PRENTICE HALL

Chemistry

Laboratory Manual

TEACHER'S EDITION

Antony C. Wilbraham
Dennis D. Staley
Michael S. Matta

Boston, Massachusetts
Upper Saddle River, New Jersey

Cover photograph: Image from Getty Images, Inc.

ISBN 0-13-190363-2
3 4 5 6 7 8 9 10 09 08 07 06 05

CONTENTS

TEACHER'S GUIDE TO SAFE LABORATORY PRACTICES

This teacher's guide is designed to assist you in working with only those chemicals that are described in the manual. If you decide to use chemicals that are not specifically listed in the Materials section of an experiment, you must refer to other sources for assistance with preparation and precautions.

Additional information concerning the hazardous properties of chemicals may be obtained from Material Safety Data Sheets (MSDS). These sheets are available from the manufacturer or supplier of every chemical you purchase. An MSDS is an important document. It contains a summary of information regarding the physical and chemical properties of the chemical; the fire and storage hazards associated with the chemical; and the cleanup and disposal procedures to be used for the chemical. A written request to the manufacturer will usually be sufficient to obtain an MSDS for any chemical in your storeroom. Remember, you have the right to know the properties of the chemicals you use. You should maintain a file of safety data sheets.

Safety Equipment

One large (15-kg) ABC dry chemical **fire extinguisher** or a BC carbon dioxide fire extinguisher should be present in the work area, in addition to the several smaller extinguishers provided in the classroom. ABC fire extinguishers will extinguish fires involving paper, flammable liquids, or electrical equipment. Class BC extinguishers are not appropriate for paper because the material used in these extinguishers has a low heat capacity and will permit embers to survive. The BC extinguishers have the advantage of leaving no residue to clean up. A key to the types of fires is provided below. Note that only class D extinguishers will put out metal fires.

A = fires involving easily combustible materials, such as paper and fabrics

B = fires involving flammable liquids

C = fires involving electrical equipment

D = fires involving flammable metals

If a student's hair or clothing catches fire, use a drenching shower and remove the clothing. However, the first course of action must be to smother the flames, even if that means rolling on the floor. Students must be warned not to run. *Running fans the flames!* A **fire blanket** can be used to smother flames. Be aware that old fire blankets may contain asbestos or wool, which may increase the severity of a burn if wrapped around a synthetic fabric such as polyester.

An **eyewash fountain** able to supply running water continuously for at least 20 minutes belongs in the work area as well as in the classroom. Simple, relatively inexpensive adapters for washing eyes can be purchased from safety supply houses and can be easily mounted on existing faucets. These adapters do not interfere with the use of the faucet for other routine operations. Eyewash bottles provide an inadequate supply of water and can become contaminated unless changed frequently.

A **drenching shower** or a hose with a sprayer attached should be readily accessible. This need not be a costly item; it can be constructed from materials available in a hardware store. Although it is unusual for a bottle of concentrated acid to break, especially if coated with a plastic, the consequences are so severe that the potential for reduction in injury provided by a nearby large-water-volume device justifies the cost. Furthermore, the sprayer can be used to extinguish fires.

A **first-aid kit** should be present in both the work area and in the classroom. The kit should include an assortment of different-sized bandages and several large sterile gauze squares that can be used to apply pressure to control bleeding. Encourage small lacerations to bleed while under running water and then protect with a bandage. Treat burns with cool running water until the pain is diminished.

Safe Storage of Chemicals

The quantities and types of chemicals that you store depend on the size and design of your storeroom. A modified scheme of storage is given below as a suggestion. The first step is to separate chemicals into inorganic and organic sections. Always date each chemical with the month and year it was received. The numbers within each section indicate groups of compatible chemicals.

Inorganic

1. Sulfur
2. Sulfates, sulfites, thiosulfates, phosphates, halogens except bromine
3. Nitrates (except ammonium nitrate, which must be stored separately), nitric acid
4. Metals
5. Hydroxides, oxides, carbonates
6. Sulfides
7. Chromates, manganates, permanganates
8. Hydrogen peroxide, hypochlorite
9. Acids, except nitric

Organic

1. Acids
2. Alcohols, glycols
3. Hydrocarbons, aldehydes
4. Ketones, halogenated hydrocarbons

Chemicals should not be stored alphabetically, because many incompatible chemicals are close together in the alphabet.

Flammables

It is tempting to store volatile liquids in a refrigerator because the low temperature will reduce the vapor pressure and the metal housing will retard a fire. However, domestic refrigerators do not have spark-free motors and flammable solvents can be ignited. Explosion-proof refrigerators have sealed light switches and motor compressors. These items are expensive and are usually beyond the budget of the average secondary school. Unless you have an explosion proof refrigerator, store flammable liquids or solids in an approved metal cabinet.

No more than 1 quart total of flammable liquids having flash points below 23°C should be stored outside a safety cabinet. In addition, no individual container of flammable liquid should be made of glass unless it has a capacity of 1 pint or less. If 1-gallon containers are used for liquids having flash points above 23°C, they must be made of metal or high-density polyethylene. Containers over 1 gallon in size should be approved safety cans available at hardware stores or from chemical supply houses. Flammable liquids and vapors must not be allowed to come into contact with strong oxidizers, open flames, sparks, or surface temperatures in excess of the auto-ignition point of the particular chemical.

Acids and Bases

Nitric acid must be stored by itself because of its powerful oxidizing properties. It is recommended that glacial ethanoic acid, which is flammable, be stored away from sulfuric acid. If glacial ethanoic acid mixes with sulfuric or nitric acids, spontaneous combustion is likely.

When concentrated acids and bases combine, substantial amounts of heat are generated, increasing the risk of combustion. Therefore, strong, concentrated mineral acids (sulfuric, nitric, hydrochloric, phosphoric) and strong concentrated bases must be stored in physically separated areas or cabinets. Because of the reactive nature of these chemicals, it is recommended that they not be stored directly on the floor or above eye level.

Spills in the Work Area

Acids

Nitric, hydrochloric, and sulfuric acids are corrosive and can cause severe injury. If a student spills acid on skin or clothing, immediately flush the affected area with water for 4–5 minutes. Instruct students to notify the teacher immediately of all acid spills. If acid should get into eyes, flush eyes immediately with running water and continue doing so for at least 20 minutes. If there is an eyewash fountain in the laboratory, use it. If acid is spilled on the laboratory bench or on the floor, neutralize the spill with solid sodium hydrogen carbonate, $NaHCO_3$, before wiping it up. The acid has been neutralized if bubbles of gas are no longer produced when more sodium hydrogen carbonate is added. Be sure to wear goggles and protective gloves when cleaning up a spill.

Bases

Sodium hydroxide is a very corrosive material, which can cause severe skin burns. Burns caused by sodium hydroxide are more serious than those caused by acids. Eye burns caused by sodium hydroxide are progressive. What at first appears to be a minor irritation can develop into a severe injury unless the chemical is completely flushed from the eye. If sodium hydroxide is splashed in the eye, flush the eye with running water continuously for at least 20 minutes. If sodium hydroxide is spilled on some other part of the body, flush the affected area with running water continuously for at least 10 minutes. If sodium hydroxide is spilled on the laboratory bench or on the floor, neutralize the spill with dilute hydrochloric acid before wiping it up. Use pH indicator paper to verify that the base has been neutralized. Be sure to wear goggles and protective gloves when cleaning up a spill.

Mercury

Spilled mercury is a serious problem because elemental mercury is a cumulative poison. Therefore, in the classroom or in the work area, only non-mercury thermometers are used.

Silver Nitrate

Be careful not to spill this material. Silver nitrate will leave dark brown stains on skin and clothing. These stains will disappear from the skin in time as the stained skin cells flake off, but the stains will not come out of clothing. Stains can be prevented by dipping the fingers into "hypo," a dilute solution of sodium thiosulfate, $Na_2S_2O_3$, immediately after touching silver nitrate solution, and then rinsing with water.

Other Liquids

Absorbents used to soak up liquid spills can be made of a range of materials. Sand, vermiculite, and fine-mesh clay such as that used in cat litter can all be used to contain a large spill. In many cases, when the spill is fully absorbed, the chemical can be placed in a plastic bag and sent to a landfill. Use gloves and a dustpan when performing this operation. For convenience, chemical suppliers produce a spill-absorbent paper, which comes in rolls or pillows. Spill kits are more expensive than vermiculite, but often include directions, bags, and disposal hints.

Safe Handling of Compressed Gas Cylinders

Compressed gas cylinders are used to contain gases at greater than 40 psi at 70°F. Pressures exceeding 5000 psi are possible for some non-condensable gases. Follow these procedures when using cylinders of compressed gas.

- Label all cylinders with date received, date of first use, vendor, and contents. Color-coded labels are not reliable indicators of cylinder contents because cylinders can be refilled with different gases.
- Know the chemical properties of the gas. Carbon dioxide, for example, is nonflammable, heavier than air, and can act as an asphyxiant.
- Use the proper regulator for the gas in the cylinder. Remember that regulators for use on cylinders containing oxygen gas have a left-handed thread.
- Leave a slight positive pressure in the cylinder and mark it "EMPTY" when finished.

Follow these steps when using a gas cylinder:

1. Secure the cylinder to the wall or cart in the area where the gas is to be dispensed. Observe fire codes when using flammable gases.
2. Remove the protecting cap over the main valve.
3. Attach the pressure regulator. Use Teflon tape on the threads to seal the points of attachment if necessary. Very low molecular weight gases such as helium can escape readily. Never lubricate the threads with oils or greases because of the risk of fire. Some connections thread to the right, others to the left. Do not force the threads, but gently check to find the proper direction. Finger-tighten the nut and further tighten it by using a crescent wrench. Do not use a pipe wrench; it will roughen the edges of the nut. Remember: Brass is soft.

4. Check that the reducing valve on the regulator is closed. The valve usually is closed in a counterclockwise fashion or until the handle feels loose! Some regulators have an additional flow control valve, which should also be closed. Both gauges should read zero.
5. To turn on the gas, open the main cylinder valve fully (a counterclockwise turn). The cylinder pressure gauge indicates the pressure inside the cylinder. The other gauge reads zero until the reducing valve is opened slightly (a clockwise turn) to the desired delivery pressure. At this point, open the flow control valve.
6. To shut off the gas, first close the main valve, then the reducing valve, and finally the flow control valve.
7. Remove the regulator and place a note on the cylinder if it is empty. Return the cylinder to the storage area and attach it properly to the wall.

Safe Preparation of Class Materials

The same precautions required for students in the laboratory are appropriate for teachers. Always wear approved safety goggles or a face shield. Lab coats protect clothing and are generally appropriate for the teacher because he or she deals with more concentrated chemicals than the student does. Gloves or aprons are needed for some chemicals, as indicated in the Table of Potential Chemical Hazards on T10.

Key to Potential Chemical Hazards

The Table of Potential Chemical Hazards on T10 provides a reference for the hazardous properties of the chemicals used in the student laboratory manual. After reading about a particular substance, you should be able to prepare materials for class use, provide precautions for your students, and evaluate the potential risks involved in the use of that chemical.

The following key is needed to interpret the information in the Table of Potential Chemical Hazards.

Hazard/Rating The nature of the hazard(s) posed by a chemical is indicated in the following way:

T/orl: toxic by ingestion
T/inh: toxic by inhalation
C: corrosive
F: flammable
Carc: carcinogenic

A numerical scale indicating the degree of the hazard posed is used together with the letters indicating the type of hazard. This scale is as follows.

1: slight to no hazard
2: moderate hazard
3: severe hazard

A chemical that is designated F/2 would pose a moderate risk of fire, for example. Note that the hazards are described for solids or for concentrated solutions of the chemical listed. For purposes of this table, concentrations of 6*M* and above are considered concentrated. For solutions less concentrated than 6*M*, the degree of hazard might be less than that indicated in the table.

Threshold Limit Value (TLV) This value indicates the maximum level of exposure that will not affect health adversely. The values listed have been determined by OSHA and are expressed either in parts per million (ppm) or in milligrams per cubic meter of respirable air (mg/m^3).

Flash Point (Fl. Pt.) The flash points of combustible liquids are given in degrees Fahrenheit (°F). The flash point is the lowest temperature at which the vapor of a combustible liquid can be made to ignite momentarily in air.

Water Pollution Level (WPL) In this category, the pollution hazard posed by a chemical is indicated. The following codes are used to indicate whether a chemical is soluble or not soluble in water:

s: soluble in water
ns: not soluble in water

A numerical scale identical to that used in the hazard/rating category is used to indicate the degree of the pollution hazard posed. An s/3 chemical, for instance, would be one that posed a severe water pollution hazard.

Incompatible Chemicals (Incomp) In this category, those chemicals that should be kept away from the chemical listed are noted. The list is not complete, but is intended to serve as a guideline.

Special Handling Recommendations (Special Handling) In this category, general comments are given on safety equipment that may be required in addition to the usual safety goggles, laboratory coat, and fire extinguisher. A key to the abbreviations used in this category follows.

Nui: use of a dust mask is recommended (nuisance dust)
Nui?: a dust mask is not needed if solid is present as large crystals
Resp: use of a respirator with appropriate cartridge is recommended
Neo: use of neoprene gloves is recommended
FH: use of a fume hood is recommended
Tongs/gloves: use of tongs or insulated gloves is required

*Reference: *Hazards in the Chemical Laboratory,* 5th Edition, edited by S.G. Luxon, published by the Royal Society of Chemistry, Burlington House, London, 1992. Distributed in the United States by the American Chemical Society.

TABLE OF POTENTIAL CHEMICAL HAZARDS

Chemical Name	Hazard/Rating	TLV	Fl.Pt. °F	WPL	Incomp	Special Handling
aluminum chloride hexahydrate	C/3; T/orl/2	2 mg/m^3	—	s/1	—	Neo
aluminum sulfate	T/orl/inh/2	—	—	s/1	forms H_2SO_4 wat.	
ammonia solution	T/orl/inh/3;C/2	25 ppm	—	s/2	acids/halogens	FH/Resp/Neo
ammonium chloride	T/orl/2	10 mg/m^3	—	—	ammon. nitrate	FH/Nui
ammonium molybdate	T/orl/2	10 ppm	—	—	—	Nui
ammonium nitrate	C/1	—	—	s/1	organic matter	keep cool/ unconfined
ammonium oxalate	T/orl/inh/3	1 mg/m^3	—	s/2	silver	FH/Nui
ammonium peroxydisulfate	—	—	—	s/2	organic matter	Nui
barium chloride	T/orl/3;C/2	0.5 mg/m^3	—	s/3	—	FH/Nui/glove
barium nitrate	T/orl/3;C/2	0.5 mg/m^3	—	s/3	Al, organic mat.	FH/Nui/glove
benzoic acid	T/orl/2;F/1	—	—	s/1	oxidizers	Nui?
calcium carbonate	T/inh/2	—	—	ns	—	Nui
calcium chloride	T/orl/2	—	—	s/1	—	Nui
calcium nitrate	T/orl/2	—	—	s/1	organic matter	Nui
camphor	T/orl/3; F/1	2 ppm	150	ns	oxidizers	FH
carbon dioxide, gas	asphyxiant	5000 ppm	—	s/1	—	enough oxygen
carbon dioxide, solid	C/3-frostbite	5000 ppm	—	s/1	—	Tongs/gloves
chromium(III) nitrate	T/inh/3/Carc	0.5 mg/m^3	—	s/3	organic matter	Nui
copper, strips/wire	T/inh/3(dust)	1 mg/m^3	—	ns	oxidizers	Nui if polished
copper(II) chloride	T/orl/inh/3	1 mg/m^3	—	s/3	—	Nui?
copper(II) nitrate	T/orl/2	—	—	s/2	ferrocyanide	Nui?
copper(II) sulfate pentahydrate	T/orl/inh/2	1 mg/m^3	—	s/2	Mg	Nui?
dibutyl phthalate	T/orl/inh/1	5 mg/m^3	315	s/3	Cl_2/oxidizers	no open flame
ethanoic acid, glacial	T/orl/inh/2 C/2; F/2	10 ppm	109	s/2	nitrates, oxidizers	FH/Neo
ethanol 95%	T/orl/inh/3;F/3	1000 ppm	56	s/3	oxidizers silver nitrate	Neo/defats skin
glycerin	T/orl/1	—	320	s/1	oxidizers	—
hexane	F/3; T/orl/inh/2	50 ppm	−9.4	ns	oxidizers	no flame/FH
hydrochloric acid	C/T/orl/inh/3	5 ppm	—	s/3	ammonia, bases	FH/Resp/Neo

TABLE OF POTENTIAL CHEMICAL HAZARDS (CONT.)

Chemical Name	Hazard/Rating	TLV	Fl.Pt. °F	WPL	Incomp	Special Handling
iron(III) chloride	T/orl/C/1	1 mg/m^3	—	s/1	water/HCl fume	—
iron(III) nitrate	T/orl/2	1 mg/m^3	—	s/1	organic matter	—
iron(III) sulfate	T/inh/2	1 mg/m^3	—	s/1	—	—
kerosene	T/orl/1/inh/1 F/1	100 mg/m^3	150	ns	oxidizers	no flames
lead, not dust	T/orl/3	0.15 mg/m^3	—	ns	ammon. nitrate	no oxidizers
lead(II) chloride	T/orl/2	0.10 mg/m^3	—	s/2	—	Nui?
lead(II) nitrate	T/orl/2	0.10 mg/m^3	—	s/2	organic matter	Nui?
magnesium, ribbon	F/1; T/orl/3	—	651	ns	water/oxidizers	very reactive
magnesium chloride	T/orl/2	—	—	s/1	—	—
manganese(II) chloride	T/orl/3; Carc	5 mg/m^3	—	s/3	—	Nui
manganese(IV) oxide	T/inh/3	5 mg/m^3	—	ns	organic matter	Nui
mercury, metal	T/inh/3	0.05 mg/m^3	—	ns	ammonia	avoid vapor
methanoic acid	F/2; T/orl/2; C/2	5 ppm	122	s/2	peroxide	no flame/Neo
methanol (methyl alcohol)	F/1 T/inh/2/orl/3	200 ppm	54	s/3	oxidizers, Br_2	defats skin/Neo
nitric acid	T/orl/inh/3; C/3	2 ppm	—	s/3	organic matter, many others	FH/Neo
1-octanol	T/orl/1	—	—	ns	oxidizers	no flames/FH
oxalic acid	T/orl/3	1 mg/m^3	—	s/2	silver salts	Nui
1-pentanol	F/2; T/orl/2	—	105	ns	oxidizers	no flames/FH
potassium chromate	T/orl/inh/3; Carc/inh	0.05 mg/m^3	—	s	organic matter	Nui?
potassium dichromate	T/orl/inh/3; Carc; respiratory	25 mg/m^3	—	s/3	organic matter	Nui?
potassium ferricyanide	T/orl/2	—	—	s/2	NH_3, $Cu(NO_3)_2$, $NaNO_3$	no hot acids
potassium hydroxide	T/orl/3; C/3	2 mg/m^3	—	s/3	acids	Neo
potassium iodide	T/orl/2	—	—	s/1	metallic salts	—
potassium nitrate	T/orl/2	—	—	s/1	organic matter, Zn, metals	—
potassium permanganate	T/orl/2	—	—	s/3	organic matter, conc. H_2SO_4	with care
potassium sulfate	T/orl/2	—	—	s/1	—	—
potassium thiocyanate	T/orl/2	—	—	s/1	—	no heat

TABLE OF POTENTIAL CHEMICAL HAZARDS (CONT.)

Chemical Name	Hazard/Rating	TLV	Fl.Pt. °F	WPL	Incomp	Special Handling
silver nitrate	T/orl/2; C/2	0.01 mg/m^3	—	s/1	alkalies + NH_3	gloves
sodium chromate	T/orl/3	0.05 mg/m^3	—	s/3	organic matter	Nui?
sodium dichromate	Carc/inh	0.05 mg/m^3	—	s/3	organic matter	Nui?
sodium hydroxide	T/orl/3; C/3	2 mg/m^3	—	s/3	acids	Neo
sodium iodide	T/orl/2	—	—	s/1	oxidizers	—
sodium hydrogen phosphate	C/2	—	—	s/1	—	—
sodium nitrate	T/orl/2	—	—	s/1	organic matter, Zn	—
sodium oxalate	T/orl/3	2 mg/m^3	—	s/2	silver salts	Nui?
sodium thiocyanate	T/orl/2	—	—	s/1	—	no heat
sodium thiosulfate	—	—	—	—	metal nitrates	—
strontium nitrate	T/orl/2	—	—	s/1	organic matter	—
sulfur, powder	T/eye	6 ppm	405	ns	oxidizers	dust very reactive
sulfuric acid	T/inh/3; C/3	1 mg/m^3	—	s/3	organic matter	no water/Neo
tin, not dust	T/inh/3	—	—	ns	halogens	Nui/dust
urea	T/orl/2; C/1	—	—	s/1	—	—
zinc, dust	Irr/inh only	—	—	ns	variety	no flame
zinc, not dust	—	—	—	ns	acids, NH_4NO_3	—
zinc chloride	T/orl/3	1 mg/m^3	—	s/2	—	no heat/avoid fumes
zinc nitrate	—	—	—	s/1	C, S, Cu, organics	—

CHEMICAL WASTE DISPOSAL

The disposal of chemical wastes from your laboratories must comply with local, state, and federal regulations. The federal regulatory agencies are the Occupational Safety and Health Administration (OSHA) and the Environmental Protection Agency (EPA). Because local regulations are often more stringent than federal regulations, you are advised to check these disposal procedures with local authorities. The disposal of chemical wastes can be expensive. But the failure to dispose of chemical wastes according to the regulations can be more expensive; it can result in fines and lawsuits.

To reduce disposal costs, you should, as far as is practical, attempt to recover, recycle, and reuse chemicals. You can also reduce chemical waste production by using smaller amounts of chemicals. However, whether your students use traditional techniques and equipment or do small-scale experiments, some chemical wastes will be generated. These wastes must be disposed of properly.

Before you select and use any of the disposal options presented here, it is *essential* that you review the procedures with officials of the regulatory agencies. These disposal guidelines assume the laboratory quantities of materials used are very small; the solution concentrations are low; and, therefore, the associated amounts of chemical wastes are small.

Beware: You are responsible forever for the chemical wastes that you and your students generate!

The following sources may be of help if you need advice in disposing of your chemical wastes or assistance in finding a waste disposal company:

- Your state Environmental Protection Agency
- The science supervisor with your state department of education
- The local section of the American Chemical Society
- The chemistry department of a local college or university
- The technical service department of chemical suppliers

The disposal procedures described here are for relatively small amounts of chemical wastes. The procedures are based, in general, upon recommendations and suggestions from the publications in the list that follows. No representation, warranty, or guarantee is made by the authors or Prentice Hall, Inc. as to the completeness or accuracy of these disposal procedures.

Flinn Chemical Catalog/Reference Manual. Flinn Scientific, Inc., (an annual publication). P.O. Box 219, Batavia, IL 60510-0219.

Prudent Practices in the Laboratory: Handling and Disposal of Chemicals. National Academies Press, 1995. 500 Fifth St., N.W., Lockbox 285, Washington, DC 20055. http://books.nap.edu/html/prudent/

Working Safely with Chemicals in the Laboratory. Genium Publishing Corporation, 1993. 1171 Riverfront Center, Amsterdam, NY 12010.

Safety in Academic Chemical Laboratories. American Chemical Society, Department of Educational Activities, 1998. 1155 Sixteenth Street, N.W., Washington, DC 20036.

A Model Chemical Hygiene Plan for High Schools. American Chemical Society, Department of Educational Activities, 1995. 1155 Sixteenth Street, N.W., Washington, DC 20036.

General Disposal Guidelines

Disposal of Chemicals in the Sanitary Sewer System

Inorganic Chemicals

Small amounts of compounds containing any combination of the following anions and cations can be disposed of, with ample water, down the drain. Solutions that are strongly acidic (pH < 3) or strongly basic (pH > 8) should be neutralized before disposal down the drain.

Anions: aluminum, Al^{3+}; ammonium, NH_4^+; calcium, Ca^{2+}; copper, Cu^{2+}; hydrogen, H^+; iron, Fe^{2+}, Fe^{3+}; lithium, Li^+; magnesium, Mg^{2+}; potassium, K^+; sodium, Na^+; strontium, Sr^{2+}; zinc, Zn^{2+}

Cations: carbonate, CO_3^{2-}; chloride, Cl^-; hydrogen carbonate, HCO_3^-; hydroxide, OH^-; iodide, I^-; nitrate, NO_3^-; phosphate, PO_4^{3-}; sulfate, SO_4^{2-}; thiocyanate, SCN^-; thiosulfate, $S_2O_3^{2-}$

Organic Chemicals

The organic compounds or their solutions that are cited in the master materials list are used in the experiments in this manual. They can be disposed of, with ample water, down the drain. Solutions that are strongly acidic or strongly basic should be neutralized before disposal. These compounds are agar gel; aspirin; cornstarch; ethanoic acid, CH_3COOH; ethanol, C_2H_5OH; methanoic acid, $HCOOH$; glycerin (glycerol), $C_3H_8O_3$; methanol, CH_3OH; 2-methyl-1-propanol, C_4H_9OH; potassium ethanoate, CH_3COOK; sodium ethanoate, CH_3COONa; sodium oxalate, $Na_2C_2O_4$; starch; sucrose, $C_{12}H_{22}O_{11}$; urea, $CO(NH_2)_2$

Shipping to a Hazardous Waste Landfill

If a waste is hazardous, it cannot be disposed of down the drain. If it cannot be recycled or made nonhazardous, it will probably have to be packed and shipped to a designated landfill by a firm approved by the Department of Transportation. Because this method of disposal is expensive, it is prudent to keep such hazardous wastes to a minimum. You can reduce the bulk and hazard of some wastes by precipitation and filtration. This procedure is the basis for the treatment of waste solutions containing the heavy-metal ions of barium, Ba^{2+}; chromium, Cr(VI); lead, Pb^{2+}; and silver, Ag^+. Briefly, barium ions are precipitated as insoluble barium sulfate, chromium(VI) ions are reduced to chromium(III) and precipitated as insoluble chromium(III) sulfide, lead ions are precipitated as insoluble lead sulfide, and silver ions are precipitated as insoluble silver chloride.

Disposal Methods

Disposal advice given in this teacher's edition is keyed to the following eight disposal methods. Throughout the lab manual, whenever a chemical must be disposed of, the number of the appropriate disposal method will appear in the margin as a note to the teacher.

1. School Trash

This solid waste material can be disposed of in your school's trash and taken to a local landfill. Materials recommended for this disposal method are inert, water insoluble, and of very low toxicity.

2. Drain Disposal

This liquid waste material can be poured, with a large amount of water, down school drains; pretreatment is not required *if the drains are connected to a sanitary sewer system that leads to a waste treatment facility.* This procedure should not be used if the drains empty into ground water through a septic tank system or into a storm sewer. Materials recommended for this disposal method are water soluble; of very low toxicity; and, if organic, readily biodegradable.

3. Neutralization

Adjust the pH of acidic liquid waste to be in the range pH 6–pH 8 by using approximately 1*M* sodium carbonate. Adjust the pH of basic liquid waste to be in the range pH 6–pH 8 by using 6*M* hydrochloric acid. Check with pH indicator paper. Dispose of the waste by flushing down the drain with large amounts of water. Add ice if the solution gets hot during the neutralization process. Read also "Drain Disposal," the preceding method. (Note: You can use waste acid solutions to neutralize waste base solutions, and vice versa.)

4. Disposal of Hydrocarbons, Nonhalogenated

These materials are flammable.

Volatile
Pour a thin layer of the substance into a metal pan under a fume hood, and allow the substance to evaporate. If you do not have a hood, the evaporation may be conducted outdoors. The process should be attended at all times.

Nonvolatile
Pour the waste material onto paper towels in a cardboard box. Do this outdoors. Ignite the paper and the absorbed waste. Stay upwind of the fire until the burning is complete. Do not burn any substance without first checking with local authorities to be sure that burning is permitted.

5. Disposal of Barium Compounds

Add dilute sulfuric acid to the waste barium solution while stirring. Continue stirring until the precipitation of barium sulfate appears to be complete. Allow the precipitate to settle for several hours. Filter off the precipitate and allow it to dry. Put the precipitate and filter paper into a labeled container suitable for burial in a designated landfill. The filtrate is acidic and must be neutralized with sodium carbonate before pouring it down the drain with ample water.

6. Disposal of Chromium Compounds

Before disposal, solutions that contain chromium(VI), chromates, and dichromates must be reduced to chromium(III) by adding the material to a twofold excess of an aqueous solution of sodium thiosulfate. While stirring, adjust the pH to 2–3 with 3*M* sulfuric acid. Allow the reaction mixture to stand for about one hour. (A rise in temperature indicates that the reaction is proceeding. Add more sulfuric acid, if necessary, to produce a temperature rise.) Add a threefold molar excess of sodium sulfide and stir occasionally for about one hour. Adjust the pH to about 7 by using 3*M* sodium hydroxide to complete the precipitation of chromium(III) sulfide. Filter off the precipitate and allow it to dry. Put the precipitate and filter paper into a labeled container suitable for burial in a designated landfill. The filtrate contains sulfide ions and must be treated before disposal. While stirring, pour the sulfide-containing solution into a beaker containing an excess of a solution of iron(III) chloride. A precipitate will form. Neutralize the solution by using sodium carbonate. Allow the precipitate to settle and filter it off. Put the dry precipitate and filter paper into a labeled container suitable for burial in a designated landfill. Pour the neutralized filtrate down the drain with ample water.

7. Disposal of Lead Compounds

Add a threefold molar excess of sodium sulfide to the solution of lead waste and stir occasionally for about one hour. Adjust the pH to about 7 by using 3*M* sodium hydroxide to complete the precipitation of lead(II) sulfide. Filter off the precipitate and allow it to dry. Put the precipitate and filter paper into a labeled container suitable for burial in a designated landfill. The filtrate contains sulfide ions and must be treated before disposal. While stirring, pour the sulfide-containing solution into a beaker containing an excess of a solution of iron(III) chloride. A precipitate will form. Neutralize the solution by using sodium carbonate. Allow the precipitate to settle and filter it off. Put the dry precipitate and filter paper into a labeled container suitable for burial in a designated landfill. Pour the neutralized filtrate down the drain with ample water.

8. Disposal of Silver Compounds

Acidify the waste solution with dilute nitric acid. Add a 50% molar excess of sodium chloride solution and stir. Filter off the silver chloride precipitate. Put the dry precipitate and filter paper into a labeled container suitable for burial in a designated landfill. Neutralize the filtrate with sodium carbonate and pour it down the drain with ample water.

REQUIRED MATERIALS

The following materials are needed for a class of 30 students working in pairs. For Experiments 23 and 24, the material is sufficient for five groups of six students each. Materials for all demonstrations in the laboratory manual are also included. The numbers in boldface indicate core experiments.

MASTER MATERIALS LIST

Material	Quantity	Experiments
agar, powdered	20 g	47
aluminum chloride hexahydrate, $AlCl_3 \cdot 6H_2O$	1.5 g	17
aluminum foil, Al	20	3, **36, 52**
aluminum rod, 1-cm diam. × 2-cm to 5-cm lengths	15	**4, 34**
aluminum sulfate, $Al_2(SO_4)_3$	3.5 g	17
ammonia, 15*M* $NH_3(aq)$	200 mL	**16,** 18, 25, 26, 29, 40
ammonium chloride, NH_4Cl	10 g	44
ammonium paramolybdate tetrahydrate, $(NH_4)_6Mo_7O_{24} \cdot 4H_2O$	100 g	**16,** 18
ammonium peroxydisulfate, $(NH_4)_2S_2O_8$	80 g	37
ammonium nitrate, NH_4NO_3	7.5 g	**16**
antacid liquid	500 mL	40
argon, gas, Ar	1 cylinder	12
aspirin tablets	30	40
ball-and-stick model set	1	**11**
barium chloride dihydrate, $BaCl_2 \cdot 2H_2O$	3 g	**16,** 17, 18
barium nitrate, $Ba(NO_3)_2$	1.3 g	**6,** 17
benzoic acid, C_6H_5COOH	200 g	33

MASTER MATERIALS LIST (CONT.)

Material	Quantity	Experiments
bleach	50 mL	40
boiling chips	4	26
brass rod, 1-cm diam. × 2-cm to 5-cm lengths	15	**4, 34**
bromthymol blue	2.5×10^{-3} g	40
calcium carbonate, $CaCO_3$	12 g	**27, 41**
calcium chloride, $CaCl_2$	0.2 g	**36**
calcium chloride dihydrate, $CaCl_2{\bullet}2H_2O$	1 g	51
calcium ethanoate monohydrate, $(CH_3COO)_2Ca{\bullet}H_2O$	25 g	1
calcium nitrate, $Ca(NO_3)_2$	14 g	**6, 16**
calcium oxide, CaO	0.1 g	**14**
camphor, $C_{10}H_{16}O$	5 g	33
carbon-14, ^{14}C, 10-μCi sealed source	1	**52**
carbon dioxide, gas, CO_2	1 cylinder	12
carbon dioxide, solid, CO_2	see "dry ice"	
carbonated beverage	1 can	40
cardboard piece with narrow slit	15	**6**
centimeter ruler	1	**10**
cesium-137, ^{137}Cs, 5-μCi sealed source	1	**52**
chromium(III) nitrate, $Cr(NO_3)_3$	1 g	8
coffee stirrers, plastic	3 packs	**10**
cold tea	50 mL	40
construction paper	15 sheets	**5**
copper rod, Cu, 1-cm diam. × 2-cm to 5-cm lengths	2	**34**
copper strips, Cu, 0.25 mm × 0.50 mm × 2.00 cm	7	**15,** 46
copper strips, Cu, 0.25 mm × 1.00 cm × 5.00 cm	20	**48**
copper wire, Cu	725 cm	1, **22, 41, 47**
copper(II) chloride dihydrate, $CuCl_2{\bullet}2H_2O$	250 g	3, **19**
copper(II) nitrate, $Cu(NO_3)_2$	20 g	**6,** 46
copper(II) sulfate pentahydrate, $CuSO_4{\bullet}5H_2O$	320 g	**14, 15,** 28, **30, 48**
cornstarch, $(C_6H_{12}O_6)_n$	90 g	1
cotton	1 wad	**25**
cotton fabric, 10-cm × 10-cm squares	15	**52**

MASTER MATERIALS LIST (CONT.)

Material	Quantity	Experiments
dibutyl phthalate, $C_6H_4(CO_2C_4H_9)_2$	1.5 L	23, **24**
disodium hydrogen phosphate, $Na_2HPO_4 \cdot 12H_2O$	4 g	18, 45
distilled water	sufficient	1, **2,** 3, 7, 8, **9, 16,** 17, 18, **19, 21, 27,** 29, **30,** 31, 32, **34,** 35, **36,** 37, 39, 40, **43,** 44, 45, **46,** 47, **50**
dry ice, $CO_2(s)$, walnut-sized pieces	2	1
ethanoic acid 6*M*, CH_3COOH	60 mL	29, 40
ethanoic acid, glacial, CH_3COOH	25 mL	29, **50**
ethanol, C_2H_5OH	140 mL	1, **27,** 29, **50**
ethanol–water mixture 50/50 (v/v)	300 mL	51
film, exposed	30 pieces	**13**
filter paper circles	20	**2, 21,** 39
filter paper strips, 1-cm × 15-cm	45	32
food coloring, yellow, blue, and green	sufficient	32
Geiger-Müller counter	1	**52**
glass delivery tube	15	12
glass, small pane	15	**52**
glycerin, $C_3H_8O_3$	20 mL	23, 26, **27**
hand soap	15 g	51
hexane, C_6H_{14}	10 mL	**27**
hydrochloric acid, HCl (conc.)	1100 mL	**2, 6,** 7, **14, 16,** 18, 25, 29, 35, **36,** 40, **41,** 42, 45, 47
hydrogen peroxide, H_2O_2, 3%	30 mL	1, **14, 36**
ice cubes, $H_2O(s)$	sufficient	1, **24, 30,** 31, **36,** 38, **50**
indicator solution	see "wide-range indicator solution"	
iron filings, Fe	150 g	**2, 14**
iron nails, Fe, 4 cm	40	**19**
iron nails, Fe, 5 cm	160	47
iron rod, 1-cm diam. × 2-cm to 5-cm lengths	15	**4**
iron wire or 2-cm nails, Fe	25	**41**
iron(II) sulfate, $FeSO_4$	0.01 g	47
iron(III) chloride hexahydrate, $FeCl_3 \cdot 6H_2O$	3 g	**36,** 38, 51
iron(III) nitrate nonahydrate, $Fe(NO_3)_3 \cdot 9H_2O$	0.5 g	**36**

MASTER MATERIALS LIST (CONT.)

Material	Quantity	Experiments
iron(III) sulfate, $Fe_2(SO_4)_3$	2.5 g	**16**
kerosene, C_{12}—C_{15}	50 mL	**27,** 29
laundry detergent	10 g	51
lauric acid, $CH_3(CH_2)_{10}COOH$	500 g	**22**
lead strips, Pb, 0.25 mm × 0.50 cm × 2.00 cm	50	**46**
lead(II) chloride, $PbCl_2$	20 g	39
lead(II) nitrate, $Pb(NO_3)_2$	175 g	**14, 15,** 18, 20, **46**
lead foil, 10-cm × 10-cm squares	15	**52**
lead shot, Pb	4 kg	**9, 34**
lemons	3	40
lithium nitrate, $LiNO_3$	10 g	**6**
litmus paper or Hydrion paper	1 roll	**16,** 47
litmus powder	1 g	40
magnesium chloride, $MgCl_2$	5 g	**15**
magnesium chloride hexahydrate, $MgCl_2 \bullet 6H_2O$	4 g	17, 51
magnesium nitrate, $Mg(NO_3)_2$	4 g	17
magnesium ribbon, Mg	850 cm	**2, 13, 15, 41**
magnesium sulfate heptahydrate, $MgSO_4 \bullet 7H_2O$	22 g	17, 28
magnesium turnings, Mg	15 g	**14**
manganese chloride, $MnCl_2$	0.5 g	**36**
manganese(IV) oxide, MnO_2	1 g	1
marble	15	**5**
matches	16 books	1, **14**
meter stick	30	7
methanoic acid, 90% solution, HCOOH	25 mL	**50**
methanol, CH_3OH	25 mL	**50**
2-methyl-1-propanol, C_4H_9OH	25 mL	**50**
methyl red solution	25 mL	40
milk	30 mL	40
nitric acid, HNO_3 (conc.)	60 mL	**16,** 18, 26, 47
1-octanol, $C_8H_{17}OH$	25 mL	**50**
paper	200	**2, 5, 41, 52**

MASTER MATERIALS LIST (CONT.)

Material	Quantity	Experiments
paper towels	6 rolls	**4, 6,** 17, 18, **19, 21, 30, 36, 48,** 51
1-pentanol, $C_5H_{11}OH$	25 mL	**50**
pH test paper	see "wide-range pH test paper"	
phenolphthalein	5 g	40, 42, **43,** 47
phenolphthalein solution, 1%	100 mL	26
photographic film, exposed	30 pieces	**2, 13**
pipe cleaners	1 box	**10**
plastic, film	1 roll	**52**
plastic-foam balls, 2-inch diameter, 1-inch diameter, 3/4-inch diameter	88	**10**
plastic foam shape	15	**5**
platinum wire loop	15	**6,** 7
plywood sheets, 60 cm × 60 cm	15	**5**
potassium chloride crystals, KCl	30 g	**15, 16,** 17, 38
potassium chromate, K_2CrO_4	90 g	17, 18, 39
potassium ethanoate, CH_3COOK	15 g	33
potassium ferricyanide, $K_3Fe(CN)_6$	0.5 g	47
potassium hydrogen sulfate, $KHSO_4$	50 g	**43**
potassium hydroxide, KOH	1 g	47
potassium iodide, KI	300 g	**14,** 37
potassium nitrate, KNO_3	20 g	**6, 36,** 37, 47
potassium sulfate, K_2SO_4	125 g	**27**
potassium thiocyanate, KSCN	1 g	**16,** 38
salicylic acid, $C_6H_4OHCOOH$	25 g	**50**
sand	100 g	**2**
scissors	1	**10**
shampoo	50 mL	40
silicon, Si, 10-g to 25-g pieces	15	**9**
silicone grease	1 tube	23
silver coins	20	**48**
silver nitrate, $AgNO_3$	6 g	1, **15, 16,** 17, 18, 26, **48**
sodium carbonate, Na_2CO_3	15 g	44, 45, 47

MASTER MATERIALS LIST (CONT.)

Material	Quantity	Experiments
sodium carbonate decahydrate, $Na_2CO_3{\cdot}10H_2O$	20 g	28
sodium chloride, NaCl	1600 g	**2,** 7, **15, 16,** 26, **27,** 28, 29, **30, 36,** 44, 47, 51
sodium chromate, Na_2CrO_4	1 g	17
sodium dichromate dihydrate, $Na_2Cr_2O_7{\cdot}2H_2O$	5 g	47
sodium dihydrogen phosphate, NaH_2PO_4	3 g	45
sodium ethanoate, CH_3COONa	10 g	44
sodium hydrogen carbonate, $NaHCO_3$	135 g	**2, 14, 16,** 40, **41,** 44, 45
sodium hydroxide, NaOH	150 g	1, **16,** 17, 29, 35, 40, **43,** 45, 47, 51
sodium iodide, NaI	80 g	20
sodium nitrate, $NaNO_3$	10 g	**6**
sodium oxalate, $Na_2C_2O_4$	2.5 g	**16,** 47
sodium phosphate, Na_3PO_4	10 g	44
sodium phosphate dodecahydrate, $Na_3PO_4{\cdot}12H_2O$	6 g	**16,** 47
sodium sulfate, Na_2SO_4	1.5 g	**16,** 17
sodium sulfate decahydrate, $Na_2SO_4{\cdot}10H_2O$	100 g	31
sodium thiocyanate, NaSCN	1 g	47
sodium thiosulfate pentahydrate, $Na_2S_2O_3{\cdot}5H_2O$	20 g	**27,** 37
stainless steel rod, 1-cm diam. × 2-cm to 5-cm lengths	15	**4,** 39
starch, $(C_6H_{10}O_5)_n$, soluble	1 g	37
steel wool	24 pads	**15, 19, 36, 46,** 47, **48**
strontium nitrate, $Sr(NO_3)_2$	25 g	**6,** 7, 29
sucrose, $C_{12}H_{22}O_{11}$	115 g	**2, 27,** 29, **30**
sulfur, powdered, S	1.1 kg	**2, 21**
sulfuric acid, H_2SO_4 (conc.)	50 mL	**16,** 47, **50**
thallium-204, ^{204}Tl-μCi sealed source	1	**52**
tin, Sn, 25–50-g pieces	15 pieces	**9**
tissue paper	1 box	8
toothpicks	1 box	**10**
universal indicator paper	1 roll	26
universal indicator solution	10 mL	1
urea, $CO(NH_2)_2$	10 g	33

MASTER MATERIALS LIST (CONT.)		
Material	**Quantity**	**Experiments**
vegetable oil	200 mL	**21,** 51
vinegar (dilute aqueous ethanoic acid, CH_3COOH)	250 mL	40, **43**
wide-range indicator solution (pH 1–14)	55 mL	44, 45, 51
wide-range pH test paper (pH 1–14)	4 rolls	44, 45, 51
wood, 10-cm × 10-cm squares, 3 mm thick	15	**52**
wood splints	75	1, **14, 36, 41**
zinc, powder, Zn	5 g	**36**
zinc chloride, $ZnCl_2$	0.5 g	**15**
zinc nitrate hexahydrate, $Zn(NO_3)_2{\bullet}6H_2O$	6.0 g	**46**
zinc rod, 1-cm diam. × 2-cm to 5-cm lengths	15	**4, 34**
zinc, sheet, 0.25 mm thick	100 cm^2	**15, 36, 41, 46,** 47

PRENTICE HALL

Chemistry

Laboratory Manual

Antony C. Wilbraham
Dennis D. Staley
Michael S. Matta

Boston, Massachusetts
Upper Saddle River, New Jersey

Cover photograph: Image from Getty Images, Inc.

ISBN 0-13-190359-4

3 4 5 6 7 8 9 10 09 08 07 06 05

CONTENTS

* *Core experiment*

TO THE STUDENT

Chemistry is exciting! Each day in the laboratory you are given the opportunity to confront the unknown, and to understand it. Each experiment holds many secrets. Look hard and you may uncover them. Work hard and you will understand them.

The word *science* comes from the Latin word *scire*, which means "to know." The goal of all science is knowledge. Scientists are men and women who devote their lives to the pursuit of knowledge.

In this class, you are given the opportunity to do what scientists do. You can wonder how things work, ask why and how, and then think of ways to answer your own questions. You are given the chance to understand what is unknown to you and to many other people.

It is a great opportunity. Do not waste it by being lazy or careless. Work hard. Master the scientist's skills of observation and experiment. These skills are tools for understanding the secrets of the unknown.

SAFETY

Chemistry is a laboratory science. As part of your laboratory experience you will handle many chemical substances and manipulate specialized laboratory equipment. Many of these substances pose a health risk if handled improperly, and some of the laboratory equipment can cause severe injury if used improperly. This section is a guide to the safe laboratory practices you will use throughout this course.

Preparation and Safety

To get the most out of your laboratory experience, you must be well prepared for each experiment. This means that you must read the experiment thoroughly before coming to the laboratory. Make sure you have a clear idea of what the experiment is about. Be sure that you understand each step of the procedure. If you are unsure of any part of the experiment, ask your teacher for help before the laboratory begins.

Preparation is important not only to understanding, but also to safety. If you are well prepared for the laboratory, it is much less likely that an accident will occur. In the laboratory, you are responsible not only for your safety, but also for the safety of your classmates. If an accident happens because you are not prepared, it can also affect your friends. This is all the more reason for you to take the time and make the effort to prepare for the laboratory.

Be sure to note the safety warnings listed in the Safety section of each experiment. Note that these warnings are emphasized by symbols appearing in the margins. The symbols mark those parts of the procedure that may be hazardous. In addition, be sure to observe the general safety precautions described in the safety section at the beginning of the manual. Finally, remember the most important safety advice of all: *Always wear safety goggles in the chemistry laboratory!*

Safety in the Chemistry Laboratory

Everyone who works in a chemistry laboratory should follow these safety precautions:

1. Wear safety goggles and a laboratory apron in the laboratory at all times.
2. Shoes must be worn in the laboratory. Avoid wearing overly bulky or loose-fitting clothing. Remove any dangling jewelry.
3. Conduct only assigned experiments, and do them only when your teacher is present.
4. Know the locations of safety equipment such as eyewash fountains, fire extinguishers, emergency shower, and fire blanket. Be sure you know how to use the equipment.
5. Do not chew gum, eat, or drink in the laboratory. Never taste any chemicals. Keep your hands away from your face when working with chemicals.
6. Wash your hands with soap and water at the end of each laboratory exercise.
7. Read all of the directions for a laboratory procedure before proceeding with the first part. Reread each instruction before you do it.
8. Notify your teacher immediately if any chemicals, especially concentrated acid or base, are spilled.
9. Report all accidents, no matter how slight, to the teacher immediately.
10. Pin or tie back long hair and roll up loose sleeves when working with flames.
11. Do not leave a lighted burner unattended.
12. Use a hot plate instead of an open flame whenever a flammable liquid is present.
13. Read the label on a reagent bottle carefully *before* using the chemical. After removing the chemical from the bottle, check to make sure that it is the correct chemical for that procedure.
14. To avoid contamination, do not return unused chemicals to a reagent bottle. Similarly, never put a pipet, spatula, or dropper into a reagent bottle. Instead, pour some of the reagent into a small clean beaker and use that as your supply.
15. Do not use chipped or cracked glassware. Discard it according to your teacher's instructions.
16. When diluting an acid, *always* pour the acid slowly into water, stirring to dissipate the heat generated. **CAUTION:** *Never pour water into a concentrated acid.*
17. When heating a liquid in a test tube, turn the mouth of the test tube away from yourself and others.
18. Clean up spills and broken glass immediately. Leave your work area clean at the end of the laboratory period.

Laboratory Hazards

You should be aware of possible hazards in the laboratory and take the appropriate safety precautions. By doing so, you can minimize the risks of doing chemistry. This safety section is intended to acquaint you with the hazards that exist in the laboratory and to indicate how you can avoid these hazards. In addition, information is provided on what to do if an accident should occur.

Thermal Burns

A thermal burn can occur if you touch hot equipment or come too close to an open flame. You can prevent thermal burns by being aware that hot and cold equipment look the same. If a gas burner or hot plate has been used, some of the equipment nearby may be hot. Hold your hand near an item to feel for heat before touching it. Treat a thermal burn by *immediately* running cold water over the burned area. Continue applying the cold water until the pain is reduced. This usually takes several minutes. In addition to reducing pain, cooling the burned area also serves to speed the healing process. Greases and oils should not be used to treat burns because they tend to trap heat. Medical assistance should be sought for any serious burn. *Notify your teacher immediately if you are burned.*

Chemical Burns

A chemical burn occurs when the skin or a mucous membrane is damaged by contact with a substance. The Materials section of each exercise indicates which substances can cause chemical burns. [C] **stands for corrosive**. It indicates that the chemical can cause severe burns. [I] **stands for irritant**. It indicates that the chemical can irritate the skin and the membranes of the eye, nose, throat, and lungs. Chemicals that are marked [C] or [I] should be treated with special care. Chemical burns can be severe. Permanent damage to mucous membranes can occur despite the best efforts to rinse a chemical from the affected area.

The best defense against chemical burns is prevention. *Without exception, wear safety goggles during all phases of the laboratory period—even during cleanup.* Should any chemical splash in your eye, immediately use a continuous flow of running water to flush your eye for a period of 20 minutes. Call for help. If you wear contact lenses, remove them immediately. This is especially crucial if the chemical involved is an acid or base. It can concentrate under the lens and cause extensive damage. Wear a laboratory apron and close-toed shoes (no sandals) to protect other areas of your body. If corrosive chemicals should contact your exposed skin, wash the affected area with water for several minutes.

An additional burn hazard exists when concentrated acids or bases are mixed with water. The heat released in mixing these chemicals with water can cause the mixture to boil, spattering corrosive chemical. The heat can also cause non-Pyrex containers to break, spilling corrosive chemical.

To avoid these hazards, follow these instructions: Always add acid or base to water, very slowly while stirring; never the reverse. One way to remember this critical advice is to think of the phrase "Pouring acid into water is doing what you ought-er."

Cuts from Glass

Cuts occur most often when thermometers or pieces of glass tubing are forced into rubber stoppers. Prevent cuts by using the correct technique for this procedure. The hole should be lubricated with glycerol or water to facilitate the movement of the glass tubing. The glass should not be gripped directly with the hands, but rather by means of cloth towels. The towels will protect your hands if the glass should break. Use a gentle twisting motion to move the tube smoothly into the stopper.

Avoid cuts from other sources by discarding chipped and cracked glassware according to your teacher's instructions. If you should receive a minor cut, allow it to bleed for a short time. Wash the injured area under cold running water, and notify your teacher. Serious cuts and deep puncture wounds require immediate medical help. Notify your teacher immediately. While waiting for assistance, control the bleeding by applying pressure with the fingertips or by firmly pressing with a clean towel or sterile gauze.

Fire

A fire may occur if chemicals are mixed improperly or if flammable materials come too close to a burner flame or hot plate. When using lab equipment, prevent fires by tying back long hair and loose-fitting clothing. Do not use a burner when flammable chemicals are present. **Flammable chemicals are designated with the symbol** [F] in the Materials section for each exercise. Use a hot plate as a heat source instead of a burner when flammable chemicals are present.

If hair or clothing should catch fire, *do not* run, because running fans a fire. Drop to the floor and roll slowly to smother the flames. Shout for help. If another person is the victim, get a fire blanket to smother the flames. If a shower is nearby, help the victim to use it.

In case of a fire on a laboratory bench, turn off all accessible gas outlets and unplug all accessible appliances. A fire in a container may be put out by covering the container with a nonflammable object. It could also be smothered by covering the burning object with a damp cloth. If not, call for a fire extinguisher. Spray the base of the fire with foam from the extinguisher. **CAUTION:** *Never direct the jet of a fire extinguisher into a person's face.* Use a fire blanket instead. If a fire is not extinguished quickly, leave the laboratory. Crawl to the door if necessary to avoid the smoke. Do not return to the laboratory.

Poisoning

Many of the chemicals used in this manual are toxic. **Toxic chemicals are identified in the Materials sections with the symbol** [T].

You should do several things to prevent poisoning. Never eat, chew gum, or drink in the laboratory. Do not touch chemicals. Clean up spills. Keep your hands away from your face. In this way you will prevent chemicals from reaching your hands, mouth, nose, or eyes.

In some cases, the detection of an odor is used to indicate that a chemical reaction has taken place. It is important to note, however, that many gases are toxic when inhaled. If you must detect an odor, use your hand to waft some of the gas toward your nose. Sniff the gas instead of taking a deep breath. This will minimize the amount of gas sampled.

Safety Symbols

Take appropriate precautions whenever any of the following safety symbols appear in an experiment.

Eye Safety
Wear safety goggles.

Clothing Protection
Wear a lab coat or apron when using corrosive chemicals or chemicals that can stain clothing.

Skin Protection
Wear plastic gloves when using chemicals that can irritate or stain your skin.

Broken Glass
Do not use chipped or cracked glassware. Do not heat the bottom of a test tube.

Open Flame
Tie back hair and loose clothing. Never reach across a lit burner.

Flammable Substance
Do not have a flame near flammable materials.

Corrosive Substance
Wear safety goggles, an apron, and gloves when working with corrosive chemicals.

Poison
Don't chew gum, drink, or eat in the laboratory. Never taste a chemical in the laboratory.

Fume
Avoid inhaling substances that can irritate your respiratory system.

Thermal Burn
Do not touch hot glassware or equipment.

Electrical Equipment
Keep electrical equipment away from water or other liquids.

Sharp Object
To avoid a puncture wound, use scissors or other sharp objects only as intended.

Disposal
Dispose chemicals only as directed.

Hand Washing
Wash your hands thoroughly with soap and water.

C **Corrosive**

I **Irritant**

F **Flammable**

T **Toxic**

Emergency Procedures

Report any injury, accident, or spill to your teacher immediately. Know the location of the closest eyewash fountain, fire blanket, fire extinguisher, and shower.

SITUATION	SAFE RESPONSE
burns	Immediately flush with cold water until the burning sensation subsides.
fainting	Provide fresh air (for instance, open a window). Move the person so that the head is lower than the rest of the body. If breathing stops, use CPR
fire	Turn off all gas outlets. Unplug all appliances. Use a fire blanket or fire extinguisher to smother the fire. **CAUTION:** *Do not cut off a person's air supply.*
eye injury	Immediately flush the eye with running water. Remove contact lenses. Do not allow eye to be rubbed if a foreign object is present in the eye.
minor cuts	Allow to bleed briefly. Wash with soap and water.
poisoning	Note what substance was responsible. Alert teacher immediately.
spills on skin	Flush with water.

Laboratory Equipment

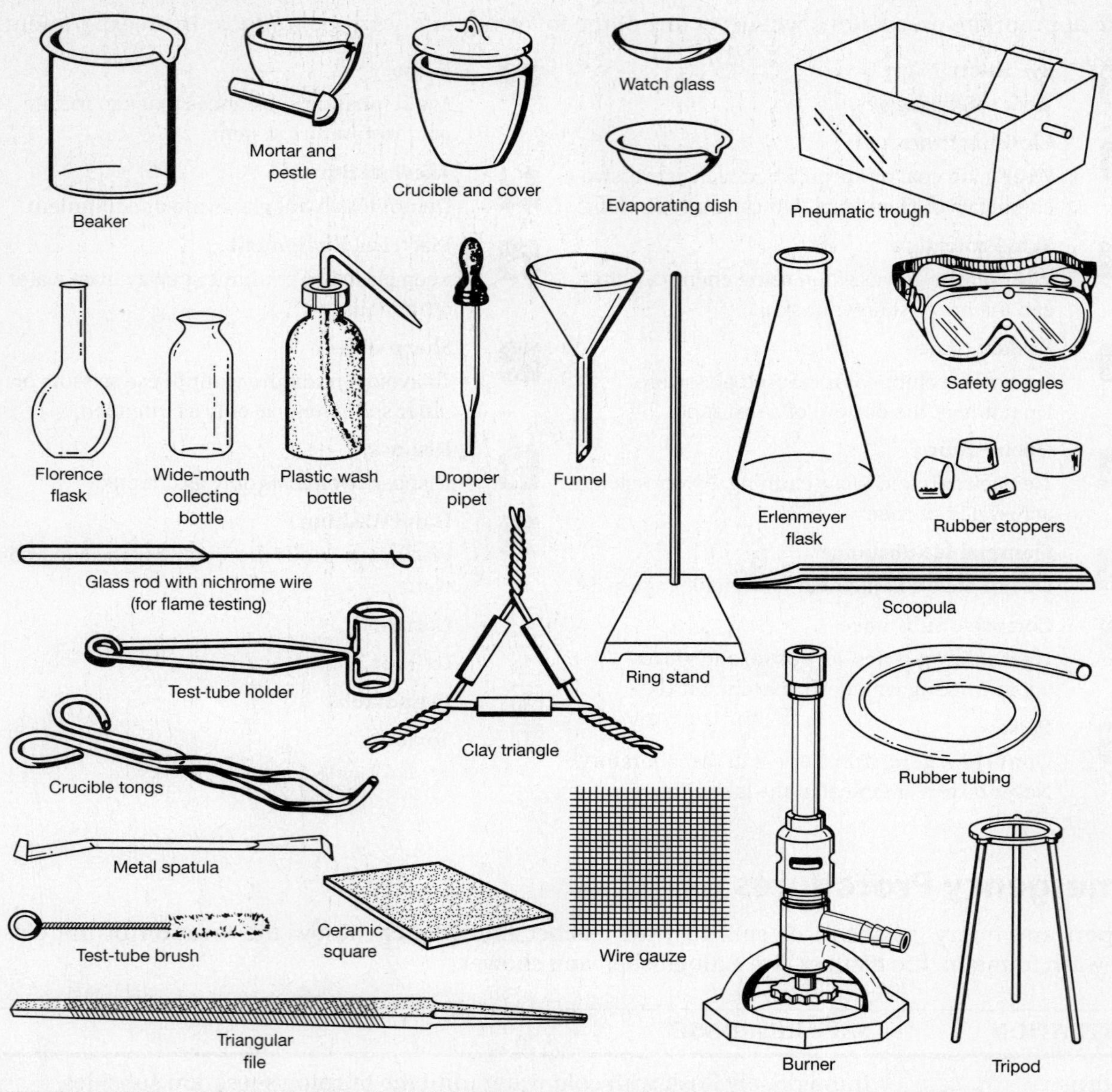

Beaker: glass or plastic; common sizes are 50 mL, 100 mL, 250 mL, 400 mL; glass beakers may be heated.
Buret: glass; common sizes are 25 mL and 50 mL; used to measure volumes of solutions in titrations.
Ceramic square: used under hot apparatus or glassware.
Clamps: the following types of clamps may be fastened to support apparatus: buret/test-tube clamp, clamp holder, double buret clamp, ring clamp, 3-pronged jaw clamp.
Clay triangle: wire frame with porcelain supports; used to support a crucible.
Condenser: glass; used in distillation procedures.
Crucible and cover: porcelain; used to heat small amounts of solid substances at high temperatures.
Crucible tongs: iron or nickel; used to pick up and hold small items.
Dropper pipet: glass tip with rubber bulb; used to transfer small volumes of liquid.
Erlenmeyer flask: glass; common sizes are 100 mL, 250 mL; may be heated; used in titrations.
Evaporating dish: porcelain; used to contain small volumes of liquid being evaporated.
Florence flask: glass; common sizes are 125 mL, 250 mL, 500 mL; may be heated; used in making and for storing solutions.
Forceps: metal; used to hold or pick up small objects.
Funnel: glass or plastic; common size holds 12.5-cm diameter filter paper.
Gas burner: constructed of metal; connected to a gas supply with rubber tubing; used to heat chemicals (dry or in solution) in beakers, test tubes, and crucibles.
Gas collecting tube: glass; marked in mL intervals; used to measure gas volumes.
Glass rod with nichrome wire: used in flame tests.
Graduated cylinder: glass or plastic; common sizes are 10 mL, 50 mL, 100 mL; used to measure approximate volumes; must not be heated.
Graduated pipet: glass; common sizes are 10 mL, 25 mL; used to measure solution volumes; less accurate than a volumetric pipet.
Mortar and pestle: porcelain; may be used to grind crystals and lumpy chemicals to a powder.
Pipet bulb: rubber; used in filling a pipet with a solution; a pipet must never be filled by mouth.

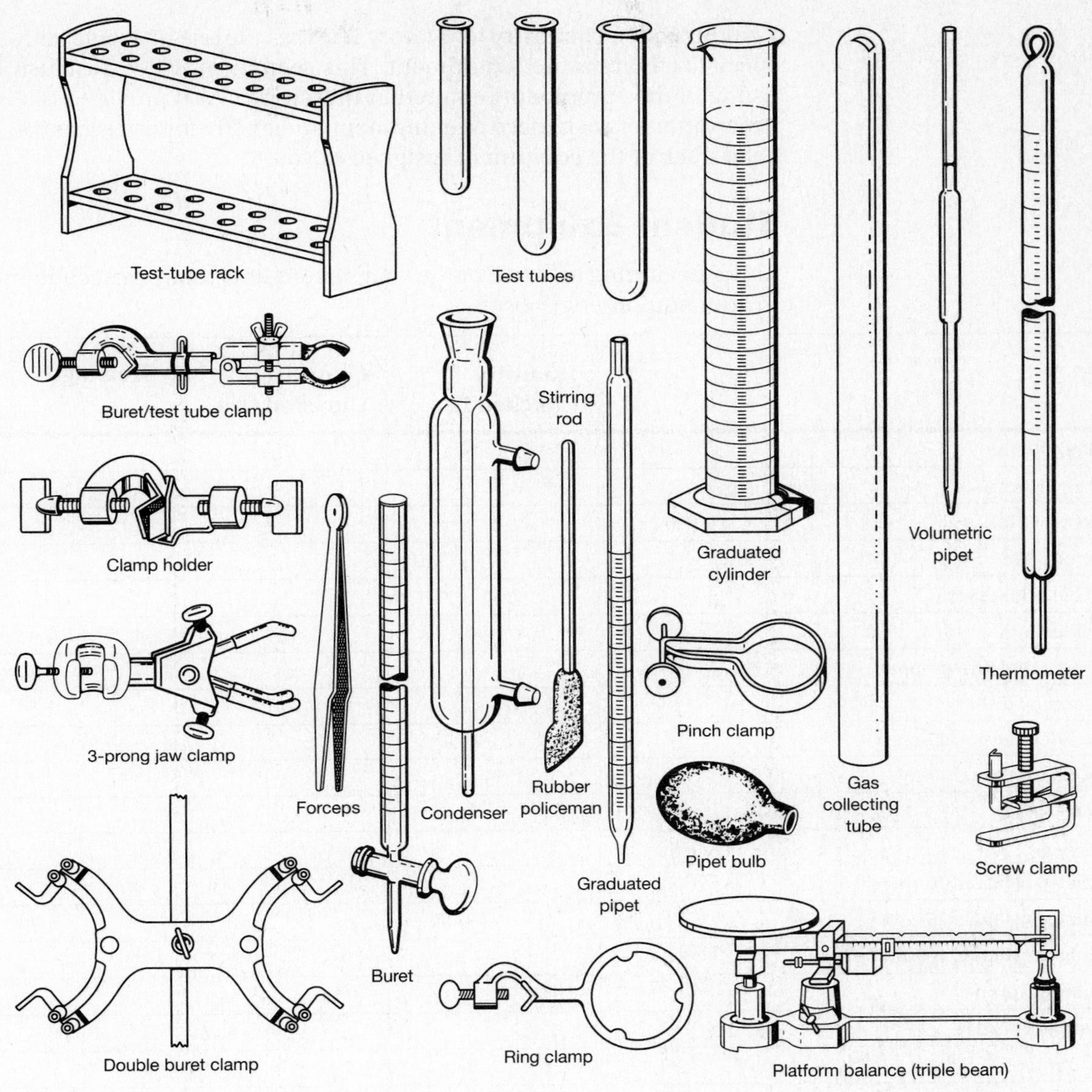

Plastic wash bottle: flexible plastic; squeeze sides to dispense water.
Platform balance: also known as a triple-beam balance.
Pneumatic trough: galvanized container with shelf; used in experiments where a gas is collected.
Ring stand: metal rod fixed upright in a heavy metal base; has many uses as a support.
Rubber stoppers: several sizes.
Rubber tubing: used to connect apparatus to transfer liquids or gases.
Safety goggles: plastic; must be worn at all times while working in the laboratory.
Screw clamp, pinch clamp: metal; used to block off rubber tubbing.
Spatula, scoopula: metal or porcelain; used to transfer solid chemicals; the scoopula has a larger capacity.
Stirring rod and rubber policeman: glass with rubber sleeve; used to stir, assist in pouring liquids, and for removing precipitates from a container.
Test-tube brush: bristles with wire handle; used to scrub small-diameter glassware.
Test-tube holder: spring metal; used to hold test tubes or glass tubing.
Test-tube rack: wood or plastic; holds test tubes in a vertical position.
Test tubes: glass; common sizes small (13 mm × 100 mm), medium (20 mm × 150 mm), large (25 × 200 mm); may be heated.
Thermometer: non-mercury; common range −10°C to 110°C.
Triangular file: metal; used to scratch glass tubing prior to breaking to desired length.
Tripod: iron; used to support containers of chemicals above the flame of a burner.
Volumetric pipet: glass; common sizes are 10 mL, 25 mL; used to measure solution volumes accurately; must not be heated.
Watch glass: glass; used to cover an evaporating dish or beaker.
Wide-mouth bottle: glass; used with pneumatic trough.
Wire gauze: used to spread the heat of a burner flame.

EQUIPMENT

Working in the chemistry laboratory requires the use of a wide variety of specialized laboratory equipment. This section provides an illustrated listing of the equipment required in this course. Also provided is a brief description of each piece of equipment and an inventory list so you can keep track of the equipment assigned to you.

Student Equipment

At the beginning and end of the year, record how many of each item are in your equipment drawer.

Item	Quantity Checked In	Quantity Checked Out	Breakage
beaker, 100-mL			
beaker, 250-mL			
beaker, 400-mL			
ceramic plate			
crucible, with cover			
crucible tongs			
dropper pipet (eye dropper)			
evaporating dish			
flask, Erlenmeyer, 125-mL			
flask, Erlenmeyer, 250-mL			
forceps			
funnel			
graduated cylinder, 10-mL			
graduated cylinder, 25-mL			
graduated cylinder, 100-mL			
laboratory apron			
mortar and pestle			
safety goggles			
screw clamp or pinch clamp			
spatula, scoopula			
stirring rod and policeman			
test tube, 13 mm × 100 mm (small)			
test tube, 20 mm × 150 mm (medium)			
test tube holder			
thermometer (−10°C to 110°C), non-mercury			
triangle			
watch glass			
wire gauze			

LABORATORY TECHNIQUES

Working in the chemistry laboratory, you will be handling potentially dangerous substances and performing unfamiliar tasks. This section provides you with a guide to the safe laboratory techniques needed in this course. While performing experiments throughout the year, refer back to this section any time you are unsure of proper laboratory techniques.

Pouring Liquids

- Always read the label on a reagent bottle before using its contents.
- Always wear safety goggles when handling chemicals.
- Never touch chemicals with your hands.
- Never return unused chemicals to their original containers. To avoid waste, do not take excessive amounts of reagents.

Follow this procedure when pouring liquids:

1. Use the back of your fingers to remove the stopper from a reagent bottle. Hold the stopper between your fingers until the transfer of liquid is complete. Do not place the stopper on your workbench.

2. Grasp the container from which you are pouring with the palm of your hand covering the label.

3a. When you are transferring a liquid to a test tube or measuring cylinder, the container should be held at eye level. Pour the liquid slowly, until the correct volume has been transferred.

3b. When you are pouring a liquid from a reagent bottle into a beaker, the reagent should be poured slowly down a glass stirring rod (Figure 1). When you are transferring a liquid from one beaker to another, you can hold the stirring rod and beaker in one hand.

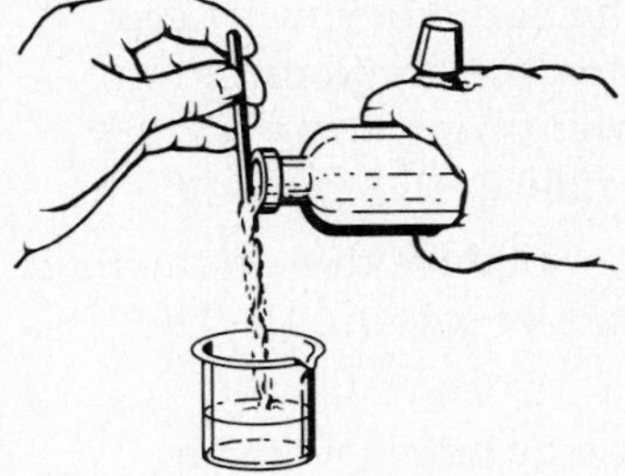

Figure 1 *Pouring from a reagent bottle into a beaker.*

Filtering a Mixture

Sometimes it is necessary to separate a solid from a liquid. The most common method of separating such a mixture is filtration.

1. Fold a filter paper circle in half and then quarters. Open the folded paper to form a cone, with one thickness of paper on one side and three thicknesses on the other (Figure 2).

2. Put the paper cone in a filter funnel. Place the funnel in an iron ring clamped to a ring stand. Moisten the filter paper with a small volume of distilled water, and gently press the paper against the sides of the funnel to achieve a good fit. (If the correct size of filter paper has been used, the top edge of the cone will be just below the rim of the filter funnel.)

3. Place a beaker beneath the funnel to collect the filtrate. The tip of the funnel should touch the inside surface of the beaker and extend about one inch below the rim (Figure 3).

Figure 2 *Folding the filter paper.*

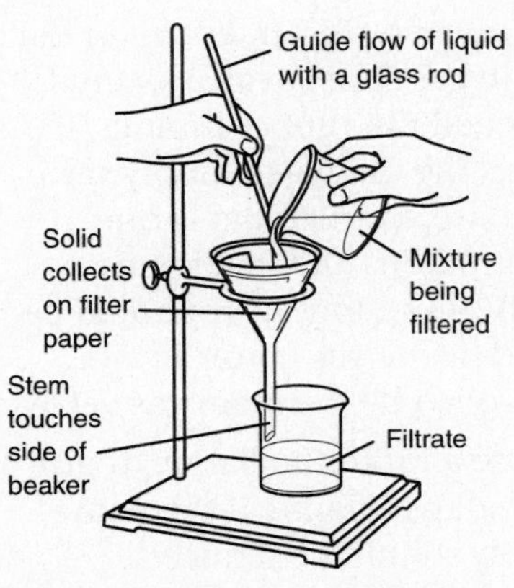

Figure 3 *Filtration assembly.*

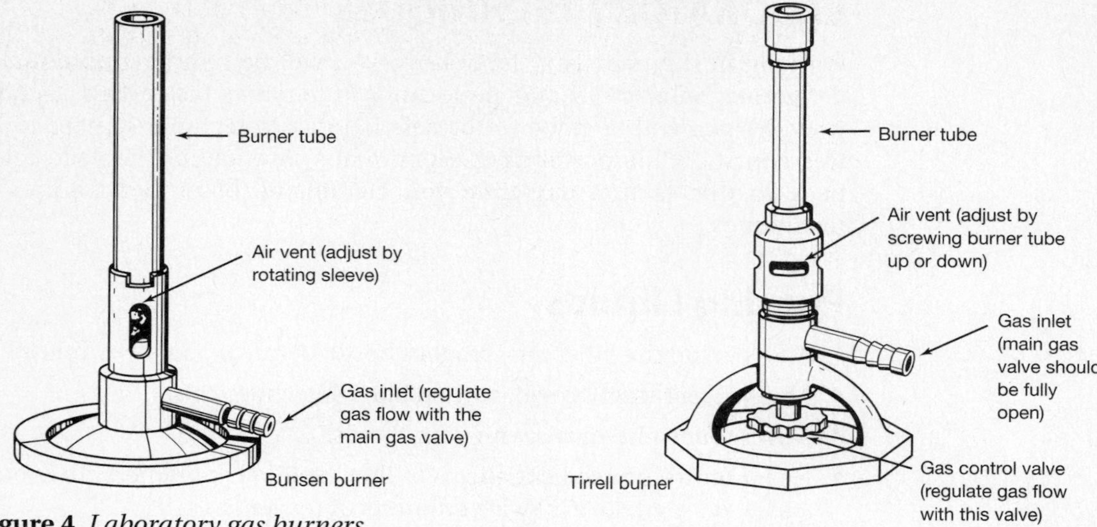

Figure 4 *Laboratory gas burners.*

4. Decant the liquid from the solid by pouring it down a glass stirring rod into the funnel. Be careful to keep the liquid below the top edge of the cone of filter paper at all times; the liquid must not overflow. Finally, use a jet of distilled water from a wash bottle to wash the solid from the beaker into the filter.
5. When the filtration is complete, wash the solid residue on the filter paper with distilled water to remove traces of solvent. Dry the solid.
6. If the filtrate contains a dissolved salt, it may be recovered by evaporation if desired.

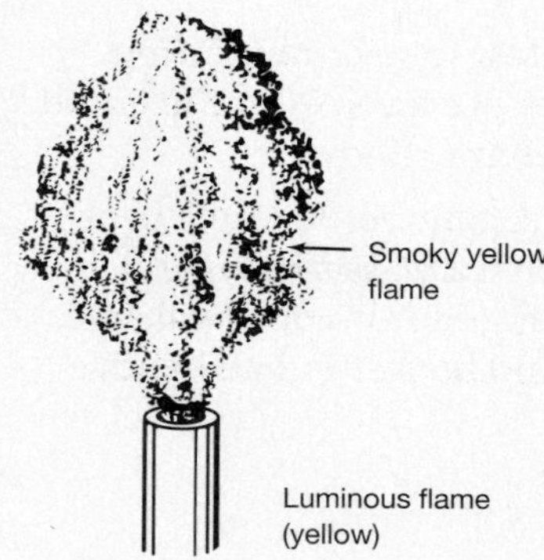

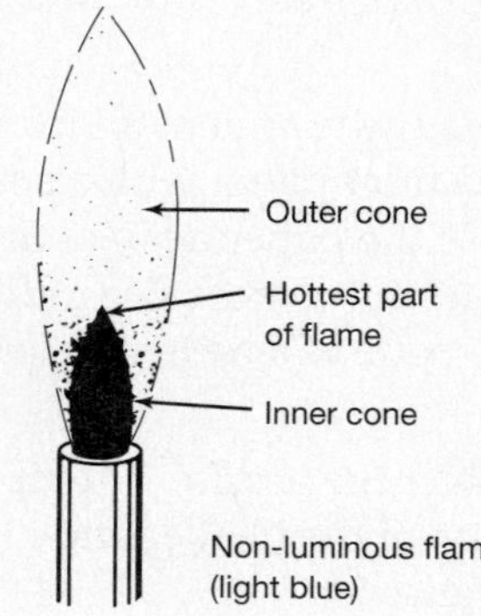

Figure 5 *Burner flame characteristics.*

Using a Gas Burner

Laboratory gas burners produce various kinds of flames when different mixtures of gas and air are burned. The two most common models are the Bunsen burner and the Tirrell burner. Both have adjustable air vents; the Tirrell burner has a gas control valve in its base (Figure 4).

1. Examine your laboratory burner. Determine which model you have.
2. Connect the burner to the gas supply with rubber tubing.
3. Close the air vents. If your model is a Tirrell burner, also close the gas control valve at the base of the burner.
4. Hold a lighted match at the top of the burner tube and turn on the gas supply. Do this by opening the main gas supply valve located on top of the nozzle to which you attached the rubber tubing. (If your model is a Tirrell burner, first open the main gas supply valve, then open the gas control valve at the base approximately one-half-turn.) You should get a yellow, or luminous, flame (Figure 5). When a Tirrell burner is used, the main gas supply valve should be opened fully and the gas flow regulated by the gas control valve. Gas supply to a Bunsen burner is controlled by the main gas valve.
5. Open the air vents slowly, to admit more air into the flame, to produce a light blue (nonluminous) cone-shaped flame. If the flame "blows out" after lighting, the gas supply should be reduced.

6. Adjust the air vents and gas supply to produce the desired size of flame. For most laboratory work, the blue inner cone of the flame should be about 1 inch high and free of yellow color. If you want a smaller flame, close the air vent slightly and reduce the gas supply. You will learn how to control the burner flame by trial and error.
7. Turn the burner off at the main gas supply valve when done.

   CAUTION: *Confine long hair and loose clothing when using a gas burner. Do not reach over a burner. Ensure that flammables are not being used when a burner is lit. Never leave a lit burner unattended. Know the location of fire extinguishers, the fire blanket, and safety shower.*

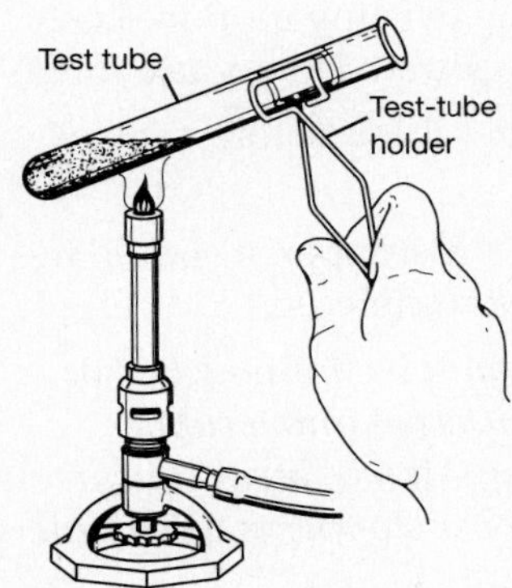

Figure 6 *Heating a liquid in a test tube.*

Heating Liquids

Heating a Liquid in a Test Tube

The correct procedure for heating liquids in the laboratory is important to laboratory safety.

1. Adjust your gas burner to produce a gentle blue flame.
2. Fill a test tube one-third full with the liquid to be heated.
3. Grasp the test tube with a test-tube holder, near the upper end of the tube.
4. Hold the test tube in a slanting position in the flame, and gently heat the tube a short distance below the surface of the liquid (Figure 6).
5. Shake the tube gently as it is being heated, until the liquid boils or reaches the desired temperature.

   CAUTION: *Never point the open end of a test tube you are heating either toward yourself or anyone working nearby. Never heat the bottom of the test tube.*

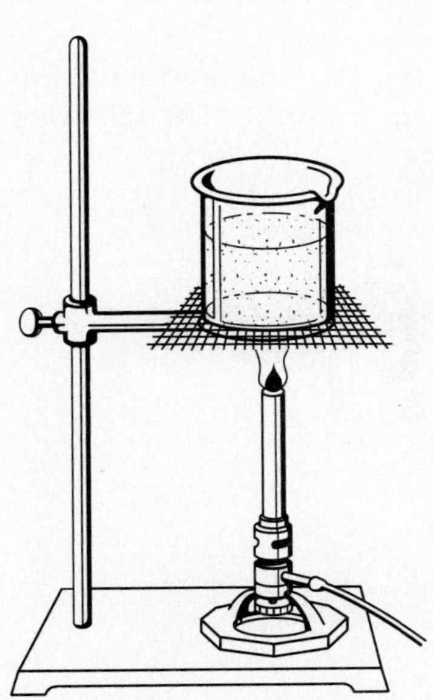

Figure 7 *Heating a liquid in a beaker.*

Heating a Liquid in a Beaker

Many laboratory experiments require the use of a hot water or boiling water bath. This procedure describes how to assemble a water bath.

1. Fasten an iron ring securely to a ring stand so that it is 2–4 cm above the top of a gas burner placed on the ring stand base.
2. Place a 250-mL beaker one-half-filled with water on a wire gauze resting on the iron ring (Figure 7).
3. Light your gas burner and adjust it to produce a hot flame.
4. Place the burner beneath the wire gauze. For a slower rate of heating, reduce the intensity of the burner flame.

   CAUTION: *Never heat plastic beakers or graduated glassware in a burner flame. Never let a boiling water bath boil dry; add water to it as necessary.*

Inserting Glass Tubing

In many experimental procedures, you are required to insert a thermometer or a length of glass tubing into a hole in a rubber stopper. It is essential that you know the correct way to do this. Otherwise, serious injury may result.

1. Lubricate the end of the glass tubing with a few drops of water, washing-up liquid, glycerol, or vegetable oil.
2. Hold the glass tubing close to where it enters the hole in the rubber stopper. Protect your hands with work gloves or pieces of cloth.
3. Ease the tubing into the hole with a gentle twisting motion. Push the tubing through the hole as far as is required. Do not use force!
4. Wipe excess lubricating material from the tubing before continuing with the experiment.
5. If the glass tubing is to be removed from the stopper, it should be done immediately after the experiment is completed.

   CAUTION: *The end of the glass tubing should be fire-polished or smoothed with emery cloth before being inserted into a rubber stopper. Do not try to bend the glass tubing—it will break. Ensure that the palm of the hand holding the rubber stopper is not in line with the emerging glass tube.*

Measuring Mass

In many experiments you are required to determine the mass of a chemical used or produced in a reaction. An object's mass is determined by measuring it on a balance. When you determine the mass of an object, you are comparing its mass with a known mass. In SI, the base unit of mass is the kilogram.

There are many types of laboratory balances. The one used most frequently in schools is the centigram balance (Figure 8). The following general rules apply to the use of all balances:

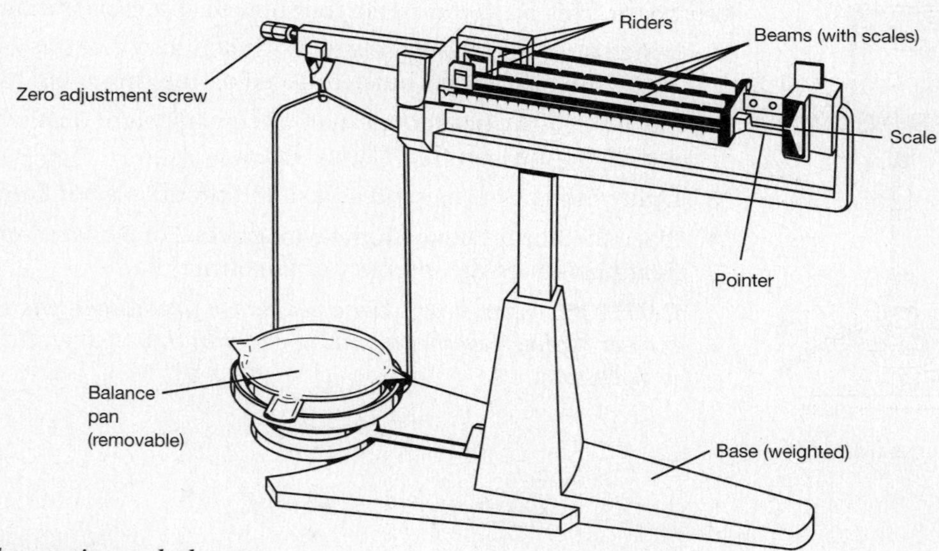

Figure 8 *The centigram balance.*

- Check the balance before you start. The balance pan should be empty and clean, and all masses (or dials) should be set on zero. The balance must be level. Check the bubble level on the base. See your teacher if you need assistance with checking your balance.
- Objects to be placed directly on the balance pan must be clean, dry, and at room temperature. Solid chemicals and liquids must never be put directly on the balance pan. Liquid samples should be placed in beakers or sealed containers. Solid chemicals can be conveniently placed in beakers, disposable plastic weighing boats, or on 10-cm squares made of glossy paper.
- The balance is a precision instrument that must be handled with care. To avoid damaging it, always be sure that the balance is in an arrested position when objects are placed on or removed from the pan. Always turn all dials slowly.
- Never move or jar either a balance or the balance table.
- If you spill a chemical on or near the balance, clean it up immediately. If in doubt, inform your teacher. A camel-hair brush is usually provided to wipe minute traces of solid from the balance pan before you use it.
- Never attempt to measure an object with a mass greater than the maximum capacity of the balance.
- When you are done, return all the masses to zero, and make sure the balance pan is clean.

Do not attempt to use a balance until your teacher has demonstrated the proper technique.

Using a Centigram Balance

1. Examine a centigram balance. The maximum capacity for this balance is 300 g and the sensitivity (limit of detection) is 0.01 g. The balance has four beams and four riders.
2. Move all the riders to their zero points (to the left side of their respective beams). Ensure that the riders rest in the notches on the beams.
3. Check to see that the beam is balanced. The pointer should move the same distance above and below the zero line on the scale or come to rest at the zero line. Use the zero adjustment screw if necessary. Always zero the balance before you begin. When the balance has been checked and adjusted, you are ready to begin.
4. Place the object whose mass is to be determined on the pan. (It must be dry and at room temperature.)
5. Slide the riders gently along the beams, one at a time, beginning with the largest. If a beam is notched, be sure that the rider is in a notch. Note that all the beams have notches except the one carrying the smallest rider. When the added masses (the positions of the riders) are equal to the mass of the object on the pan, then the pointer will be on the zero line. It may also swing equal distances above and below the zero line.
6. To record the mass of the object, sum the masses indicated by the positions of the riders on their respective beams.
7. Return all riders to zero and remove your sample. Make sure that the balance pan is left clean.

Measuring Volume

Volume measurements are important in many experimental procedures. Sometimes volume measurements must be accurate; other times they can be approximate. Most volume measures in the laboratory are made using equipment calibrated in milliliters. Although some beakers have graduation marks, these marks are designed only for quick, rough estimates of volume. Accurate volumes must be measured with pipets, burets, or volumetric flasks.

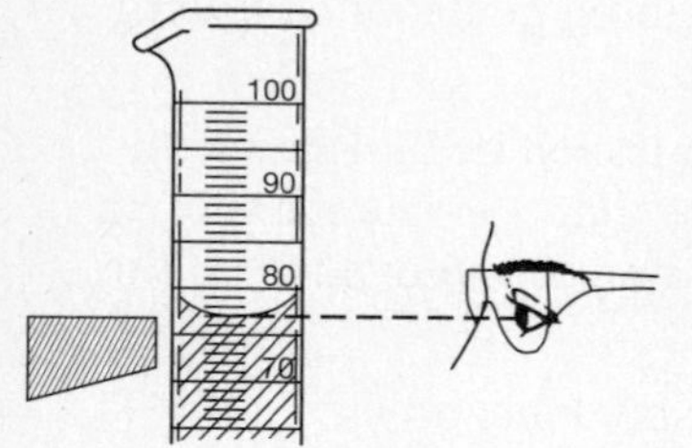

Figure 9 *Reading volume in a graduated cylinder.*

Using a Graduated Cylinder

Half-fill a 100-mL graduated cylinder with water, and set the cylinder on your laboratory bench. Examine the surface of the water. Notice how the surface curves upward where the water contacts the cylinder walls. This curved surface is called a *meniscus.*

A volume measurement is always read at the bottom of the meniscus, with your eye at the same level as the liquid surface. To make the meniscus more visible, you can place your finger or a dark piece of paper behind and just below the meniscus while making the reading (Figure 9).

Graduated cylinders are available in many capacities. The 100-mL cylinder is marked in 1-mL divisions, and volumes can be estimated to the nearest 0.1 mL. The last digit in these measurements is therefore significant but uncertain.

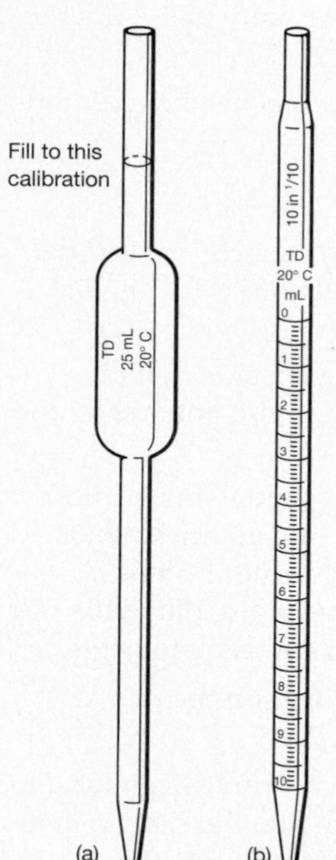

Figure 10 *(a) The volumetric pipet and (b) the graduated pipet.*

Using a Pipet

A pipet is used to accurately measure and deliver volumes of liquids. Two types are in common use: volumetric pipets and graduated, or measuring, pipets (Figure 10). The use of a volumetric pipet will be described. A volumetric pipet has a single calibration mark and delivers the volume printed on the bulb of the pipet at the temperature specified. (A graduated pipet has calibrations along the length of the pipet.) Volumes can be measured more accurately with a volumetric pipet than with a graduated pipet.

1. Place the tip of the pipet below the surface of the liquid to be dispensed.
2. Compress a pipet bulb and press the hole in the bulb against the upper end of the pipet. **CAUTION:** *Never fill a pipet by applying suction with your mouth.* Never push the pipet bulb over the end of the pipet.
3. Slowly release pressure on the bulb so that liquid is drawn into the pipet to a level about 2 cm above the calibration mark.
4. Remove the bulb and simultaneously place your index finger over the end of the pipet. If you are right-handed, you should hold the pipet in your right hand and the pipet bulb in your left (Figure 11).
5. Keep your index finger pressed firmly against the end. Withdraw the pipet from the liquid, and carefully wipe the outside of the stem with a paper towel.

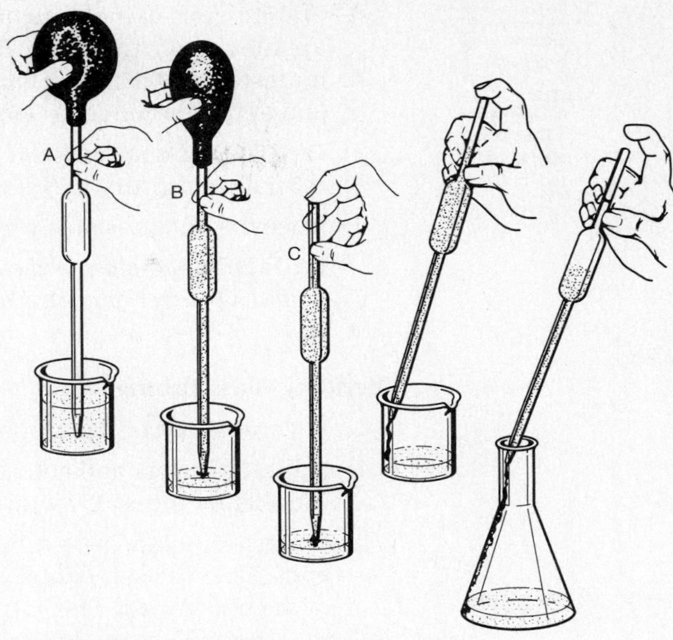

Figure 11 *Filling and emptying a pipet.*

6. Slowly reduce the pressure on your finger to allow the excess liquid to drain into a waste receiver, until the bottom of the meniscus is at the calibration mark.
7. Now, deliver the remaining liquid in the pipet into the designated receiver. When releasing liquid from a volumetric pipet, let it drain completely. Wait 20 seconds, then touch the pipet tip to the side of the flask or surface of the liquid. This action will remove some, but not all, of the liquid in the tip. The pipet delivers the stated volume when this procedure is followed. A small amount of liquid remains in the tip. Do not blow this out into your receiver.

Glassworking

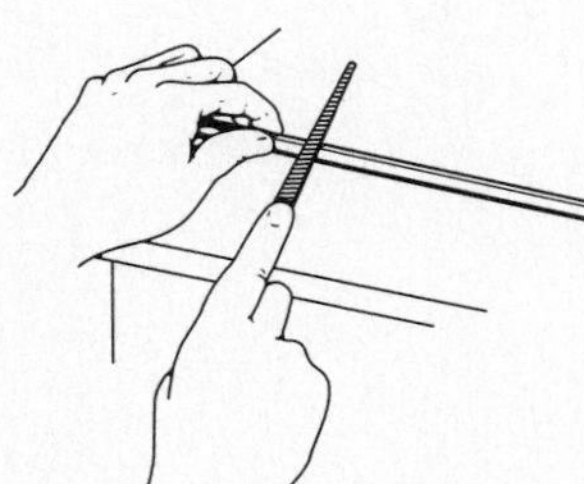

Figure 12

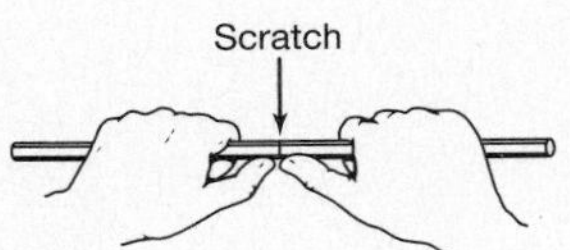

Figure 13

Cutting and Fire Polishing

1. Place the glass tubing or glass rod on a flat surface (such as the laboratory bench).
2. Hold the glass tightly with one hand close to the area to be cut.
3. Using a firm stroke, make a *single* deep scratch with a triangular file (Figure 12).

   CAUTION: *Do not use a sawing motion or repeated scratching.*
4. Grasp the glass in both hands with the scratch facing away from you and both thumbs directly behind the scratch (Figure 13).
5. Push firmly with the thumbs and pull with your fingers. The glass should snap with a clean break.

   CAUTION: *Be careful with the cut ends of the glass. They may be sharp and jagged. Do not attempt to break glass tubing having an outside diameter greater than 6 mm.*

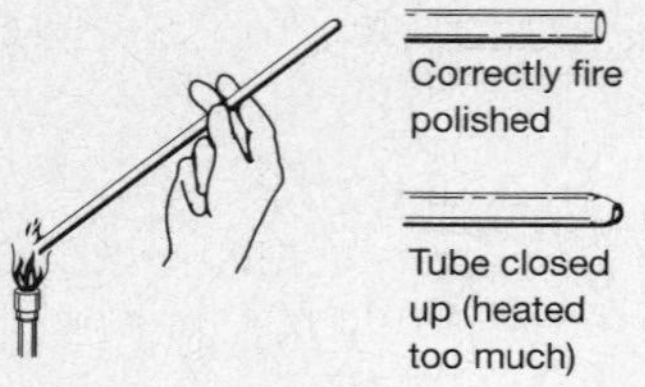

Figure 14

6. The cut ends of the glass tubing should be fire-polished to make the tubing safe to handle. Rotate one end of the glass tube in the hottest part of a burner flame, until the sharp edges have softened and become rounded (Figure 14).

   CAUTION: *Do not hold the tubing in the flame too long. If you do, the hole in the tube will close.*

7. Place the hot glass on a wire gauze square to cool.

   CAUTION: *Hot glass and cold glass look alike. Make sure one end of a piece of glass has cooled before you attempt to fire-polish the other end.*

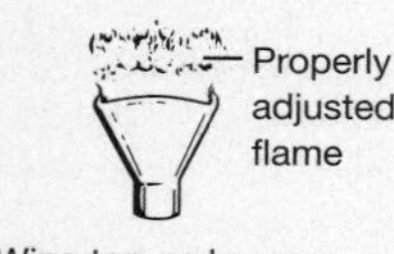

Wing top on burner

Figure 15

Bending Glass Tubing

1. Put a wing top or flame spreader on your gas burner.
2. Light the burner and adjust the flame to produce an even blue (hot) flame across the wing top (Figure 15).
3. Grasp a length of glass tubing that has been fire-polished at both ends. Hold the center of it lengthwise in the flame, just at the top of the blue region. This is the hottest part of the flame (Figure 16).
4. Rotate the tubing in the flame to heat approximately a 5-cm section uniformly, until it becomes soft and just begins to sag.
5. Remove the tubing from the flame and bend it to the desired shape in one movement (Figure 17). Examples of good and bad bends are shown in Figure 18.
6. When it has hardened, put the glass tubing on a wire gauze to cool.

   CAUTION: *Hot and cold glass look alike.*

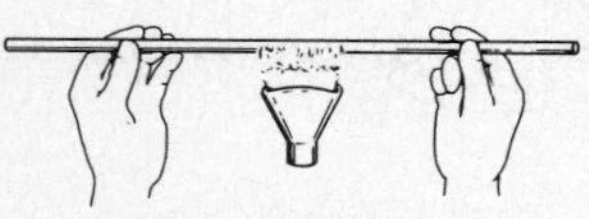

Heating glass tubing over a wing top prior to bending

Figure 16

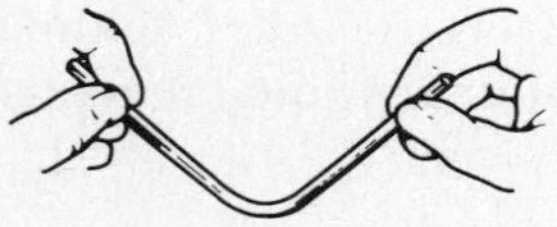

Bend and hold at desired angle

Figure 17

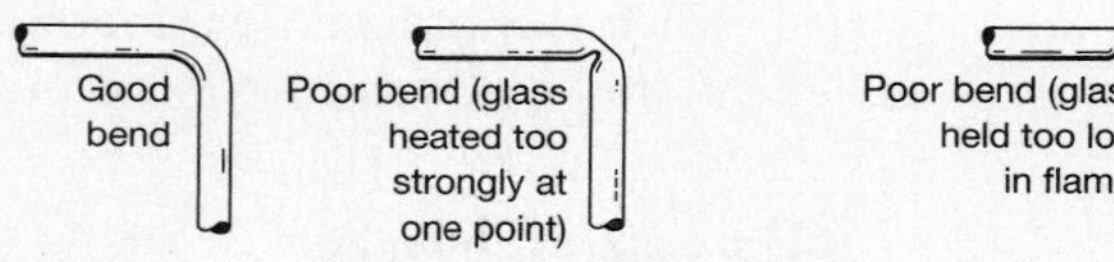

Figure 18

Name ______________ Date ______________ Class ______________

1 OBSERVING AND INFERRING

Text Reference
Section 1.3

Time Required
50 minutes

Objectives
- Make observations about the behavior of physical and chemical systems.
- Propose possible explanations, or hypotheses, for the observations.

Advance Preparation
saturated calcium ethanoate
The solubility of $(CH_3COO)_2Ca{\bullet}H_2O$ is approximately 50 g/100 mL distilled water.
0.05M silver nitrate
Dissolve 1.7 g of $AgNO_3$ in 200 mL of distilled water. Store the solution in brown or foil-wrapped bottles.
0.1M sodium hydroxide
Add 3.0 mL of 6*M* NaOH to 190 mL of distilled water and dilute to 200 mL. Keep sodium hydroxide solutions in full and tightly capped bottles to prevent formation of Na_2CO_3 by reaction of NaOH with atmospheric CO_2.
copper wire
Cut 10 lengths of copper wire that are each 7.5 cm long. Twist the strands of copper to form a "tree" as shown in Figure 1.1.

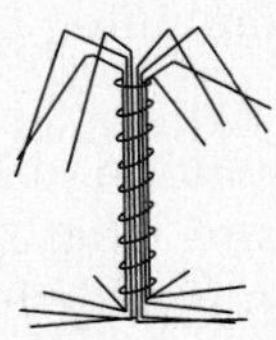

Figure 1.1
Copper wire tree

PURPOSE

To practice making observations and to learn how to formulate hypotheses that account for these observations.

BACKGROUND

Throughout the day, you use your senses to observe the world. You hear your alarm clock go off in the morning, you smell familiar odors as you approach the school cafeteria, and you see your friend walking down the hall toward you.

Observation, followed by the development of a hypothesis, are often the first steps in a scientific method. Experiments are then designed and carried out to test the hypothesis under controlled conditions. If the results of the initial experiment support the hypothesis, additional testing is done to further test the hypothesis. If, however, the experimental results do not support the original hypothesis, then the hypothesis must be changed or modified. When the results of many, many experiments support a hypothesis, it may become a theory. A theory is a well-tested explanation for a broad set of observations.

Your teacher will do a series of demonstrations, and you will make and record observations. You will then formulate hypotheses to explain your observations.

MATERIALS

(Teacher demonstration)
2 insulated gloves
crucible tongs
safety goggles and apron
3 watch glasses
3 100-mL beakers
4 glass stirring rods
3 250-mL beakers
plastic wash bottle
2-L graduated cylinder
ice
dry ice [C]
cornstarch
copper wire
0.05*M* silver nitrate [C] [T]
distilled water
manganese(IV) oxide [T]
3% hydrogen peroxide
wood splints
matches
calcium ethanoate
95% ethanol [F] [T]
universal indicator solution
0.1*M* sodium hydroxide [C] [T]

Name ______________________ Date ________________ Class ______________

You can use petri dishes and an overhead projector for the comparison of ice and dry ice.

Use of MnO_2 powder will permit a rapid reaction in Step 5. If MnO_2 chips are used, the reaction will take longer and 2–3 minutes should be allowed for the concentration of $O_2(g)$ to build up before administering the splint test.

Skin discoloration by $AgNO_3$ can be prevented by dipping the affected part in a dilute (0.1*M*) solution of sodium hyposulfite ($Na_2S_2O_3 \bullet 5H_2O$, also called sodium thiosulfate) immediately after contact with the $AgNO_3(aq)$.

Use the following disposal methods for chemical waste.

Disposal 1: Cu(*s*) in Step 3.

Disposal 3: The reaction solution in Step 7.

Disposal 2: All other chemical wastes.

Step 3.

$Cu(s) + 2Ag^+(aq) \rightarrow Cu^{2+}(aq) + 2Ag(s)$

Step 5.

$2H_2O_2(aq) \xrightarrow{MnO_2(s)} 2H_2O(l) + O_2(g)$

Step 6.

After the gel forms, invert the beaker.

Step 7.

$2NaOH(aq) + CO_2(g) \rightarrow Na_2CO_3(aq) + H_2O(l)$

The equilibrium reactions that occur when CO_2 dissolves in water are:

$CO_2(g) + H_2O(l) \rightleftharpoons H_2CO_3(aq)$

$H_2CO_3 \rightleftharpoons H^+(aq) + HCO_3^-(aq)$

SAFETY FIRST!

In this lab, your teacher will perform the demonstrations. Some of the solutions may contain harmful materials. Handle chemicals only when instructed to do so by the teacher. Observe all precautions, especially the ones listed below. If you see a safety icon beside a step in the Procedure, refer to the list below for its meaning.

Caution: Do not touch the dry ice. It can cause frostbite. Use insulated gloves or tongs. (Step 1.)

Caution: Wear your safety goggles. (All steps.)

Caution: Avoid contact with silver nitrate solution. It can cause temporary skin discoloration and skin burns. (Step 3.)

Caution: Ethanol is flammable. (Step 6.)

Note: Your teacher will properly dispose of the materials.

PROCEDURE

Your teacher will perform the demonstrations. Record your observations in Data Table 1.

1. Place a piece of ice and a piece of dry ice on separate watch glasses. Observe what happens with time.
2. Add 30 g of cornstarch to three 100-mL beakers containing 10 mL, 15 mL, and 20 mL of water, respectively. Observe what happens when each mixture is stirred with its own glass stirring rod and when some of each mixture is picked up with the rod.

3. Place the copper wire tree (Figure 1.1) in a 250-mL beaker containing 200 mL of the silver nitrate solution. Observe this system at intervals during the class period.
4. Place several small pieces of dry ice in a plastic wash bottle half-filled with distilled water. Observe what happens when the jet assembly of the wash bottle is replaced and tightened.
5. Add a small amount of manganese(IV) oxide powder to 50 mL of hydrogen peroxide solution in a 250-mL beaker. Cover the beaker with a watch glass for 15 seconds. Observe what happens when a *glowing* wood splint is inserted into the upper part of the beaker.

6. Observe what happens when 50 mL of calcium ethanoate solution is poured into a 250-mL beaker containing 50 mL of ethanol.
7. Add about 20 drops of universal indicator solution to 1500 mL of water in a 2-L graduated cylinder. Record what happens when 150 mL of sodium hydroxide solution is added and the mixture is stirred. Observe what occurs when several small pieces of dry ice are added.

Name ______________ Date ______________ Class ______________

OBSERVATIONS

DATA TABLE 1: OBSERVATIONS	
System	Observations
ice dry ice	The ice melts; the volume of water produced is almost the same as that of ice. The volume of dry ice becomes smaller (as the dry ice sublimes). At the same time, water vapor from the air condenses on the dry ice and forms ice crystals—$H_2O(s)$. When all the dry ice has sublimed, the ice melts and forms a pool of water. Student observations should be consistent with this explanation.
cornstarch 10 mL water cornstarch 15 mL water cornstarch 20 mL water	These systems (actually suspensions) have the appearance of thick white paint. When stirred or scraped, however, they tend to solidify. It is almost impossible to stir the system with the least amount of water. When stirring is stopped, the system again flows freely. Material picked up with a glass rod quickly changes from a "solid" to a free-flowing "liquid" and drips off the rod.
copper silver nitrate	The bright copper wire is coated immediately with a black substance. After a while, the colorless solution of $AgNO_3$ slowly turns blue. Silver-colored crystals collect on the copper wire.
dry ice wash bottle	The dry ice bubbles in the water. Water squirts from the jet until the wash bottle is empty.
manganese(IV) oxide hydrogen peroxide	Bubbles of O_2 form in the hydrogen peroxide and accumulate above the solution. A glowing splint bursts into flame when inserted into the upper part of the beaker.
calcium ethanoate ethanol	When the two liquids are mixed, the mixture instantly sets to form a white translucent gel. The mixture stays in the inverted beaker.
water universal indicator sodium hydroxide dry ice	When sodium hydroxide is added, the color of the solution changes from green to violet. When dry ice is added, the color slowly changes from violet through blue, green, and yellow [because the $CO_2(g)$ neutralizes the NaOH]. The solution becomes pale orange (when saturated with CO_2).

ANALYSES AND CONCLUSIONS

For each demonstration, suggest at least one explanation for the behavior that you observed.

1. ice and dry ice

   If students are having difficulty offering an explanation, have them compare what happens to the dry ice (a change from a solid to a vapor) and what happens when ice crystals form on the dry ice (a change from a vapor to a solid).

Name ______________________ Date ________________ Class ________________

2. cornstarch and water

Students may suggest that stirring causes some interaction between the cornstarch and water that is reversed when the stirring stops.

3. copper and silver nitrate

Students may recognize that the color changes and the formation of a solid are indicators that a chemical reaction has taken place. They might infer that copper "goes into" the water while silver "comes out of" the water.

4. dry ice in water-filled wash bottle

Students may correctly infer that the gas produced from the dry ice occupies a greater volume than the dry ice and, thus, forces the water out of the wash bottle.

5. manganese(IV) oxide, hydrogen peroxide, and wood splint

If students have seen a glowing splint used before, they may know that it is a test for oxygen. Otherwise, they may infer that a gas is produced that can support burning.

6. calcium ethanoate and ethanol

Mixtures of water and calcium ethanoate or water and ethanol do not form gels. Thus, students may infer that the water, ethanol, and calcium ethanoate interact to produce the gel.

7. sodium hydroxide, dry ice, and water with an indicator

Students are unlikely to know exactly what is happening. They might infer that the indicator reacts with the NaOH and the dry ice, or that the indicator, as its name implies, changes color in response to reactions among water, NaOH, and dry ice.

GOING FURTHER

Design an Experiment

Propose an experiment to test one of your explanations. If resources are available and you have your teacher's permission, perform the experiment.

2 PHYSICAL AND CHEMICAL CHANGE

Text Reference
Section 2.4

Time Required
50 minutes

Objectives
- Learn to discern the physical and chemical properties of substances.
- Classify observed changes in matter as physical or chemical.
- Demonstrate that mass is conserved in a chemical reaction.

Advance Preparation
Sulfur, iron filings, sodium hydrogen carbonate, sodium chloride, sucrose, and sand
Place a small amount (5–6 g) of each substance into labeled wide-mouth bottles. Provide a set for each work-station. Place a dedicated spatula next to each bottle.
Magnesium ribbon
Cut 40 strips of magnesium ribbon, 20 5-cm strips and 20 1-cm strips. Distribute the strips to students as needed. Do not allow them to have free access to the Mg.
6M hydrochloric acid
Pour 10 mL of concentrated HCl slowly into 10 mL of distilled water while stirring. Dispense in dropper bottles and distribute as needed.
Other materials
Cut 200 10 cm × 10 cm squares of paper for use in Parts A and B. Check to see that you have enough filter paper (30 circles) and distilled water on hand.

PURPOSE

To investigate the criteria used to distinguish between physical and chemical changes in matter.

BACKGROUND

Matter has both physical and chemical properties. A *physical property* is a quality or condition of a substance that can be observed or measured without changing the composition of the substance. Color is an example of a physical property. During a *physical change,* some properties of a sample of matter change, but the composition of the sample does not change. Melting and dissolving are examples of physical changes. A *chemical change* produces matter with a different composition than the original sample. A *chemical property* describes the ability of a substance to undergo a specific chemical change. The ability to rust is a chemical property of iron.

In this experiment, you will observe various materials and describe their physical properties. You will then cause some of the materials to undergo changes. Based upon your observations, you will determine whether the changes are physical changes or chemical changes.

MATERIALS (PER PAIR)

(Student Experiment)
safety goggles
spatula
magnifying glass
magnet
12 small test tubes
test-tube rack
2 100-mL beakers
glass stirring rod
funnel
ring stand
ring support
evaporating dish
gas burner
watch glass
plastic wash bottle
crucible tongs
wire gauze
test-tube holder
9 pieces paper, 10 cm × 10 cm
magnesium ribbon, Mg [F] [T]
sulfur, powdered, S [F] [T]
iron filings, Fe
sodium hydrogen carbonate, $NaHCO_3$
sodium chloride, NaCl
sucrose, $C_{12}H_{22}O_{11}$
sand
distilled water
coarse filter paper
2 pieces of exposed film
6*M* hydrochloric acid, HCl [C] [T]

(Teacher Demonstration)
small test tube
centigram balance
fume hood
gas burner
test-tube holder
magnet

Name ______________________ Date ______________ Class ______________

Point out the location of the $NaHCO_3$ for neutralizing acid spills and demonstrate the proper way to clean up a spill. When the acid is HCl, copious amounts of water should be used on spills affecting the skin or clothing. Caution students that 6*M* HCl looks just like water and that any stray drops of acid should be cleaned up immediately. Make certain that the students know the location of the eyewash station.

SAFETY FIRST!

In this lab, observe all precautions, especially the ones listed below. If you see a safety icon beside a step in the Procedure, refer to the list below for its meaning.

Caution: Wear your safety goggles. (All steps.)

Caution: Hydrochloric acid is very corrosive and can cause burns. (Steps 10, 12.)

Caution: Do not look directly at burning magnesium. The intense light may damage your eyes. View the magnesium reaction through exposed pieces of film. Do not inhale the smoke that is produced when magnesium burns. (Step 9.) Powdered sulfur is irritating to the moist membranes of the eyes, nose, and throat. Avoid getting the dust into the air. (Step 6.)

Caution: Do not taste any of the substances or touch them with your hands. (All steps.)

Caution: Hot glass looks just like cool glass. Once a test tube has been heated over an open flame, it may take several minutes for it to cool. Be sure that test tubes are cool before handling them. (Step 11.)

Caution: Magnesium is extremely flammable. Keep unused strips away from open flames. (Step 9.)

Note: Return or dispose of all materials according to the instructions of your teacher. (Steps 5, 13, 15.)

PROCEDURE

Part A. The Physical Properties of Matter

Record your observations for Part A in Data Table 1.

Step 1.
Warn students that using a single spatula for multiple chemicals will contaminate the chemicals. Emphasize that once chemicals have been taken out of their containers they should not be put back in.

1. Label a separate piece of paper for each of the seven substances to be examined. Place two pieces of magnesium ribbon, one 5 cm long and one 1 cm long, on the paper labeled "magnesium." Using the spatula supplied for each substance, transfer a pea-sized sample of the other substances to their correctly labeled papers.
2. Examine each substance with a magnifying glass. Record your observations in Data Table 1.
3. Test the effect of a magnet on each substance by passing the magnet under the sheet of paper.
4. In separate small test tubes, test the solubility of each substance by mixing a small amount of each sample with 3 mL of distilled water. "Flick" each test tube to mix the contents.

Step 4.
Demonstrate the height of about 3 mL of water in a small test tube. Demonstrate the proper technique for mixing solutions in a test tube. Hold the test tube at the top and flick the bottom of the tube repeatedly.

5. Return the strip of magnesium ribbon in the test tube to its paper. Follow your teacher's instructions for proper disposal of the other materials.

Name ____________ Date ____________ Class ____________

Part B. Causing a Physical or Chemical Change

Step 6.
Fine sulfur particles may adhere to the surface of the iron filings. A fairly good separation can be achieved with the magnet.

Step 8.
Demonstrate gravity filtration. The filtrate is NaCl(*aq*). After heating, the evaporation dish contains NaCl(*s*). The residue in the filter paper is sand, which generally contains a significant amount of quartz, SiO_2.

Record your observations for Part B in Data Table 2.

6. Mix the iron filings and sulfur on a clean piece of paper. Examine the mixture with a magnifying glass. Test the effect of a magnet by passing the magnet under the paper. Give this mixture to your teacher for use in Part C.

7. Mix the sodium chloride and sand on a clean piece of paper. Examine the mixture with a magnifying glass, and test the effect of a magnet.

8. Transfer the salt-sand mixture to a clean 100-mL beaker. Add about 30 mL of tap water and stir. Record your observations. Prepare a filtration setup as shown in Figures 2.1 and 2.2. Filter the mixture and record your observations. Pour about 10 mL of the filtrate into an evaporating dish. Convert your filtration setup into a setup you can use to heat the liquid in the evaporating dish. Heat the dish gently until the filtrate has completely evaporated. Examine both the dry residue in the evaporating dish and the wet residue on the filter paper.

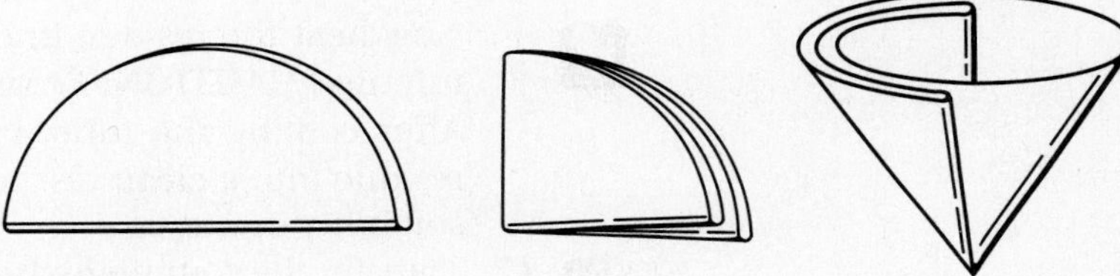

Figure 2.1

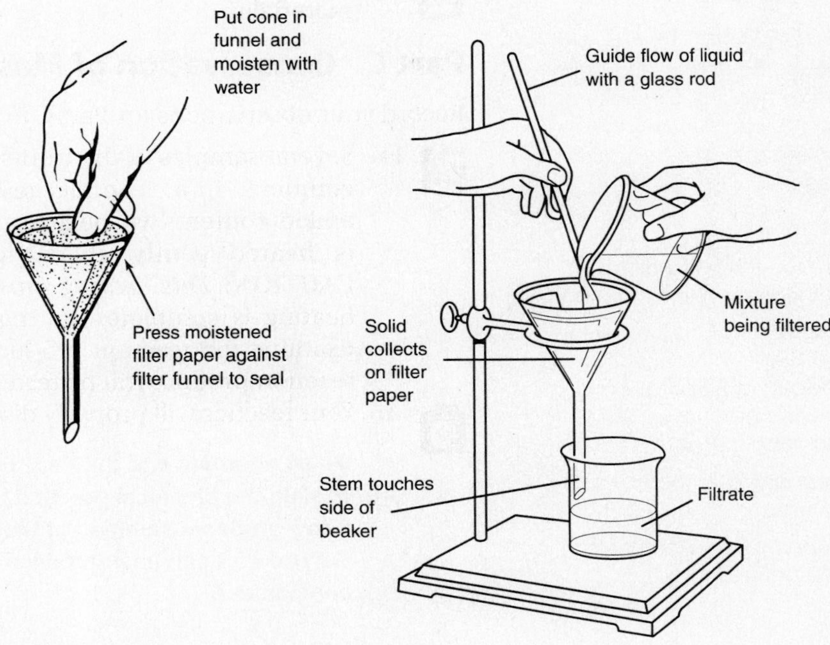
Put cone in funnel and moisten with water
Press moistened filter paper against filter funnel to seal
Guide flow of liquid with a glass rod
Mixture being filtered
Solid collects on filter paper
Stem touches side of beaker
Filtrate

Figure 2.2

Steps 9 and 10.
$2Mg(s) + O_2(g) \rightarrow 2MgO(s)$
$Mg(s) + 2HCl(aq) \rightarrow MgCl_2(aq) + H_2(g)$
$MgO(s) + 2HCl(aq) \rightarrow MgCl_2(aq) + H_2O(l)$

9. CAUTION: *Do not look directly at burning magnesium; look through the exposed film.* Position a watch glass near the gas burner. Using crucible tongs, grasp one end of the 5-cm strip of magnesium ribbon and hold it in the burner flame until the magnesium ignites. Quickly position the burning magnesium so that the combustion products fall on the watch glass. Compare the appearance of this product with that of the original magnesium ribbon.

10. Place the unburned 1-cm strip of magnesium and the combustion product from the watch glass into separate test tubes. Add 10 drops of 6*M* hydrochloric acid to each tube. Feel the bottom of each test tube. Record your observations.

Step 11.
Caution: Be sure that the students heat sucrose, not sulfur. Keep these chemicals separated so that students do not confuse them.
$C_{12}H_{22}O_{11}(s) + heat \rightarrow 12C(s) + 11H_2O(g)$

11. Put half of your sucrose sample into a test tube. **CAUTION:** *When heating a test tube, never point the mouth of it at yourself or anyone else.* Heat the tube gently in a burner flame and watch carefully for changes. Periodically remove the tube from the flame and check for odors by fanning the fumes toward your nose. Grasp the test tube with a test-tube holder and hold the test tube about 3–5 inches from your nose while fanning the vapors toward your nose.

Now heat the residue in the test tube more vigorously for 1–2 minutes. **CAUTION:** *Be sure the tube is cool before handling it.* After cooling the tube, use a spatula to scrape some of the residue into a clean test tube. Examine the residue and test its solubility in water.

Step 12.
$NaHCO_3(s) + HCl(aq) \rightarrow NaCl(aq) + H_2O(l) + CO_2(g)$

12. Transfer the sodium hydrogen carbonate sample to a test tube. Carefully add 5 drops of 6*M* hydrochloric acid. Touch the bottom of the test tube with your hand. Record your observations.

13. Follow your teacher's instructions for proper disposal of the materials.

Part C. Conservation of Mass (Teacher Demonstration)

Record your observations for Part C in Data Table 2.

Step 14.
Ideally, Fe and S should be combined in a mass ratio of approximately 1.7 to 1.0.
$Fe(s) + S(s) \rightarrow FeS(s)$
Mix the Fe and S thoroughly before heating. Because of incomplete reaction, the sample may still be slightly magnetic.

14. Several samples of the iron-sulfur mixture from Part B will be combined in a clean, dry test tube. The mass of the test tube and its contents will be determined and recorded. The test tube is heated gently, then vigorously, for several minutes. **CAUTION:** *This heating must be done in a fume hood.* After heating is complete, the mass is remeasured and recorded. Examine the reaction product. The effect of a magnet on the reaction product will be tested.

15. Your teacher will properly dispose of the materials.

As an alternative to the Fe-S demonstration, Step 14, explain the chemical reaction between Fe and S. Show students samples of the reaction product, FeS. Bars of FeS can be purchased from chemical supply companies.

Use the following disposal methods for chemical waste.
Disposal 1: Fe(s) in Part A and Step 14; NaCl(s) in Step 7; Mg(s) in Step 10; C(s) reaction product in Step 11; and sand in Part A.
Disposal 2: All other wastes in Part A.
Disposal 3: All materials in solution in Step 10.

Name ______________________ Date ________________ Class ________________

OBSERVATIONS

DATA TABLE 1: PHYSICAL PROPERTIES OF MATTER

Substance and Formula	Physical State	Color	Odor	Dissolves in water	Effect of Magnet
sulfur, S	solid	yellow	unique	no	not attracted
iron filings, Fe	solid	gray	none	no	attracted
sodium hydrogen carbonate, $NaHCO_3$	solid	white	none	yes	not attracted
sodium chloride, NaCl	solid	white	none	yes	not attracted
sucrose, $C_{12}H_{22}O_{11}$	solid	white	none	yes	not attracted
sand, SiO_2	solid	sandy	none	no	not attracted
magnesium, Mg	solid	gray	none	no	not attracted

DATA TABLE 2: OBSERVATIONS OF PHYSICAL AND CHEMICAL CHANGES

System	Observations
Fe and S mixture —tested with magnet	Fe is still attracted to the magnet.
NaCl and sand mixture —mixed with water —filtered —filtrate allowed to evaporate	Can still see particles of salt and sand; salt "disappears" (dissolves) when water is added; filtration leaves sand on filter paper; evaporation of water leaves salt in evaporating dish.
Mg —burned in air	Burning of magnesium leaves a residue of white solid, MgO.
Mg —reacted with 6*M* HCl	Magnesium "disappears"; gas (H_2) is produced; clear, colorless solution is obtained.
product of burning —reacted with 6*M* HCl	White solid dissolves to give clear, colorless solution; no gas is produced.
$C_{12}H_{22}O_{11}$ —heated	The sugar turns brown, then black; some solid dissolves in water to give a deep brown solution; the solution has the odor of caramel or burnt toffee.
$NaHCO_3$ —reacted with 6*M* HCl	Sodium hydrogen carbonate dissolves; gas (CO_2) is produced.
Fe and S mixture —heated initial mass final mass	Color changes from yellow to dark gray. The product is not attracted to the magnet. 31.74 g 31.67 g

Name ______________________ Date ________________ Class ________________

ANALYSES AND CONCLUSIONS

1. The following is a list of changes you observed in Parts B and C. Indicate whether each change was a physical change or a chemical change and give reasons for your answer.

   a. Mixing iron and sulfur. (Part B, Step 6)

   Physical change. The iron is still attracted to the magnet, and the particles of iron and sulfur can still be distinguished.

   b. Mixing salt, sand, and water. (Part B, Step 8)

   Physical change. Water, salt, and sand can be recovered, unchanged, from the mixture by filtration, then evaporation.

   c. Burning magnesium. (Part B, Step 9)

   Chemical change. The burning of magnesium involves a change in color, a change in physical appearance, the production of heat and light, and the production of smoke.

   d. Mixing magnesium and the product of burning magnesium with hydrochloric acid. (Part B, Step 10)

   Mg: Chemical change. Gas is produced.

   Combustion product: Chemical change. Heat is produced.

   e. Heating sucrose. (Part B, Step 11)

   Chemical change. Sucrose changes color from white to black, and gases are produced. The black product (consisting of carbon and a variety of other products) does not readily dissolve in water.

   f. Mixing sodium hydrogen carbonate and hydrochloric acid. (Part B, Step 12)

   Chemical change. Gas is produced.

   g. Heating iron and sulfur. (Part C, Step 14)

   Chemical change. The mixture of iron and sulfur changes appearance. The reaction product is not attracted to the magnet.

Name ______________ Date ______________ Class ______________

2. Was mass conserved in the reaction of iron and sulfur? Explain.

Yes. The mass after heating is essentially the same as before heating.

3. Except for the reaction between iron and sulfur, none of the reactions in this experiment can be used to demonstrate the law of conservation of mass. Explain why.

The other reactions involved the production of gases. These gases escaped into the atmosphere. Thus, the mass of the gas was "lost." The mass of this escaped gas was not measured and, as a consequence, the results would not have been consistent with the law of conservation of mass.

4. How do you decide whether an observed property of matter is a physical or chemical property?

A physical property can be observed and measured without changing the composition of a substance. A chemical property can be observed only during a chemical change.

5. What criteria are used to distinguish between a chemical change and a physical change?

A physical change does not change the composition of a substance. A chemical change does involve a change in the composition of a substance.

6. State in your own words the law of conservation of mass.

Mass is neither created nor destroyed in a chemical reaction.

Name ____________ Date ____________ Class ____________

GOING FURTHER

Develop a Hypothesis

The black residue left in Step 11 has a smaller mass than the original sucrose sample. Propose a hypothesis to explain this loss of mass.

Students may notice the condensation of a liquid at the mouth of the test tube. If so, their hypothesis should be that the sucrose breaks down into carbon (the black residue) and water.

Design an Experiment

Propose an experiment to test your hypothesis. If resources are available and you have your teacher's permission, perform the experiment.

To test this hypothesis, students can test the condensate with cobalt chloride paper to confirm that the second product is water.

Name ____________ Date ____________ Class ____________

3 OBSERVING A CHEMICAL REACTION

Text Reference
Section 2.4

Time Required
15–30 minutes

Objectives
- Record observations for the reaction of copper(II) chloride with aluminum.
- Distinguish between observations and interpretations.
- Classify observations as qualitative or quantitative.

Advance Preparation
Copper(II) chloride dihydrate
You will need approximately 80 g of reagent grade $CuCl{\bullet}2H_2O$ for 15 student pairs. Reagent grade copper(II) chloride crystals will give a clear, brilliantly colored solution. Technical grade crystals will yield a murky solution. The crystals should be placed in labeled wide-mouthed bottles and made available at each lab station.
Aluminum foil
Cut 20 8 cm × 8 cm squares. Dispense the aluminum foil yourself.

Demonstrate how easily a small beaker can be tipped over by a long thermometer.

PURPOSE

To learn how qualitative and quantitative observations of a chemical reaction are used to formulate a hypothesis.

BACKGROUND

You and a friend may have very different feelings about a movie you've just seen. You may disagree about whether you liked the movie or about the movie's intended meaning. Although you both have observed the same movie, your interpretations of the movie may differ. Distinguishing between observation and interpretation is very important in chemistry. An *observation* is a statement of fact, based on what you detect by your senses. An *interpretation* is your judgment or opinion about what you have observed. A statement such as "the liquid is clear and colorless" is an observation. It would be an interpretation to say, without further testing, that the clear and colorless liquid is water.

The purpose of this experiment is to help you distinguish observation from interpretation while examining a chemical reaction. Try to make as many observations of the reaction as possible. There are two types of observations. A *quantitative* observation is an observation that involves a measurement; a *qualitative* observation is a general description and does not involve a measurement. "The liquid is hot" is a qualitative observation. "The temperature of the liquid is 95.0°C" is a quantitative observation.

MATERIALS (PER PAIR)

safety goggles
100-mL beaker
plastic spoon
glass stirring rod
thermometer
copper(II) chloride dihydrate, $CuCl_2{\bullet}2H_2O$ [T] [I]
distilled water
aluminum foil, 8 cm × 8 cm

SAFETY FIRST!

In this lab, the solution you are working with may become quite hot following the addition of aluminum foil. Observe all precautions, especially the ones listed below. If you see a safety icon beside a step in the Procedure, refer to the list below for its meaning.

Caution: Wear safety goggles. (All steps.)

Caution: Copper(II) chloride is an irritant. Avoid skin contact with this chemical. (All steps.)

Name ______________________ Date ________________ Class ________________

Caution: Copper chloride is toxic by ingestion and inhalation. (Step 1.)

Note: Return or dispose of all materials according to the instructions of your teacher. (Step 5.)

PROCEDURE

As you perform the experiment, record your observations in Data Table 1.

1. Obtain and describe a sample of copper(II) chloride dihydrate, $CuCl_2{\cdot}2H_2O$.

2. Fill the 100-mL beaker about one-fourth full with distilled water. Without stirring, add 1 level teaspoonful of the solid to the water. Record your observations of both the solid and the water.
3. Use the glass stirring rod to stir the mixture until the solid is completely dissolved. Record your observations of the solution.

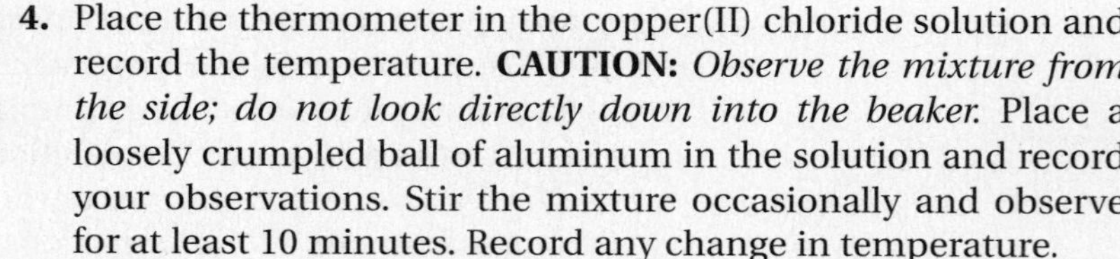

4. Place the thermometer in the copper(II) chloride solution and record the temperature. **CAUTION:** *Observe the mixture from the side; do not look directly down into the beaker.* Place a loosely crumpled ball of aluminum in the solution and record your observations. Stir the mixture occasionally and observe for at least 10 minutes. Record any change in temperature.

5. Follow your teacher's instructions for proper disposal of the materials.

Step 1.
Copper(II) chloride crystals are blue-green, rhombic needles.

Step 2.
Remind students to pay attention to quantities required in Step 2. Too dilute a solution of $CuCl_2$ will react very slowly with Al. If the instructions (one-fourth full and 1 teaspoon) are followed, the reaction proceeds nicely.

Step 4.
Students will observe the blue-green solution of $CuCl_2$ change to clear upon reaction with aluminum foil. A red-brown precipitate forms, heat is released, and H_2 gas is produced.

$$3Cu^{2+}(aq) + 4Al(s) + 6H^{+}(aq) \rightarrow 3Cu(s) + 4Al^{3+}(aq) + 3H_2(g)$$

Warn students that the beaker may become quite hot in the course of this reaction. Some spitting of the solution can occur as the gas is produced.

Use the following disposal methods for chemical waste.

Disposal 1: Cu(s) precipitate in Step 4.

Disposal 2: The reaction solution in Step 4.

Name ______________________ Date ________________ Class ________________

OBSERVATIONS

DATA TABLE 1: OBSERVATIONS	
System	Observations
dry copper(II) chloride dihydrate	The crystals are small in size and pale blue to dark blue-green in color. They resemble short needles in shape.
copper(II) chloride in water	The crystals on the bottom of the beaker appear green; the solution above becomes pale blue. After a few seconds, the solution just above the crystals becomes a deep green.
stirred copper(II) chloride in water	The crystals dissolve readily; the solution becomes blue-green.
copper(II) chloride solution plus aluminum foil	The foil is plated with copper and corrodes rapidly. A gas is produced and the solution becomes very warm. A red-brown precipitate drops to the bottom of the beaker.
initial temperature:	
final temperature:	

ANALYSES AND CONCLUSIONS

1. Check your observations. Cross out any that are interpretations rather than observations.
2. List each of your observations in one of four following sections. Number your observations consecutively. Circle the number of any observation that is quantitative.
   a. observations of the dry solid
   Ask each group to present one observation of the dry solid. Repeat the process with each section, starting with a different group each time.
   b. observations of the wet solid before stirring
   c. observations of the solution before addition of aluminum

d. observations of the reaction that occurs when the aluminum is added to the solution

3. Would you expect your observations or your interpretations to most closely match those of your classmates? Explain.

Observations should most closely match, because everyone is observing the same changes. Everyone may have a slightly different interpretation of the same events, depending on their previous experiences.

GOING FURTHER

Develop a Hypothesis

Based on the observations you made during this lab, develop a hypothesis about what happened when aluminum metal was added to the solution of copper(II) chloride.

Hypothesis: When aluminum metal is dropped into a solution of copper ions, a chemical reaction occurs. Copper is formed during the reaction. A compound of aluminum forms and dissolves in water.

Design an Experiment

Propose an experiment to test your hypothesis. If resources are available and you have the permission of your teacher, perform the experiment.

Repeat the experiment using a solution of copper(II) chloride and a thin rod of aluminum metal. Then perform similar experiments in which the copper(II) chloride solution is replaced with (a) copper(II) sulfate and (b) copper(II) nitrate.

Name ______________________ Date ______________ Class ______________

4 MASS, VOLUME, AND DENSITY

Text Reference
Section 3.2, 3.3, and 3.4

Time Required
30–40 minutes

Objectives
- Measure the mass and volume of different metals, using a balance and the method of water displacement.
- Show that the relationship between mass and volume is a constant for each unknown metal.
- Compute the density of each metal from its mass and volume.
- Draw conclusions and make predictions about the densities of different substances, based on data.

Advance Preparation
Metal samples
Obtain a sufficient amount of each metal as 1-cm-diameter rods. Saw the rods into different lengths between 2 cm and 5 cm. Each lab pair will test samples of the same two unknown metals: aluminum (A) and another metal (B). Sample B can be brass, iron, zinc, or stainless steel. Samples A and B should be different lengths in order to provide different data points for the graphical determination of density.

PURPOSE

To determine the densities of unknown metals.

BACKGROUND

An old riddle asks "Which is heavier, a pound of feathers or a pound of lead?" The question is nonsensical, of course, since a pound of feathers and a pound of lead both weigh the same, one pound. Nevertheless, there is a clearly something different about a small lead brick and a large bag of feathers, even though they weigh the same. The key to answering the riddle is understanding the relationship that exists between a substance's mass and the volume it occupies. This relationship is expressed by the physical property called density. *Density* is defined as the ratio of a substance's mass to the volume it occupies.

$$\text{Density} = \frac{\text{mass of substance (g)}}{\text{volume of substance (mL)}}$$

In this experiment, you will measure the mass and volume of several unknown materials. You will then use your data to explore the relationship between the mass and volume of the materials and to calculate their density.

After performing this lab, if someone asks you the riddle about feathers and lead, you can explain to them the difference between weight and density.

MATERIALS (PER PAIR)

safety goggles	ruler
centigram balance	metal samples
25-mL graduated cylinder	paper towels

SAFETY FIRST!

In this lab, observe all precautions, especially the ones listed below. If you see a safety icon beside a step in the Procedure, refer to the list below for its meaning.

Caution: Wear your safety goggles. (All steps.)

Note: Your teacher will properly dispose of the materials.

Name ____________________ Date ______________ Class ______________

Students will determine the mass/volume ratios for samples of two different metals. Class data will be combined and graphed. Students should learn that the mass/volume ratio is constant for a particular metal and that this constant ratio is called *density*. If time permits, students can test and analyze additional samples.

Analyses and Conclusions
Remind students that the measurement with the least number of significant figures determines the number of significant figures in a calculated answer (multiplication and division). The number of significant figures in a volume measurement made in a graduated cylinder generally depends on the size of the cylinder in the following way:

100 mL¬= ±1 mL
25 mL¬= ±0.5 mL
10 mL¬= ±0.2 mL

Refer students to the graphing review section in Appendix C of the textbook.

Provide students with clear plastic rulers for use in drawing the "best fit" line through their data points. The *y*-intercept for this line should be 0.

PROCEDURE

As you perform the experiment, record your data in Data Tables 1 and 2.

1. Determine the mass of two different unknown metal samples to the nearest 0.01 gram, using a centigram balance. Record the masses in Data Tables 1 and 2.
2. Find the volume of each metal sample by water displacement. Fill a 25-mL graduated cylinder about half-full with water, measure the volume, and record as "volume of water alone" in Data Table 1. Tilt the graduated cylinder and carefully slide one of the metal samples down the side. Make sure the metal sample is completely submerged in the water. Measure the volume and record the measurement as "volume of water + metal" in Data Table 1.

3. Repeat Step 2, using the other metal sample. Dry both samples and return them to your teacher.

Name ______________________ Date ________________ Class ________________

OBSERVATIONS

DATA TABLE 1: INDIVIDUAL DATA AND CALCULATIONS			
	Metal A	Metal B	Additional Metal Sample
mass (g)	10.10 g	33.41 g	
volume of water alone (mL)	12.0 mL	19.7 mL	
volume of water + metal (mL)	15.8 mL	23.5 mL	
volume of metal (mL)	3.8 mL	3.8 mL	
density of metal (g/mL)	10.10 g/3.8 mL = 2.7 g/mL	33.41 g/3.8 mL = 8.8 g/mL	

All sample data is for aluminum (Metal A) and brass (Metal B).

DATA TABLE 2: CLASS DATA: MASS AND VOLUME OF METAL SAMPLES						
	Metal A		Metal B		Additional Metal Sample	
Lab Pair	mass (g)	volume (mL)	mass (g)	volume (mL)	mass (g)	volume (mL)
1	10.10	3.8	33.41	3.8		
2	4.31	1.7	34.62	3.9		
3	8.05	3.0	27.63	3.1		
4	8.21	3.1	21.00	2.4		
5	10.35	4.1	20.92	2.5		
6	8.22	3.2	26.92	3.2		
7	4.51	1.7	34.00	3.6		
8	9.93	3.7	21.22	2.5		
9	4.70	1.8	27.15	3.2		

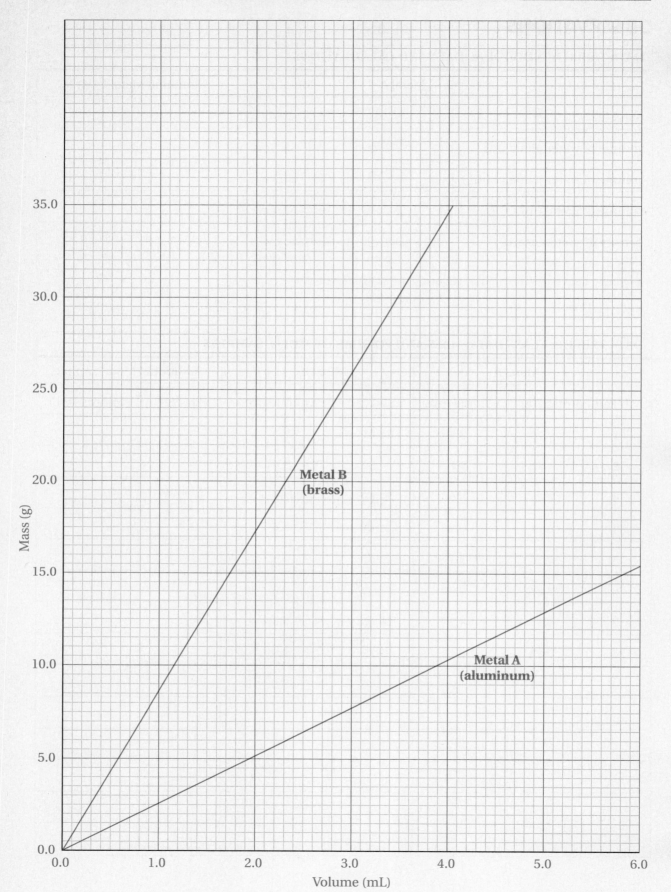

Name ______________________ Date ________________ Class ________________

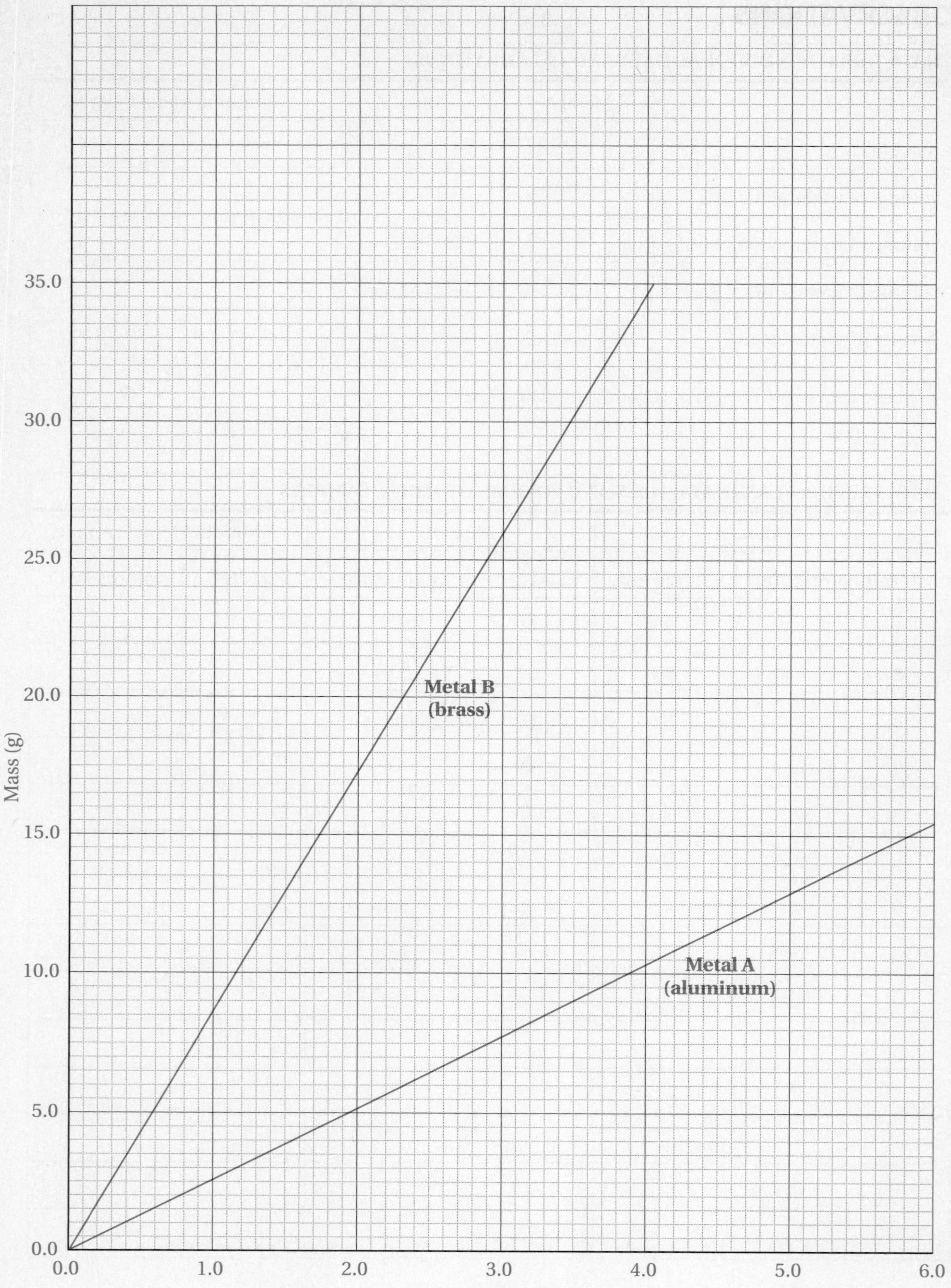

Name ______________________ Date ________________ Class ______________

ANALYSES AND CONCLUSIONS

1. Compute the volume of each metal sample, using data from Data Table 1. Compute the density of each metal sample, showing your work (including units), in Data Table 1. Remember,

$$\text{density} = \frac{\text{mass (g)}}{\text{volume (mL)}}.$$

2. Complete Data Table 2 by recording the mass and volume data collected by you and your classmates.

3. Using the class data, plot a graph of mass versus volume. Represent the plotted points for each metal with a different symbol. Draw a "best fit" straight line through each group of plotted points.

4. Determine the slope of each of the lines on your graph. Record the slope of each line and your method of calculation in Data Table 3. (**Hint:** The general equation for a line is $y = mx + b$ where m is the value for the slope and b is the value for the y-intercept.) Pay special attention to the units of the slope.

DATA TABLE 3: DENSITY CALCULATIONS FROM CLASS DATA (SLOPES)	
Metal A	Metal B
$\frac{y}{x} = \frac{15.5\text{ g}}{6.0\text{ mL}} = 2.6\text{ g/mL}$	$\frac{y}{x} = \frac{34.5\text{ g}}{4.1\text{ mL}} = 8.5\text{ g/mL}$

5. What does the slope of the line for each metal represent? (**Hint:** Look back at Data Table 1.)

The slope is the density. If you use the origin as one of the points in the slope formula, then the slope equals the ratio of the mass to volume.

6. Looking at your graph, what does this experiment demonstrate about the density of a metal? What does it demonstrate about the densities of different metals?

This experiment indicates that the density of a specific metal is constant. It also indicates that the densities of different metals can be quite different.

7. Calculate the percent error in the density calculations for the two samples. (See Analyses and Conclusions, Step 1.) Your teacher will provide the accepted value for the density of each metal.

$$\text{percent error} = \frac{|\text{experimental value} - \text{accepted value}|}{\text{accepted value}} \times 100\%$$

Densities of suggested metals are Al (2.70 g/cm^3), brass (8.44 g/cm^3), Zn (7.04–7.16 g/cm^3), Fe (7.85–7.88 g/cm^3), stainless steel (7.75 g/cm^3). For the examples of aluminum (Metal A) and brass (Metal B) used here, a sample calculation follows, based on the sample density data provided.

$$\text{experimental density (Al)} = 2.7\ \text{g/cm}^3$$

$$\text{experimental density (brass)} = 8.8\ \text{g/cm}^3$$

$$\text{percent error (Al)} = \frac{|2.7\ \text{g/cm}^3 - 2.7\ \text{g/cm}^3|}{2.7\ \text{g/cm}^3} \times 100\%$$

$$= \frac{|0\ \text{g/cm}^3|}{2.7\ \text{g/cm}^3} \times 100\%$$

$$= 0\%$$

$$\text{percent error (brass)} = \frac{|8.8\ \text{g/cm}^3 - 8.4\ \text{g/cm}^3|}{8.4\ \text{g/cm}^3} \times 100\%$$

$$= \frac{|0.4\ \text{g/cm}^3|}{8.4\ \text{g/cm}^3} \times 100\%$$

$$= \frac{0.4}{8.4} \times 100\%$$

$$= 0.048 \times 100\%$$

$$= 4.8\%$$

8. Calculate the percent error in the values of density obtained from the slopes of the lines in your graph. (See Analyses and Conclusions, Step 4.)

$$\text{percent error (Al)} = \frac{|2.7\ \text{g/cm}^3 - 2.6\ \text{g/cm}^3|}{2.7\ \text{g/cm}^3} \times 100\%$$

$$= \frac{0.1}{2.7} \times 100\%$$

$$= 3.7\%$$

$$\text{percent error (brass)} = \frac{|8.5\ \text{g/cm}^3 - 8.4\ \text{g/cm}^3|}{8.4\ \text{g/cm}^3} \times 100\%$$

$$= \frac{|0.1|}{8.4} \times 100\%$$

$$= \frac{0.1}{8.4} \times 100\%$$

$$= 0.012 \times 100\%$$

$$= 1.2\%$$

Name ______________________ Date ________________ Class ________________

9. Look back at the percent errors calculated in problems 7 and 8. Generally, the slope of the line will give a more accurate value for density than a single sample. Explain why this is usually true.

Ordinarily, a number of determinations are better than a single determination; witness the results obtained for brass. The 0% error in the single determination for aluminum is probably the result of canceling measurement uncertainties. The 3.7% error found by using the slope method is more realistic.

10. Can you identify a metal if you know its density? Explain your answer. Try to identify the metals used in this experiment by referring to tables of density.

Density can be used to identify a metal because density is constant for a particular metal and generally different for different metals. For the densities of some common metals, see the answer to problem 7 in the Analyses and Conclusions section.

11. Do you think that determining the volumes of your metal samples by measuring their dimensions and calculating would be more accurate or less accurate than determining these volumes by water displacement? Explain. Would measuring the dimensions of a solid always be possible? Explain.

If the dimensions of a regular solid cylindrical sample of metal were measured more accurately (to more than two significant figures), the calculated value for the volume would be more accurate. This increased accuracy could be achieved by using a vernier caliper to make the measurements. If a cylinder is used, the following volume formula applies:

$$V = \pi r^2 h$$

Measuring the dimensions of an irregularly shaped object is usually not possible.

Name ____________ Date ____________ Class ____________

12. How would you modify this experiment to determine the density of table sugar, wood chips, and milk?

The sugar would dissolve in water; use a solvent in which it would not dissolve. Wood chips would float in water; use a metal cylinder of known volume to weigh down the wood chips. Since milk is a liquid, determine the mass of an empty 25-mL volumetric flask (or some container of known volume). Fill the flask with milk and remeasure the mass. The mass of the known volume of milk is the difference between the two mass measurements.

GOING FURTHER

Develop a Hypothesis

Based on the results of this lab, develop a hypothesis about how and why unknown substances can be distinguished from one another by measuring their densities.

Design an Experiment

Propose an experiment to test your hypothesis. If resources are available and you have your teacher's permission, perform the experiment.

Name ______________________ Date __________________ Class ________________

ATOMIC STRUCTURE: RUTHERFORD'S EXPERIMENT

Text Reference
Section 4.2

Time Required
30 minutes

Objectives
- Measure the shape of a hidden object by analyzing entry and rebound paths for a marble rolled at the object.

Advance Preparation
Plastic-foam shapes
Cut geometric shapes from a sheet of 1-inch plastic foam. Even simple shapes—such as a triangle, circle, half circle, rectangle, square, or L—are a challenge for students. More complicated shapes can be used in a second trial. Make the largest dimension of the shapes approximately 20 cm. Place a shape under a cover board at each lab station before the students come into the lab.
Cover boards
The cover boards must be sturdy enough not to bend when students write on them. Masonite or 1/4-inch plywood is adequate.

PURPOSE

To discover how the physical properties, such as size and shape, of an object can be measured by indirect means.

BACKGROUND

As you have done experiments, you have learned to make useful observations and to draw reasonable conclusions from data. But imagine how little you would be able to accomplish if the room in which you worked were so dark that you could not see the materials you were working with. Imagine how limited your observations would be if the object of your scrutiny were so small that it could not be seen, even with a microscope. When you think of how difficult experimentation would be under such adverse conditions, you will gain some appreciation for the enormous technical problems confronting early atomic scientists.

These scientists had as their target the atom—a bit of matter so small that there was no hope of seeing it directly. Nevertheless, these ingenious experimenters were able to infer that the atom had a nucleus.

It is impractical to reproduce the classic experiments that led to the discovery of the nucleus in a high school laboratory. You can get some idea of the challenge that these researchers faced, however, by playing the game described in this experiment. You will infer the size and shape of an object you cannot see or touch.

MATERIALS (PER PAIR)

safety goggles
sheet of heavy cardboard or thin plywood sheet, 60 cm × 60 cm
plastic-foam shape
marble
sheet construction paper
sheet notebook paper

SAFETY FIRST!

Caution: Wear your safety goggles. (All steps.)

Name ______________________ Date ________________ Class ________________

Review with students how to relate each marble's angle of reflection to its angle of incidence. Meter or yard sticks can be used to retrieve "lost" marbles without posing the associated hazard of revealing the mystery shape.

PROCEDURE

1. At your lab station, you will find a sheet of cardboard resting on top of a hidden object. *Do not look under the cardboard!* Roll a marble under the cardboard from various directions and observe where it comes out. (Have your teacher retrieve the marble if it stays under the board; no peeking!)
2. Place a sheet of construction paper on top of the board and trace the entry and exit path for each roll of the marble.
3. Continue rolling the marble and recording its path until you think you know the size and shape of the object. Draw a full-sized sketch of the object on a sheet of paper. Check your results with your teacher. Do not look under the board until your teacher confirms your results.
4. Ask your teacher for a second mystery object if you have time to repeat the game.

Name ______________________ Date ______________ Class ______________

ANALYSES AND CONCLUSIONS

1. How does this game simulate early efforts to determine the structure of the atom? In what ways is it different?

   Like the students, Rutherford and other scientists were faced with the problem of identifying properties of an object not visible to the unaided eye. The game and Rutherford's efforts to solve the structure of the atom are similar because, in each instance, the angles of deflection of particles were used to infer the size and shape of the unseen object. Thus, Rutherford's experiment and this game used a similar indirect means to study the structure of an object. The two activities are also dissimilar. In the game, the board can be lifted to check the shape of the object. The atomic nucleus, however, is invisible because of its small size. The theory that the nucleus exists can only be supported by indirect evidence.

2. You eventually had the satisfaction of seeing the shape under the board. Did the early atomic scientists have this same opportunity? Do scientists today have this opportunity?

   Student answers will vary. The scanning tunneling microscope makes it possible to view atoms and molecules on a solid surface.

GOING FURTHER

Develop a Hypothesis

On the basis of the results in this lab, develop a hypothesis about how the size, shape, or identity of other kinds of objects could be determined by indirect means.

The shadow of an object can be very dissimilar from the shape of the real object. By shining a light on the object from different angles, it is sometimes possible to identify the object. Players of games such as Twenty Questions (animal, vegetable, or mineral?) attempt to identify an object that, for purposes of the game, exists only in someone's mind.

Name ______________________ Date ________________ Class ________________

Design an Experiment

Propose an experiment to test your hypothesis. If resources are available and you have your teacher's permission, perform the experiment.

Name ______________________ Date ________________ Class ______________

6 FLAME TESTS FOR METALS

Text Reference
Section 5.3

Time Required
30 minutes

Objectives
- Observe the flame test for seven different metallic ions.
- Identify an unknown metallic element, using the flame test.

Advance Preparation
6M hydrochloric acid
Pour 150 mL concentrated HCl into 150 mL of water.

Fill small labeled screw-top jars with chemicals for groups of four students to use at their lab stations.

Platinum wire is more expensive, but also more durable, than nichrome wire. Nichrome wire can deteriorate rapidly, especially if it is used in the hottest region of the burner flame.

Review the safety procedures and caution the students about the corrosive nature of acids before they begin to work.

PURPOSE

To observe and identify metallic ions, using flame tests.

BACKGROUND

Have you ever wondered why a candle flame is yellow? The characteristic yellow of a candle flame comes from the glow of burning carbon fragments. The carbon fragments are produced by the incomplete combustion reaction of the wick and candle wax. When elements, such as carbon, are heated to high temperatures, some of their electrons are excited to higher energy levels. When these excited electrons fall back to lower energy levels, they release excess energy in packages of light called photons, or light quanta. The color of the emitted light depends on its energy. Blue light is more energetic than red light, for example. When heated, each element emits a characteristic pattern of light energies, which is useful for identifying the element. The characteristic colors of light produced when substances are heated in the flame of a gas burner are the basis of flame tests for several elements.

In this experiment, you will perform the flame tests used to identify several metallic elements.

MATERIALS (PER PAIR)

safety goggles
8 small test tubes
test-tube rack
paper towel
scoopulas
50-mL beaker
platinum wire or nichrome wire loop
gas burner
cobalt-blue glass
potassium nitrate, KNO_3 [T]
calcium nitrate, $Ca(NO_3)_2$ [T]
strontium nitrate, $Sr(NO_3)_2$ [T]
lithium nitrate, $LiNO_3$
copper(II) nitrate, $Cu(NO_3)_2$ [T]
sodium nitrate, $NaNO_3$ [T]
barium nitrate, $Ba(NO_3)_2$ [T] [C]
6*M* hydrochloric acid, HCl [C] [T]
unknown salt

SAFETY FIRST!

In this lab, the solutions you will be using contain harmful materials. Avoid skin contact with these chemicals. Observe all precautions, especially the ones listed below. If you see a safety icon beside a step in the Procedure, refer to the list below for its meaning.

Caution: Wear your safety goggles. (All steps.)

Name ______________________ Date ________________ Class ________________

Caution: Hydrochloric acid is corrosive and can cause severe burns. (Step 2.)

Caution: Do not taste any of the substances or touch them with your hands. (Step 1.)

Caution: Do not at any time touch the end of the wire loop used in the flame tests. This wire gets extremely hot and can cause severe burns. (Steps 2–5.)

Note: Return or dispose of all materials according to the instructions of your teacher. (Step 6.)

PROCEDURE

As you perform the experiment, record your observations in Data Table 1.

1. Place a test-tube rack on a paper towel. Write the chemical name for each of the seven metal salts next to a position in the rack where a test tube will be placed. Use scoopulas supplied with each salt to place pea-sized samples of each metal salt into a test tube. Place the tubes in the test-tube rack.
2. Pour about 15 mL of 6*M* HCl into a clean, labeled 50-mL beaker. Dip the wire loop into the 6*M* HCl and then heat it in the hot flame of a gas burner, as shown in Figure 6.1a. Continue this procedure until no color comes from the wire when it is put into the flame.
3. Dip the clean wire loop into a sample of metal salt and heat the sample in the burner flame, as shown in Figure 6.1b. Record the color of the flame in Data Table 1. Test the remaining samples, cleaning the wire loop as described in Step 2, before each new sample is tested. Record your observations.
4. View the flame colors produced by $NaNO_3$ and KNO_3 through cobalt-blue glass. Record your observations.
5. Perform a flame test on your unknown salt. Record your observations.

6. Dispose of the unused portions of your samples as directed by your teacher.

The solutions can be stored and reused or use the following disposal methods for chemical waste.

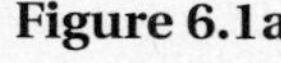

Disposal 1: $NaNO_3$, KNO_3, $Ca(NO_3)_2$, $Sr(NO_3)_2$, $LiNO_3$, $Cu(NO_3)_2$.

Disposal 2: HCl(*aq*).

Disposal 3: $Ba(NO_3)_2$.

Figure 6.1a

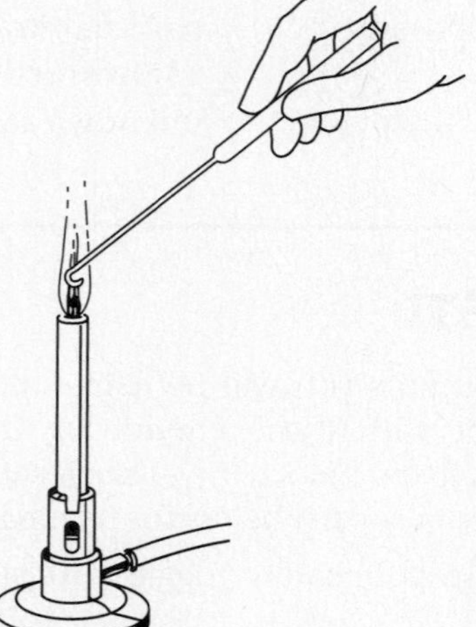

Figure 6.1b

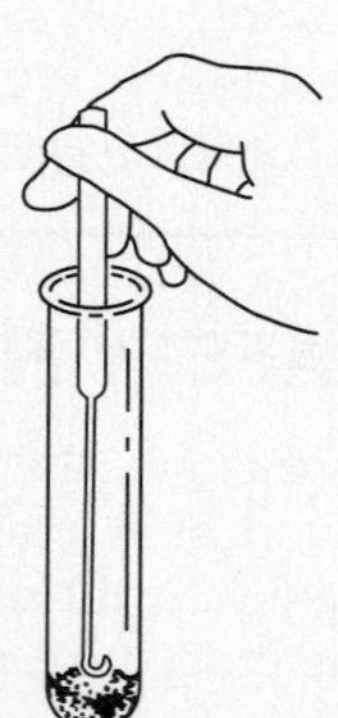

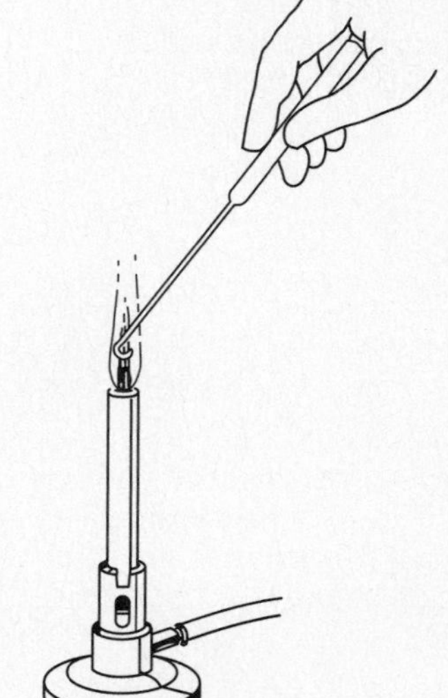

Name ______________________ Date ______________ Class ______________

OBSERVATIONS

DATA TABLE 1: FLAME TESTS	
Ion	Flame Color
sodium, Na^{+}	yellow
potassium, K^{+}	violet and yellow
calcium, Ca^{2+}	brick red
barium, Ba^{2+}	green
strontium, Sr^{2+}	bright red
lithium, Li^{+}	crimson
copper, Cu^{2+}	blue-green
sodium, Na^{+} (cobalt glass)	none
potassium, K^{+} (cobalt glass)	violet
unknown	

ANALYSES AND CONCLUSIONS

1. List the elements that produced the most easily identified colors.

   Ca^{2+}, Ba^{2+}, Sr^{2+}, Li^{+}, Cu^{2+} are quite easily identified.

2. Which elements are least easily identified? Explain.

   Na^{+} and K^{+} are difficult to distinguish.

3. Which element produces the most intense color?

   The color given by Sr^{2+} is a very bright red and is probably the most intense.

4. Would flame tests be useful for detecting metal ions present in a mixture of metal ions? Explain.

   The detection of metal ions in mixtures would be difficult. For example, Li^{+} and Sr^{2+} both give red flames and cannot be distinguished in a mixture.

Name ______________ Date ______________ Class ______________

5. The energy of colored light increases in the order red, yellow, green, blue, violet. List the metallic elements used in the flame tests in increasing order of the energy of the light emitted.

(Sr^{2+} Li^{+} Ca^{2+} red) (Na^{+} yellow) (Ba^{2+} Cu^{2+} green) (K^{+} violet)

low energy → high energy

6. What is the purpose of using the cobalt glass in the identification of sodium and potassium?

K^{+} nearly always gives a yellow flame because of the presence of trace amounts of Na^{+}. Cobalt glass filters out the yellow, allowing the violet of K^{+} to be seen. The glass helps to distinguish Na^{+} from K^{+}. If only Na^{+} is present, no flame is seen through the cobalt glass. If K^{+} is present, violet light is seen through the glass.

GOING FURTHER

Do Research

In this lab, you observed that each element emits a unique color of light when heated in a flame. If these light emissions were examined through a prism, you would observe that the emitted light is actually composed of different wavelengths of light that may lie in the violet region, the green region, or the red region of the visible spectrum. Each element has a unique *emission spectrum*. Look up the emission spectra for the elements tested in this lab. Do research on how scientists apply these emission spectra to investigate the chemical composition of stars. For example, what is the emission spectrum of the sun, and what does this spectrum reveal about the types of elements in the sun?

Scientists compare the emission spectrum of the sun with the wavelengths of lines emitted by elements in the laboratory to determine the kinds of elements in the sun. At least 67 different elements have been detected in the sun's emission spectrum. The sun is mainly composed of helium and hydrogen.

Name ____________________ Date ______________ Class ______________

ENERGIES OF ELECTRONS

Text Reference
Section 5.3

Time Required
40 minutes

Objectives
- Construct a simple flame spectrograph.
- Measure the 589-nm flame omission line of the sodium ion.

Advance Preparation
6M hydrochloric acid
Dilute concentrated HCl 1:1 with distilled water. Approximately 200 mL will be required to meet the needs of 15 student lab pairs.

1M sodium chloride
Dissolve 5.8 g of NaCl in 80 mL of distilled water and dilute to 100 mL.

Other materials
The width of the slit should be 1 mm or less. The slit height should be approximately 2 cm.

PURPOSE

To construct a simple flame spectrograph and measure a wavelength of light produced by the electronic excitations of sodium ions.

BACKGROUND

You should recall from Experiment 6 that flame tests are useful for identifying metal ions that produce characteristic colors. Separating these characteristic colors into discrete wavelengths of light produces a pattern of individual lines that uniquely identifies the metal ion. This pattern of lines is called an *emission spectrum*. With a reference source of emission spectra, you would find it relatively easy to identify a particular metal ion.

You can separate the lines in the visible region of a flame emission spectrum by using an optical prism or a diffraction grating. A *spectrograph* is an instrument designed to produce electronic excitations, separate the emitted light into its component wavelengths, and then record the wavelengths of emitted light. In this experiment, you will construct a simple spectrograph and measure the wavelength of a strong excitation of sodium ions.

MATERIALS (PER PAIR)

safety goggles
2 meter sticks
diffraction grating
cardboard piece with narrow slit
50-mL beaker
watch glass
platinum or nichrome wire loop
gas burner
6*M* hydrochloric acid, HCl [C] [T]
1*M* sodium chloride, NaCl

SAFETY FIRST!

In this lab, observe all precautions, especially the ones listed below. If you see a safety icon beside a step in the Procedure, refer to the list below for its meaning.

 **Caution:** Wear your safety goggles. (All steps.)

 **Caution:** Hydrochloric acid is corrosive and can cause severe burns. (Step 2.)

 **Caution:** Do not let your skin or clothing contact the burner flame or the hot wire used in the flame tests. (Steps 2–4.)

Name ______________________ Date ______________ Class ______________

Caution: Exercise care when working with an open flame. Tie back hair and loose clothing. Do not use the burner near flammable materials. (Steps 2–4.)

Note: Return or dispose of all materials according to the instructions of your teacher. (Step 7.)

PROCEDURE

As you perform the experiment, record your data and calculation results in Data Table 1.

1. Set up the apparatus shown in Figure 7.1.

2. Pour approximately 15 mL of 6*M* hydrochloric acid, HCl, into a 50-mL beaker. Always cover the beaker with a watch glass when the beaker is not being used. Clean the wire loop by first dipping it into the HCl and then heating it in the hot flame of a gas burner. Continue to dip and heat the wire until no color comes from the wire as it is heated.

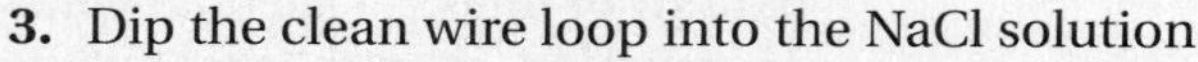

3. Dip the clean wire loop into the NaCl solution.
4. Place the wire loop in the burner flame. Observe the flame through the slit in the cardboard and the diffraction grating, as shown in Figure 7.1. You should see a series of lines to the left and right of the slit. Pick out the brightest line to the left side of the slit and have your partner record this position on the meter stick as position A. Repeat this procedure on the right side of the slit and record this as position B.
5. Measure the distance from the diffraction grating to the slit and record this as distance Y.
6. Dispose of the solutions as directed by your teacher.

Use the following disposal methods for chemical waste.

Disposal 2: NaCl(*aq*).

Disposal 3: HCl(*aq*).

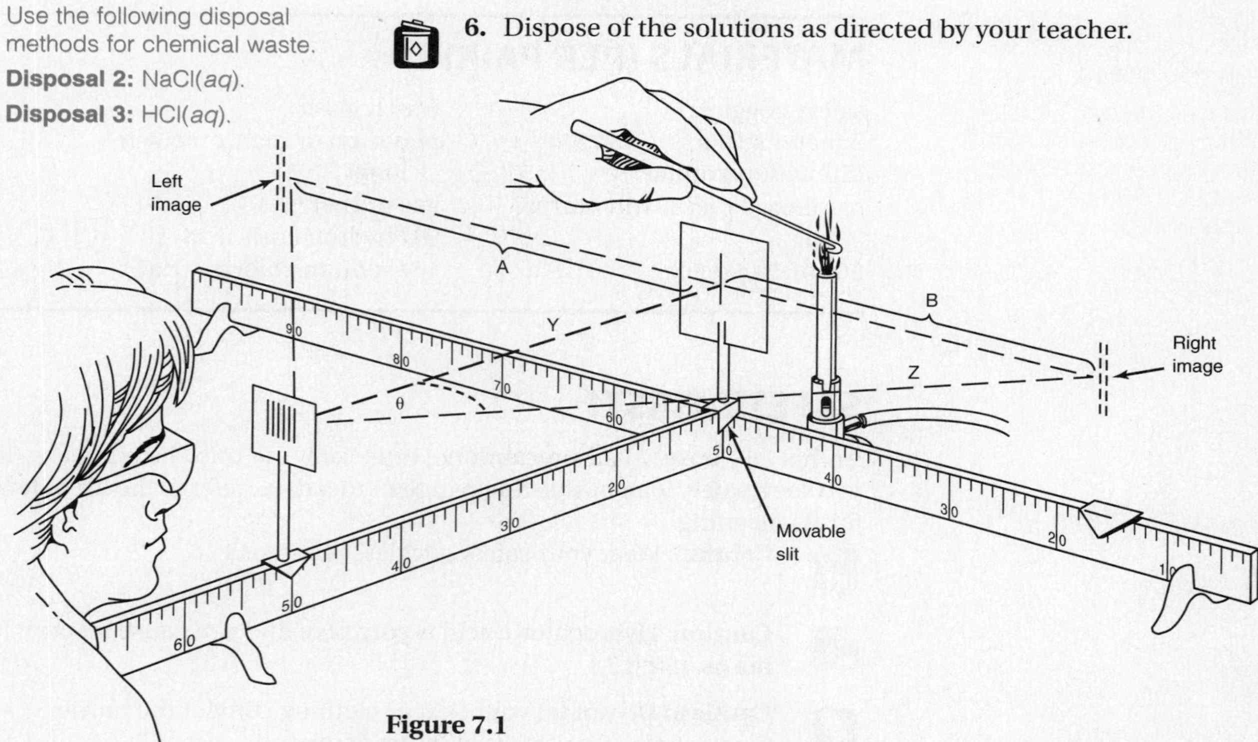

Figure 7.1

Name ______________________ Date ________________ Class ________________

OBSERVATIONS

DATA TABLE 1: WAVELENGTH FOR THE SODIUM EMISSION LINE	
left image (A)	15.0 cm
right image (B)	15.8 cm
distance X (average of left and right images)	15.4 cm
distance Y	40.0 cm
distance Z	42.9 cm
diffracting grating constant (d)	1.90×10^{-4} cm/line
sin θ	0.359
wavelength (λ)	682 nm

ANALYSES AND CONCLUSIONS

1. Find the average of distances A and B (in centimeters). Record this answer as distance X in your data table.

$$\frac{15.0 \text{ cm} + 15.8 \text{ cm}}{2} = 15.4 \text{ cm}$$

2. Calculate the distance Z, using the Pythagorean theorem. Refer to Figure 7.1 for relationship of distances.

$$Z = \sqrt{X^2 + Y^2}$$

Record the value of Z in the data table.

$$Z = \sqrt{(15.4 \text{ cm})^2 + (40.0 \text{ cm})^2}$$
$$= \sqrt{237.16 \text{ cm}^2 + 1600 \text{ cm}^2}$$
$$= 42.9 \text{ cm}$$

3. Calculate sin θ, using the following relationship:

$$\sin\theta = \frac{X}{Z}$$

Record sin θ in the data table.

$$\sin\theta = \frac{15.4 \text{ cm}}{42.9 \text{ cm}}$$
$$= 0.359$$

4. The wavelength (λ) of the sodium flame emission line being investigated in this experiment is given, in nanometers, by the Bragg equation:

$$\lambda = d \times \sin\theta \times \left(\frac{1 \times 10^7\ \text{nm}}{1\ \text{cm}}\right)$$

d represents a diffraction grating constant: $d = \frac{1}{n}$ where n is the number of lines, per centimeter, scribed on the diffraction grating. Calculate the value of d for your grating and enter it in Data Table 1.

The number of lines per inch is often 13 400; *d* may be calculated as follows:

$$d = \frac{1\ \text{in.}}{13\,400\ \text{lines}} \times \frac{2.54\ \text{cm}}{1\ \text{in.}} = 1.90 \times 10^{-4}\ \text{cm/line (constant)}$$

5. Compute the wavelength of the bright line you viewed on the meter stick, using the Bragg equation. Record this value in the data table.

$$\lambda = (1.90 \times 10^{-4}\ \text{cm}) \times (0.359) \times \left(\frac{1 \times 10^7\ \text{nm}}{\text{cm}}\right) = 682\ \text{nm}$$

6. The accepted value of λ for the observed transition is 589.0 nm. Calculate the percent error in your value.

$$\text{percent error} = \frac{682\ \text{nm} - 589\ \text{nm}}{589\ \text{nm}} \times 100 = 15.8\%$$

7. Identify the possible sources of error in your determination of λ.

The major source of error is the measurement of the values for X and Y.

8. How can a spectrographic experiment help identify a particular metal ion?

The ions of each element give characteristic patterns of lines in the spectrograph. Even elements that produce flame-test results that appear to the eye to be the same color produce very different sets of flame emission lines.

GOING FURTHER

Do Research

Atomic absorption spectroscopy is one of the most sensitive methods available for the detection of various metals. Do research to find out how this method is used to quantify the amount of an element in a particular sample and compare the detection limits of this method with other spectroscopic methods of analysis.

The detection limits of many modern atomic spectroscopic methods lie well below 1 ppm for a number of metallic elements. The ultrasensitivity of this technique is a valuable asset to scientists studying materials that contain only trace amounts of a given metal.

Name ______________________ Date ______________ Class ______________

INTRODUCTION TO THE SPECTROPHOTOMETER

Text Reference
Section 5.3

Time Required
50 minutes

Objectives
- Examine the use of a spectrophotometer to study the light-absorbing properties of a chemical substance.
- Observe how the absorption of light by a compound varies with the wavelength of light.
- Construct a graph of wavelength versus absorption for an aqueous solution of chromium(III) nitrate.

Advance Preparation
0.02M chromium(III) nitrate
Dissolve 4.8 g of $Cr(NO_3)_3$ in 900 mL of distilled water and dilute to 1 L.

PURPOSE

To determine the absorption spectrum of an aqueous solution of chromium(III) ions.

BACKGROUND

Many compounds absorb light from regions of the electromagnetic spectrum. A *spectrophotometer* is a device designed to determine the wavelengths of light that a compound absorbs. When an aqueous sample of a compound is placed in the light path of a spectrophotometer, the sample may absorb all the light, some of the light, or no light at all. The absorption of light depends upon the materials in the sample and the wavelength of the light. Light absorption occurs at wavelengths whose energy corresponds to the energy necessary to cause electronic excitations of atoms, ions, or molecules in the sample. From the spectrophotometer data, a graph can be made that plots the light intensity transmitted through the sample versus the wavelength of the light; such a graph is called an *absorption spectrum.* The range of wavelengths absorbed by the sample appear as bands of minimum intensity.

Absorption spectra are useful for two reasons. First, the absorption spectrum of a substance is a unique characteristic of that substance. This makes the spectrum useful for the identification of unknown substances. Second, the intensity of the absorption bands can be related to the concentration of the substance in the sample. Thus, the intensity of the absorption band can be used to determine the amount of a particular substance in a mixture.

In this experiment, you will determine the absorption spectrum of an aqueous solution of chromium(III) ions.

MATERIALS (PER PAIR)

- safety goggles
- Spectronic 20 spectrophotometer
- 2 small test tubes or 2 glass cuvettes
- 10-mL graduated cylinder
- plastic wash bottle
- distilled water
- 0.02*M* chromium(III) nitrate, $Cr(NO_3)_3$ [T] [I]
- tissue paper

SAFETY FIRST!

In this lab, observe all precautions, especially the following ones. If you see a safety icon beside a step in the Procedure, refer to the following list for its meaning.

Name ______________________ Date ______________ Class ______________

Caution: Wear your safety goggles. (All steps.)

Caution: Chromium(III) nitrate is toxic and can irritate your skin. (Steps 5–8.)

Note: Return or dispose of all materials according to the instructions of your teacher. (Step 8.)

PROCEDURE

As you perform the experiment, record your percent transmittance data in Data Table 1.

1. Turn on the spectrophotometer and allow it to warm up for about 20 minutes.
2. Set the wavelength control knob to 375 nanometers (375 nm). Adjust the amplifier control knob to produce 0 percent transmittance (0%T) at this wavelength.
3. Add 3 mL of distilled water to a clean, small test tube. Wipe the outside of the tube with a tissue to make certain that it is clean and dry. Avoid getting fingerprints on the tube. Dislodge any air bubbles present in the water by gently tapping the tube with a finger.
4. Place the tube in the sample holder and close the cover. Adjust the light control knob until the spectrophotometer reads 100%T.

5. Remove the first sample from the spectrophotometer. Add 3 mL of 0.02*M* chromium(III) nitrate, $Cr(NO_3)_3$, to another clean test tube. Use a tissue to clean and dry the tube. Insert the tube of chromium(III) nitrate into the sample holder. Close the cover of the holder. Read the percent transmittance and record the reading in Data Table 1. Remove the sample from the holder.
6. Turn the wavelength dial to 400 nm. Use the amplifier control knob to adjust the percent transmittance to 0%T. Place the water sample in the holder. With the light control knob, adjust the meter to 100%T. Replace the water sample with the chromium(III) nitrate sample. Measure and record the percent transmittance at 400 nm.
7. For the remainder of the wavelengths listed in Data Table 1, continue the procedure of setting 0%T, setting 100%T, and measuring the percent transmittance of the chromium(III) nitrate solution.

8. Unless directed otherwise by your teacher, return the aqueous chromium(III) nitrate to the dropper bottle.

Step 2.
To avoid damage, the spectrophotometer knobs must not be twisted past the point at which resistance is encountered. Twisting the amplifier control knob counterclockwise past the resistance point turns the spectrophotometer off.

Step 4.
Show students how to tilt the bottom of the test tube slightly to the right (facing the spectrophotometer) to fit into the holder.

The energy of the radiation striking the detector is not constant at all wavelengths, because the energy output of the source is not constant. The amplifier control knob opens or closes the slit to bring the energy at the detector to the constant value designated 100%T. Failure to adjust to 100%T at each wavelength will produce an "absorption spectrum" that includes the energy profile of the source as well as the spectrum of the absorbing species in the sample solution.

Use the following disposal method for chemical waste.

Disposal 6: $Cr(NO_3)_3$.

Name ______________________ Date ______________ Class ______________

OBSERVATIONS

DATA TABLE 1: PERCENT TRANSMITTANCE AND ABSORBANCE OF 0.02*M* $Cr(NO_3)_3$ SOLUTION AT VARIOUS WAVELENGTHS

Wavelength (nm)	% Transmittance (%T)	Absorbance
375	64.0	0.194
400	48.5	0.314
405	47.0	0.328
415	46.5	0.333
425	53.2	0.274
440	60.0	0.222
455	71.5	0.146
470	80.0	0.097
490	82.5	0.084
500	83.0	0.081
520	72.0	0.143
530	67.5	0.171
540	63.0	0.201
550	58.5	0.233
570	54.0	0.268
575	53.0	0.276
580	53.0	0.276
600	56.0	0.252
625	66.3	0.178

ANALYSES AND CONCLUSIONS

1. Graph percent transmittance versus wavelength. The curve you plot is the absorption spectrum of chromium(III) ions in the visible region of the electromagnetic spectrum.

2. At what wavelengths do chromium(III) ions absorb the maximum amounts of light? What colors of light correspond to these wavelengths?

   There are two absorption maxima (transmittance minima). One is at about 420 nm and the other is at about 580 nm. These wavelengths of light correspond to the wavelengths of violet (400–450 nm) and orange (600–650 nm) light.

Name ______________________ Date __________________ Class __________________

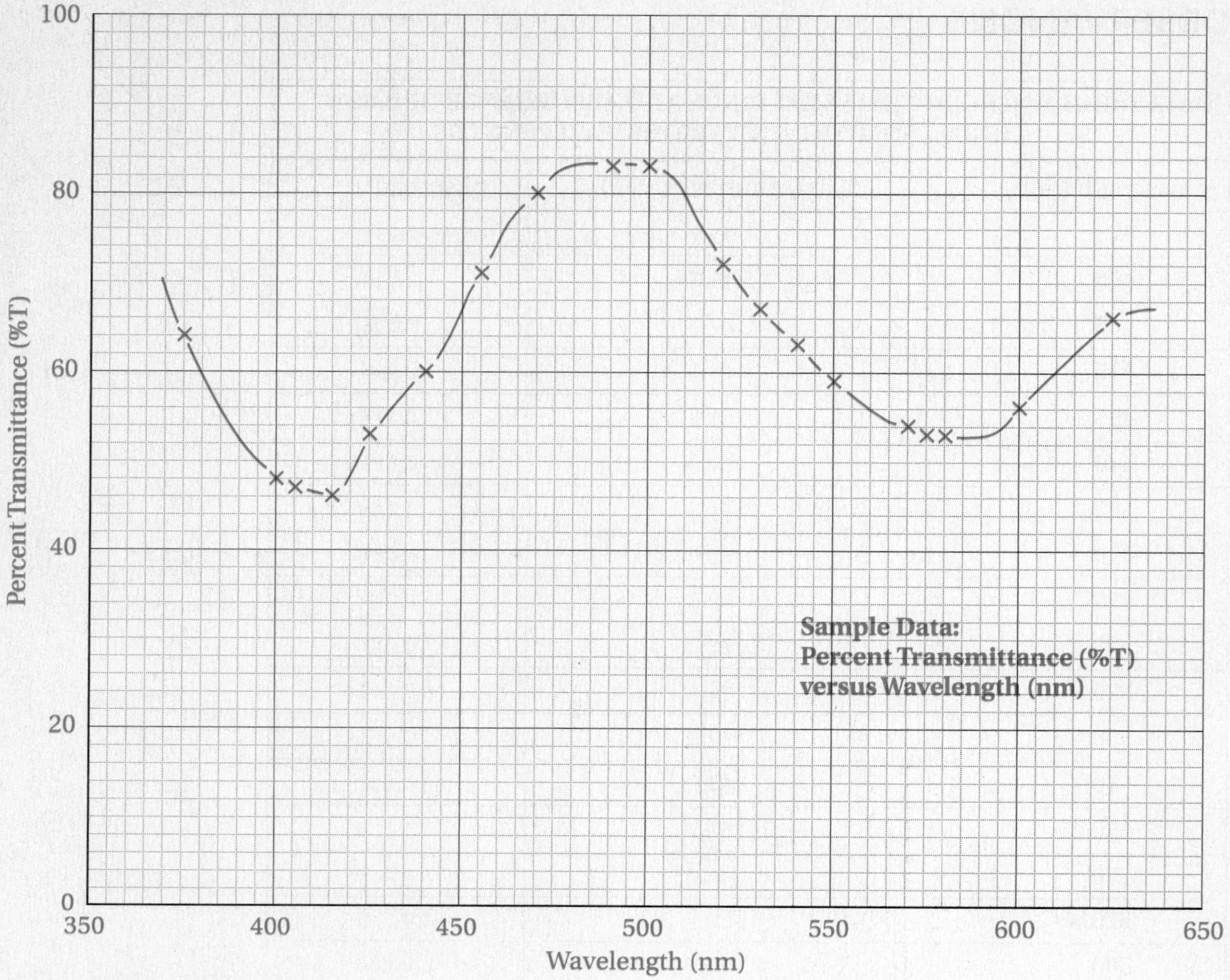

100
80
60
40
20
0
Percent Transmittance (%T)
350
400
450
500
550
600
650
Wavelength (nm)
Sample Data:
Percent Transmittance (%T)
versus Wavelength (nm)

Absorbance (A)
0.4
0.2
0
350
400
450
500
550
600
650
Wavelength (nm)
Sample Data:
Absorbance (A)
versus Wavelength (nm)

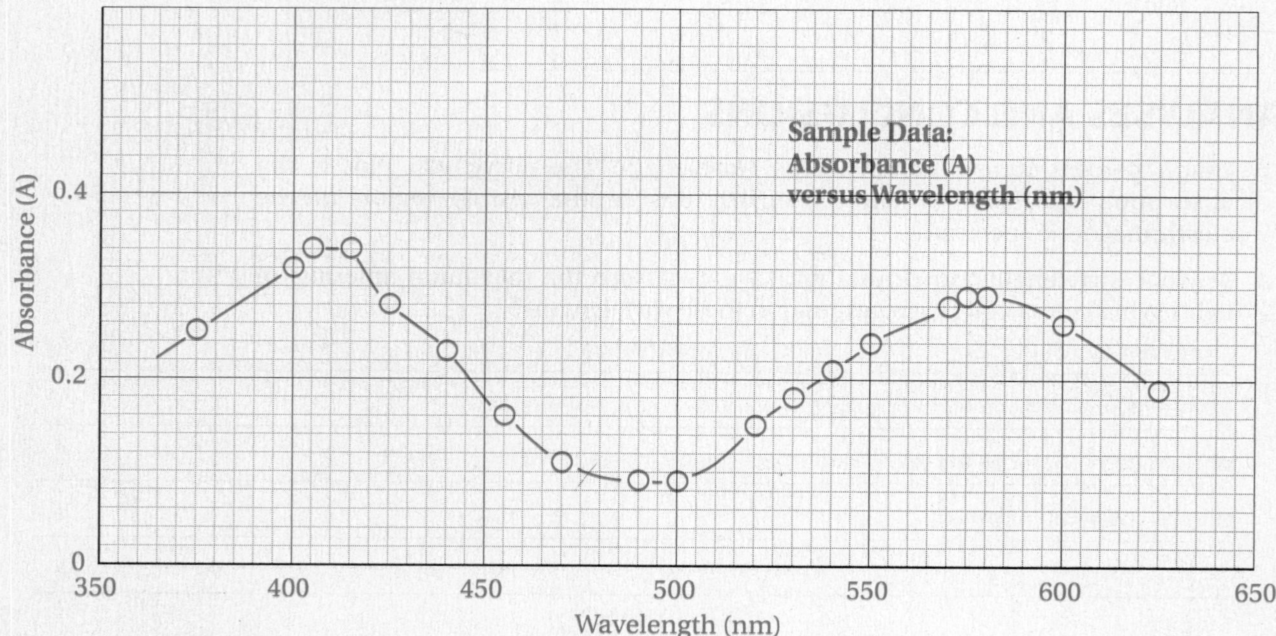

Name ______________ Date ______________ Class ______________

3. Based on the answer to problem 2, would you expect a red solution to absorb or transmit red light? Explain.

The previous answer suggests that colored solutions absorb light of a complementary color. Blue $Cr(NO_3)_3$ solution absorbs orange light. (Orange is the complement of blue.) A red solution absorbs green light (the complement of red) and transmits red light. (A yellow solution would absorb its complement, yellow.)

4. The amount of light that is absorbed by a solution is commonly expressed either in terms of percent transmittance, as in this experiment, or in terms of absorbance (A). Absorbance is defined as: 2 − log of percent transmittance

or

$$A = 2 - \log \%T$$

Given the relationship shown in the preceding formula, convert the percent transmittance values in Data Table 1 to absorbance values. Plot a graph of absorbance versus wavelength. Compare and analyze the shapes of the two curves. Might it be more useful to use transmittance values sometimes and absorbance values at other times? Explain the advantages and disadvantages of using these different units.

An absorption maximum appears to be sharper than its corresponding transmittance *minimum.* The concentration of a substance is directly proportional to the area under the peaks in an absorbance spectrum, but not in a transmittance spectrum. For this reason, analytical work is most often expressed in absorbance.

Name ______________________ Date ________________ Class ________________

GOING FURTHER

Develop a Hypothesis

Based on the results of this lab, propose a hypothesis about how the absorption of light by a solution of $Cr(NO_3)_3$ varies with the concentration of Cr^{3+} ions in solution.

The amount of light absorbed is directly proportional to the concentration of the absorbing species in solution.

Design an Experiment

Propose an experiment to test your hypothesis. In your protocol, include a method for determining the concentration of Cr^{3+} ions in an unknown solution of $Cr(NO_3)_3$. If resources are available and you have your teacher's permission, perform the experiment.

Measure the absorption of a series of standard solutions of chromium(III) ions at the wavelength of an absorption maximum determined in this experiment. Construct a plot of absorption versus concentration. Draw a best-fit line through these points. The concentration of chromium(III) solutions in an unknown solution can be determined by measuring the absorption and reading its concentration from the graph.

Name ______________________ Date ________________ Class ______________

9 PERIODIC PROPERTIES

Text Reference
Section 6.2

Time Required
50 minutes

Objectives
- Measure the densities of three elements in Group 4A.
- Describe periodic variation in the density of elements within a group.
- Predict the density of an untested Group 4A element.

Analyses and Conclusions
Remind students that the measurement with the least number of significant figures determines the number of significant figures in a calculated answer (multiplication and division). The number of significant figures in a volume measurement made in a graduated cylinder generally depends on the size of the cylinder in the following way:
100 mL = ±1 mL
25 mL = ±0.5 mL
10 mL = ± 0.2 mL

Refer students to the graphing review section in Appendix C of the textbook.

Provide students with clear plastic rulers for use in drawing the "best fit" line through their data points. The y-intercept for this line should be 0.

PURPOSE

To investigate the periodic variation of density in Group 4A elements.

BACKGROUND

When the elements are arranged in order of increasing atomic number, they exhibit a periodic recurrence of properties. Elements in the same group in the periodic table tend to have similar physical and chemical properties. These similarities are due, in large part, to similarities among the electron configurations of the elements in a group. You can find periodic trends in certain properties, such as density, among the elements within a given group.

In this experiment, you will investigate the variation in density among three Group 4A elements. You will use your results to predict the density of another Group 4A element.

MATERIALS (PER PAIR)

safety goggles and apron
centigram balance
100-mL graduated cylinder
tin, Sn
lead shot, Pb [T]
silicon, Si
distilled water

SAFETY FIRST!

In this lab, observe all precautions, especially the ones listed below. If you see a safety icon beside a step in the Procedure, refer to the list below for its meaning.

Caution: Wear your safety goggles. (All steps.)

Note: Return or dispose of all materials according to the instructions of your teacher. (Step 4.)

Note: Wash your hands thoroughly after completing this experiment.

Name ______________________ Date ________________ Class ______________

PROCEDURE

You will determine the densities of the tin (Sn), lead (Pb), and silicon (Si) samples by water displacement. As you perform the experiment, record your data in Data Table 1. Note the appearance of these elements.

1. Determine the mass of the samples to the nearest 0.01 gram, using a centigram balance. Record the masses in Data Table 1.
2. Fill a 100-mL graduated cylinder about three quarters full with water, measure the volume, and record the measurement as "volume of water alone" in Data Table 1. Tilt the graduated cylinder and carefully slide one of the samples down the side. Make sure the sample is completely submerged in the water. Measure the volume and record the measurement as "volume of water + sample" in Data Table 1.
3. Repeat Step 2, using the other samples.

4. Dry the samples and return them to your teacher. Then wash your hands thoroughly with soap or detergent.

OBSERVATIONS

DATA TABLE 1: DENSITIES OF GROUP 4A ELEMENTS			
	tin (Sn)	lead (Pb)	silicon (Si)
mass of sample (g)	27.11 g	44.30 g	9.15 g
volume of water alone (mL)	77.0 mL	76.2 mL	76.2 mL
volume of water + sample (mL)	80.8 mL	80.1 mL	80.0 mL
volume of sample (mL)	3.8 mL	3.9 mL	3.8 mL
density of sample (mass/volume)	7.1 g/cm³	11 g/cm³	2.4 g/cm³
appearance	silver-white	bluish white	brown

Name ______________________ Date ________________ Class ________________

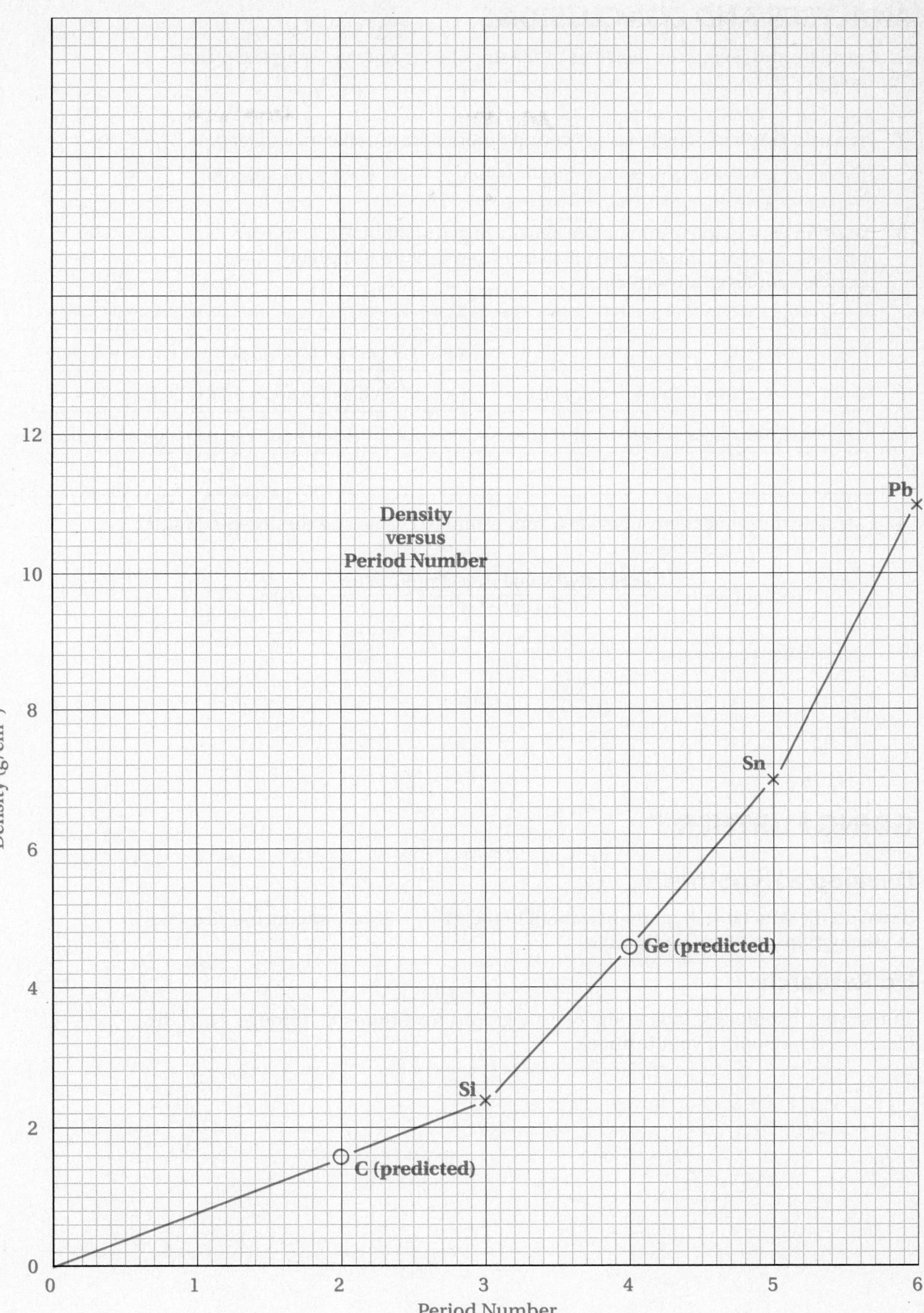

Name ______________________ Date ________________ Class ________________

ANALYSES AND CONCLUSIONS

1. Calculate and record the densities of the tin, silicon, and lead samples in Data Table 1.

   Sample data is provided in Data Table 1.

2. Prepare a graph of density versus period number for tin, silicon, and lead.

   The plot of density versus period number, although not linear, shows a regular trend toward higher density with increasing period number.

3. Based on your graph, estimate the density of germanium, Ge. Compare your estimate with the accepted density of germanium (5.3 g/cm^3). Give possible sources of any errors.

   The graph indicates that the relationship between density and period number is not linear. Lines drawn between the experimental points of Sn and Si suggest an interpolated density of 4.6 g/cm^3 for Ge (fourth period). The agreement between the predicted and accepted densities for Ge is acceptable. The major source of error in the experiment is the physical determination of the densities.

4. Calculate the percent error between your estimated value and the accepted value for the density of germanium.

$$\text{percent error} = \frac{|\text{estimated value} - \text{accepted value}|}{\text{accepted value}} \times 100\%$$

$$\textbf{germanium percent error} = \frac{|4.6\text{ g/cm}^3 - 5.3\text{ g/cm}^3|}{5.3\text{ g/cm}^3} \times 100\%$$

$$= \frac{0.7\text{ g/cm}^3}{5.3\text{ g/cm}^3} \times 100\%$$

$$= 13\%$$

GOING FURTHER

Develop a Hypothesis

Based on the data table, hypothesize about how density will vary among the elements in other groups in the periodic table.

Do Research

To test your hypothesis, look at the density graphs for Groups 1A through 8A in the Elements Handbook of your textbook.

Name ______________________________ Date ____________________ Class ____________________

10 CRYSTAL STRUCTURES

Text Reference
Sections 7.2 and 7.3

Time Required
40 minutes

Objectives
- Construct models of crystalline solids.
- Use models to identify the coordination number of atoms in three different crystalline structures.

PURPOSE

To investigate the geometric arrangement of atoms in crystalline solids.

BACKGROUND

The regular geometric shapes of crystals reflect the orderly arrangement of the atoms, ions, or molecules making up the crystal lattice. In this experiment, you will gain insight into the ways crystals are formed. To do this, you will model crystal structures using plastic-foam spheres. Using the models, you will determine the number of nearest neighbors (the coordination number) of the particles in each of these structures. The effect of the size of the anions and cations in the crystal structure on determining the coordination number will also be investigated. Your investigation will include three types of packing: hexagonal closest packing, face-centered cubic packing, and body-centered cubic packing.

MATERIALS (PER 8-STUDENT GROUP)

safety goggles
box of toothpicks, or 3 packs of plastic coffee stirrers, or box of pipe cleaners
62 plastic-foam balls, 2-inch diameter
13 plastic-foam balls, 1-inch diameter
13 plastic-foam balls, 3/4-inch diameter
scissors
centimeter ruler

SAFETY FIRST!

Caution: Wear safety goggles when you are working in the lab. (All steps.)

Safety goggles need not be required if this experiment is conducted in a classroom setting. If the experiment is done in the laboratory, though, goggles should be required because of the hazards posed to the eye by equipment and materials normally present in the lab.

PROCEDURE

As you perform the experiment, answer the questions in the Analyses and Conclusions section.

Part A. Hexagonal Closest Packing

1. Use toothpicks (or plastic coffee stirrers) to connect three sets of 2-inch spheres, as shown in Figure 10.1.
2. Place one of the sets of three spheres on a table. This is the first layer.

Name ______________________ Date ________________ Class ________________

Figure 10.1

3. Place the set of seven spheres on the three spheres so that its center sphere fits snugly into the depression in the first layer.
4. Place the second set of three spheres over the center sphere of the second layer. The spheres in this third layer should be directly above the spheres in the first layer. The arrangement you have constructed, hexagonal closest packing, is found in crystals of zinc, magnesium, and many other metals. Record the number of nearest neighbors (the coordination number) of the central sphere in the structure you formed. Retain your model for Part C.

Part B. Face-Centered Cubic Packing

5. Construct the layers shown in Figure 10.2. Use 2-inch foam spheres and toothpicks, as before.

Figure 10.2

6. Place the first layer (five spheres) on the table. Place the second layer (four spheres) over the first in such a way that the spheres of the second layer rest in the spaces between the corner spheres of the first layer.
7. Place the third layer on the second layer so that the spheres of the third layer are directly over the spheres in the first layer. Study this model carefully to determine why crystals with this structure are described as face-centered cubic packing. This is the type of packing that is found in copper, silver, aluminum, and many other metals.

Part C. Comparison of Hexagonal Closest Packing and Face-Centered Cubic Packing

8. Rearrange the model from Part A so the top layer (three spheres) is no longer directly over the first layer, but is rotated 60° with respect to it.
9. Rotate this rearranged model and look for four spheres forming a square facing you. Once you have found the four-sphere square, obtain the model made in Part B. Remove the top layer of the Part B model and place it over the four-sphere square of rearranged model A. Note that this new model contains a face-centered cube, just as model B did.

Name ______________________ Date __________________ Class __________________

Part D. Body-Centered Cubic Packing

10. Use 2-inch foam spheres to construct the layers depicted in Figure 10.3. Leave a space of approximately 0.5 cm between the spheres.

11. Place the single sphere in the center of the first layer, and then position the third layer in such a way that its spheres are directly over the spheres of the first layer. Examine the symmetry of this model and comment on the term *body-centered cubic.* This type of packing is typical of the alkali metals, which include sodium and potassium.

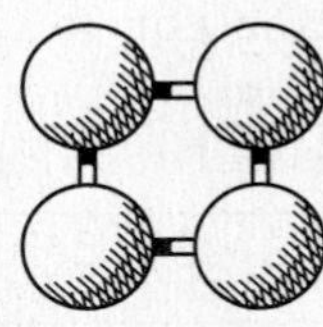

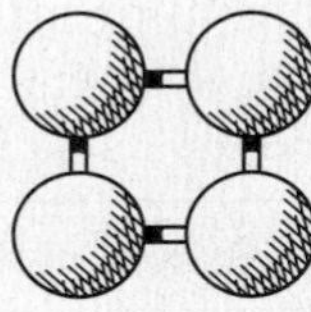

Figure 10.3

Part E. The Sodium Chloride Lattice

12. Ionic crystals are formed by packing positive and negative ions alternately into a lattice. A single sodium ion has a diameter of 0.19 nm; a chloride ion has a diameter of 0.36 nm. Because the diameters are in a ratio of roughly 1:2, the relative sizes of Na^+ and Cl^- can be approximated by using 1-inch and 2-inch spheres.

13. Use model B, with its 2-inch spheres, to represent the face-centered cubic arrangement of the chloride ions in a sodium chloride crystal. Insert thirteen 1-inch spheres, representing sodium ions, into the holes between the chloride ions in each layer. Note that the sodium chloride lattice is an interpenetrating set of face-centered cubes, one set of cubes made up of Na^+ ions and the other made up of Cl^- ions.

Part F. The Zinc Sulfide (Wurtzite) Lattice

14. Because each individual zinc ion has a diameter of 0.15 nm and the diameter of the sulfide ion is 0.37 nm, use 3/4-inch spheres for the Zn^{2+} ion and 2-inch spheres for the S^{2-} ion to approximate the relative sizes of these ions.

15. Use model A, with its hexagonal closest-packing orientation, to represent the lattice of the larger sulfide ions. Secure one 3/4-inch sphere directly above each of the larger spheres in each of the three layers of model A. The 3/4-inch spheres represent Zn^{2+} ions.

16. Place the largest layer of spheres on the table with the small spheres down. Place one of the smaller layers on the top of this layer so the smaller spheres fit into alternate depressions. Invert the two layers and place the other small layer, with small spheres upward, above the larger layer so that the spheres in the top layer are directly above the spheres in the bottom layer.

Name ____________ Date ____________ Class ____________

ANALYSES AND CONCLUSIONS

Part A. Hexagonal Closest Packing

1. What is the coordination number of the central atom in the model of hexagonal closest packing?

The coordination number is 12; the central atom has 12 nearest neighbors.

Part B. Face-Centered Cubic Packing

2. Explain the appropriateness of this name for describing the model you constructed.

In face-centered cubic packing, there is an atom at each corner of a cube and in the center of each face of the cube.

Part C. Comparison of Hexagonal Closest Packing and Face-Centered Cubic Packing

3. Compare the coordination numbers for the two types of closest packing.

The coordination number for each of these two crystal structures is 12.

4. If both a hexagonal closest-packed model and a cubic closest-packed model were constructed from spheres of the same size and mass, would the densities of the models differ? Explain.

No; spheres of the same size and mass arranged in either hexagonal closest packing or face-centered cubic packing would have the same density.

Name ____________ Date ____________ Class ____________

Part D. Body-Centered Cubic Packing

5. Below 906°C, metallic iron crystallizes in a body-centered cubic form called alpha-ferrite. Above this temperature, the stable form is gamma-ferrite, which is a face-centered cube. At 140°C, the crystal form changes back to a body-centered cube form called delta-ferrite. What is the coordination number of iron in each of these forms?

   α-ferrite is a body-centered cube with coordination number 8.

   γ-ferrite is a face-centered cube with coordination number 12.

   δ-ferrite is a body-centered cube with coordination number 8.

Part E. The Sodium Chloride Lattice

6. What ions most closely surround each Na^+ ion? What ions most closely surround each Cl^- ion?

   Each Na^+ ion is most closely surrounded by Cl^- ions.

   Each Cl^- ion is most closely surrounded by Na^+ ions.

7. What is the coordination number of the Na^+ ions? What is the coordination number of the Cl^- ions?

   The coordination number of Na^+ is 6.

   The coordination number of Cl^- is 6.

Part F. The Zinc Sulfide (Wurtzite) Lattice

8. What is the coordination number of the Zn^{2+} ions?

   The coordination number of Zn^{2+} in the Wurtzite lattice is 4. (The coordination number of S^{2-} is also 4.)

9. Use plastic-foam balls and toothpicks to explore some other types of crystal structures. Possibilities include cesium chloride (both ions have a coordination number of 8) and titanium dioxide (coordination numbers of 6 and 3, respectively).

GOING FURTHER

Do Research

Many physical properties of a solid, such as melting point, hardness, and electrical conductivity, can be directly related to its structure. Do research on the properties and structures of other crystalline solids including alloys and minerals and compare their properties to the crystalline solids studied in this lab. What trends if any are observed?

11 MOLECULAR MODELS

Text Reference
Section 8.3

Time Required
30 minutes

Objectives

- Construct three-dimensional models of molecules.
- Convert three-dimensional molecular models into two-dimensional molecular drawings.
- Examine the concept of structural isomerism.

PURPOSE

To investigate the three-dimensional shapes of molecules by building molecular models.

BACKGROUND

You can represent a molecule on paper with either a molecular formula or a structural formula. However, molecular formulas, such as NH_3, provide no information concerning the actual arrangement of atoms in the molecule. Structural formulas, such as the following, give some information about the arrangement of atoms in the molecule.

```
                                    H
                                    |
H—O—H         H—N—H            H—C—H
                  |                 |
                  H                 H
```

However, these structural formulas provide only limited information because they are two-dimensional. Actual molecular shapes are three-dimensional. A molecular model is far superior to a structural formula when it comes to visualizing atomic arrangement. Compared to molecular formulas and structural formulas, molecular models provide much more information about the true shapes of the molecules.

In this experiment, you will use ball-and-stick models to help you visualize the shapes of molecules. The balls are color-coded and sized to represent different atoms. The balls are also drilled with holes to accept sticks and springs; the number of holes in a ball reflects the maximum number of bonds a given atom can form. Single bonds are represented by short wooden sticks; double and triple bonds are represented by springs.

Plastic-foam balls or balls of clay can be used to represent atoms. Toothpicks or pipe cleaners can be used to represent the bonds that hold the atoms together.

MATERIALS (PER 6-STUDENT GROUP)

safety goggles
ball-and-stick model set

Safety goggles need not be required if this exercise is done in a classroom setting. If it is done in the laboratory, though, safety goggles should be required because of the hazards posed to the eye by equipment and materials normally present in the laboratory.

SAFETY FIRST!

Caution: Wear your safety goggles. (All steps.)

Name ______________ Date ______________ Class ______________

PROCEDURE

Data Table 1 shows color codes for balls representing different atoms. As you build the models, draw the structural formulas of the molecules in Data Table 2.

DATA TABLE 1: Description of Model Set

Atom	Symbol	Color of Ball	Number of Holes	Maximum Number of Bonds
hydrogen	H	yellow	1	1
carbon	C	black	4	4
oxygen	O	red	2	2
nitrogen	N	blue	3 or 5*	3
chlorine	Cl	green	1	1
bromine	Br	orange	1	1
iodine	I	purple	1	1

* If the nitrogen has five holes, connect two adjacent holes with a spring bond.

1. Using the ball-and-stick model set, construct models of water, H_2O; ammonia, NH_3; and methane, CH_4. Draw a sketch of each molecule in Data Table 2. The shape shown by the water molecule is described as *bent*, the shape of the ammonia molecule is called *trigonal pyramidal*, and the shape of the methane molecule is called *tetrahedral*. Write these names below the matching structures you have drawn in the table.
2. Construct models of hydrogen sulfide, H_2S; carbon tetrachloride, CCl_4; dichlorodifluoromethane, CCl_2F_2; and ethane, C_2H_6. Give the molecular formula for each of these compounds, and draw a sketch of each molecule in Data Table 2. Name the shape of each molecule.
3. The air above a burning candle contains nitrogen gas, carbon dioxide gas, and oxygen gas. Construct models of these substances. In Data Table 2, draw a sketch of each molecule.
4. The compound urea has the molecular formula $CO(NH_2)_2$. The structural formula of urea is:

```
          O
          ‖
   H—N—C—N—H
      |       |
      H       H
```

Construct a model of urea and sketch its shape in Data Table 2.

Step 3.
N_2 (N≡N); O_2 (O=O); CO_2 (O=C=O)

This is a good time to review the properties of compounds and mixtures. The components of a mixture can be physically separated.

Name ______________________ Date ________________ Class ________________

Step 5.
Inform students that, although they may rotate the molecule about the C–C single bonds, the identity of the molecule will be unchanged. To change the model of one molecule into the model of another molecule requires bond breaking and bond making, not bond rotation.

Step 6.
Have students try to superimpose the two models they have made in Step 6. If the models are superimposable (match up on an atom-to-atom basis), they represent the same molecules. True stereoisomers cannot be superimposed.

5. Construct a model of butane, C_4H_{10}. (**Hint:** The carbons are bonded to one another in a continuous, unbranched chain.) Draw a sketch of this molecule in Data Table 2. Can you construct a model of a different molecule that has the same molecular formula as butane? Make a model of such a molecule and sketch its structure in the data table.

The two different compounds having the molecular formula C_4H_{10} are called *structural isomers*. They have identical molecular formulas but different structural formulas. They also have different physical and chemical properties. Structural isomers play a very important role in organic chemistry.

6. Construct a model of bromochlorofluoromethane, CHBrClF. Sketch the compound in the table. Can you construct an isomer of this compound? (**Hint:** Is your left hand identical to your right?) Draw the new compound if you can.

The compound and the isomer have the same molecular formula, CHBrClF, but they are different from each other in the way that a left hand is different from a right hand. The compounds are mirror images of each other and are called *stereoisomers*. The phenomenon of "handedness" exhibited by pairs of stereoisomers is very important in organic chemistry and biochemistry.

Name ______________________ Date ________________ Class ________________

OBSERVATIONS

DATA TABLE 2: SKETCHES OF MOLECULES			
H_2O bent triatomic	NH_3 trigonal pyramidal	CH_4 tetrahedral	
H_2S bent triatomic	CCl_4 tetrahedral	CCl_2F_2 tetrahedral	C_2H_6
N_2	CO_2 linear triatomic	O_2	
$CO(NH_2)_2$	CHBrClF, stereoisomers		
C_4H_{10}, structural isomers			

Name ______________________ Date ________________ Class ________________

GOING FURTHER

Develop a Hypothesis

Although the VSEPR model allows one to predict the geometry of a molecule, the prediction must still be verified through experiment. One experimental method involves measuring the dipole moment of a molecule, a quantity that reflects the degree of charge separation in a molecule—the polarity. Based on your models of CCl_4 and NH_3, propose a hypothesis about the polarities of these molecules.

The polar C–Cl bonds are symmetrically distributed around the central carbon atom in CCl_4. The dipoles therefore cancel out and CCl_4 is not expected to be polar overall. The trigonal pyramidal shape of NH_3 is expected to produce a net dipole moment.

Design an Experiment

To test your hypothesis, look up dipole moments of each molecule in a chemistry handbook.

The dipole moment of CCl_4 is 0 debye. The dipole moment of NH_3 is 1.47 debyes.

Name ______________________ Date ______________ Class ______________

12 THE MASSES OF EQUAL VOLUMES OF GASES

Text Reference
Section 10.2

Time Required
50 minutes

Objectives
- Measure the masses of equal volumes of two different gases—argon and carbon dioxide.
- Compute the ratio for masses of equal volumes of Ar and CO_2 and compare this ratio to the ratio between the molar masses of these gases.
- Evaluate the data and compare the results to the predictions made by Avogadro's hypothesis.

Advance Preparation
Carbon dioxide and argon Order one cylinder each of Ar and CO_2 gas.

Because of the relatively small mass differences involved in these measurements, it is advisable to have students use the same balance for each of their mass determinations.

PURPOSE

To determine the ratio of masses of equal volumes of argon and carbon dioxide gases.

BACKGROUND

Because many gases are colorless, odorless, and have low densities, you might think they would be difficult to work with in the laboratory. For example, you cannot place an unconfined gas on a balance and find its mass. However, surprisingly, many experiments involving gases are quite easy to perform. In fact, you can easily find the mass of a volume of a contained gas by using a simple laboratory balance.

Molecules of different gases have different masses. A molecule of oxygen (O_2) has a mass of 32 atomic mass units (amu); a molecule of nitrogen (N_2) has a mass of 28 amu. Thus, the mass ratio of oxygen molecules to nitrogen molecules is 32/28. As a result of Avogadro's hypothesis, if equal volumes of oxygen and nitrogen are compared at the same temperature and pressure, the mass ratio between the molecules will always be 32/28. This fact forms the basis of the investigation in this experiment.

In this experiment, you will determine the masses of equal volumes of two different gases—argon and carbon dioxide. The volumes you will work with will contain only about 0.01 mol of gas molecules. You will calculate the ratio between these masses and compare this ratio with the established value for the ratio between the molar masses of these gases.

MATERIALS (PER PAIR)

safety goggles
250-mL Erlenmeyer flask
rubber stopper
glass delivery tube
rubber connecting tube
pinch clamp
centigram balance
glass-marking pencil
500-mL graduated cylinder
thermometer
barometer
argon, Ar
carbon dioxide, CO_2
distilled water

Stress laboratory safety

SAFETY FIRST!

Wear your safety goggles. (All steps.)

Name ______________________ Date ________________ Class ________________

Tips

1. Students should not be permitted to dispense the gas themselves.

2. Keep the tanks of gas in their safety harnesses. Have wrenches of the appropriate sizes available for putting on and taking off the pressure regulators.

3. Tanks of compressed gas (unless they are lecture bottle-size) should be chained to the wall or to a cart designed for compressed gas tanks. Compressed gas tanks should also have regulators, which not only open and close the tank, but which permit an adjustment to the rate of flow. This permits the tank to be turned off in two locations. Never check to see if a tank contains gas by opening the main valve unless a regulator is attached.

At 760 mm Hg and 25°C, the density of Ar is 1.753 g/L, the density of CO_2 is 1.931 g/L, and the density of dry air is 1.185 g/L.

PROCEDURE

As you perform this experiment, record your data in Data Table 1.

1. Obtain a 250-mL Erlenmeyer flask and set it up as shown in Figure 12.1. Keep the assembly dry throughout the experiment. Adjust the glass delivery tube so that it does not touch the bottom of the flask when the stopper is pushed firmly into the neck.
2. Determine and record the mass of the flask assembly to the nearest 0.01 g.
3. Attach the rubber tube to the delivery jet on the argon tank. Loosen the rubber stopper in the flask and loosen the pinch clamp on the rubber tube so the tube is open. Allow argon gas to flow into the flask for 20–30 seconds—this flushes out all the air in the flask. Quickly push the stopper firmly into the neck of the flask and close the pinch clamp on the rubber tube. Shut off the argon gas and disconnect the rubber tube from the delivery jet. Remeasure the mass of the flask, now full of argon, to the nearest 0.01 g.
4. Repeat Step 3 until you obtain a constant measurement for the mass of the argon-filled flask. Measurements that agree within 0.01 g can be considered constant.
5. Repeat Steps 3 and 4, using carbon dioxide gas.
6. Use a glass-marking pencil to draw a line on the neck of the flask, at the bottom of the rubber stopper. Set the stopper assembly aside to keep it dry.
7. Fill the Erlenmeyer flask with water to the height of the pencil mark. Carefully pour the water into a 500-mL graduated cylinder. Measure and record the volume.
8. Measure and record the room temperature and pressure.

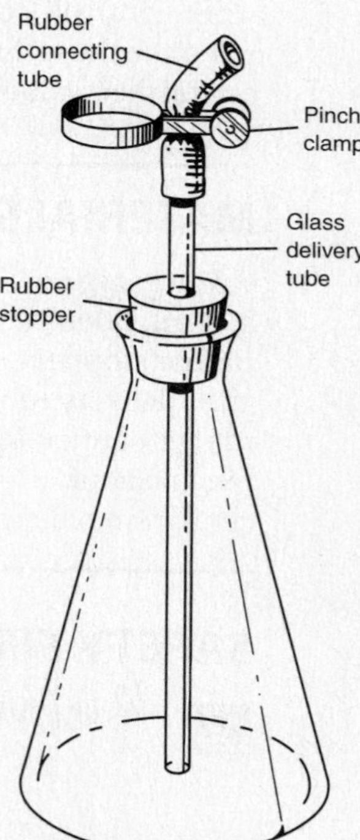

Figure 12.1

Name ______________________ Date ______________ Class ______________

OBSERVATIONS

DATA TABLE 1: QUANTITATIVE DATA		sample data
mass of flask assembly with air		274.47 g
mass of flask assembly with Ar	(1) (2)	274.64 g 274.63 g
mass of flask assembly with CO_2	(1) (2)	274.69 g 274.69 g
volume of flask		237 mL
room temperature		25°C
room pressure		740 mm Hg

ANALYSES AND CONCLUSIONS

1. Calculate the mass of air in the flask. To do this, use the density relationship between mass and volume.

density = mass/volume

Solve this equation for mass. In your calculation, use Data Table 2 to find the density of air at the conditions recorded in Data Table 1, and use the volume determined in Step 7.

If the pressure is not an even multiple of ten, students may need to interpolate from the data in the table.

DATA TABLE 2: DENSITY OF DRY AIR (g/cm^3)

	Pressure (mm Hg)					
Temperature (°C)	720	730	740	750	760	770
20	0.001141	0.001157	0.001173	0.001189	0.001205	0.001221
21	0.001137	0.001153	0.001169	0.001185	0.001201	0.001216
22	0.001134	0.001149	0.001165	0.001181	0.001197	0.001212
23	0.001130	0.001145	0.001161	0.001177	0.001193	0.001208
24	0.001126	0.001142	0.001157	0.001173	0.001189	0.001204
25	0.001122	0.001138	0.001153	0.001169	0.001185	0.001200
26	0.001118	0.001134	0.001149	0.001165	0.001181	0.001196
27	0.001115	0.001130	0.001146	0.001161	0.001177	0.001192

At 25°C and 740 mm Hg:

$$\text{mass of air} = 237\ \text{cm}^3 \times \frac{0.001153\ \text{g}}{1\ \text{cm}^3} = 0.273\ \text{g}$$

2. Calculate the mass of the flask by subtracting the mass of the air in the flask from the mass of the flask when it was full of air.

mass of flask and air − mass of air = mass of flask

274.47 g − 0.27 g = 274.20 g

3. Use the mass of the flask to calculate the masses of argon and carbon dioxide contained in the flask.

mass of Ar = mass of flask and Ar − mass of flask
= 274.64 g − 274.20 g
= 0.44 g

mass of CO_2 = mass of flask and CO_2 − mass of flask
= 274.69 g − 274.20 g
= 0.49 g

4. Determine the ratio of the mass of carbon dioxide contained in the flask to the mass of argon gas contained in the flask.

$$\frac{\text{mass of } CO_2}{\text{mass of Ar}} = \frac{0.49 \text{ g}}{0.44 \text{ g}}$$
$$= 1.1$$

5. Using data from the periodic table, calculate the actual ratio of the molar masses of carbon dioxide and argon.

$$\frac{\text{molar mass } (CO_2)}{\text{molar mass (Ar)}} = \frac{44 \text{ g}}{40 \text{ g}}$$
$$= 1.1$$

6. Avogadro's hypothesis states that equal volumes of different gases, at the same temperature and pressure, contain equal numbers of particles (or moles) of gases. Explain why similarity between the ratios calculated in problems 4 and 5 would support Avogadro's hypothesis.

The same ratios should be obtained from the experimentally determined masses and the molar masses of CO_2 and Ar if equal volumes of these gases contain the same number of moles of gas. This is essentially a statement of Avogadro's hypothesis.

7. Calculate the percent error in the experimentally determined mass ratio of equal volumes of argon and carbon dioxide. Use the ratio of the actual molar masses as the accepted value.

$$\text{Percent error} = \frac{|\text{accepted value} - \text{experimental value}|}{\text{accepted value}} \times 100\%$$

$$\text{Percent error} = \frac{|1.1 - 1.1|}{1.1} \times 100\%$$
$$= 0\%$$

8. Why must the flask assembly be kept absolutely dry during this experiment? How would your results be affected if the flask became wet any time after Step 2 in the procedure?

The experimentally determined mass of CO_2 would be too high, and the CO_2/Ar mass ratio would, consequently, be too large.

9. Is it still accurate to call Avogadro's hypothesis a *hypothesis*? Explain.

Yes and no. Yes, in the sense that it was originally introduced as an explanation of observed phenomena—the behavior of gases—but had not been tested. No, in the sense that the so-called hypothesis can now be categorized as a scientific law because it is supported by the results of many, many tests that have been done since Avogadro's time.

10. Could you find the relative mass of helium by using the procedure in this experiment? Propose a modified experimental procedure for helium and other "light" gases.

Yes. Helium is less dense than air and, therefore, it would not be possible to flush the air from the flask in the same way as was done with argon. When helium is used, the air may be flushed out by inverting the helium flask as it is being filled.

11. Demonstrate with calculations how this procedure could be used to identify an unknown gaseous element.

Suppose the mass of the unknown gaseous element, G, is 0.84 g and the mass of argon, Ar, is 0.44 g. The mass ratio of G/Ar is 0.84 g/0.44 g = 2.1.
According to Avogadro's hypothesis, the ratio of the molar mass of G to the molar mass of Ar is:

$$\frac{\text{molar mass G}}{\text{molar mass Ar}} = \frac{\text{molar mass G}}{39.9\ \text{g/mol}} = 2.1$$

$$\text{molar mass G} = 2.1 \times 39.9\ \text{g/mol}$$

$$= 83.8\ \text{g/mol}$$

The gaseous element is krypton, Kr.

Name ______________ Date ______________ Class ______________

GOING FURTHER

Develop a Hypothesis

In this experiment, it was important to compare the masses of the gases at the same temperature and pressure. Hypothesize about how the ratio of the masses of the two gases would be affected if they were each measured under different conditions of temperature and pressure.

Avogadro's hypothesis applies only when gases are measured under the same conditions. Thus, if the conditions of the measurements of two gases are different, the masses of the two gases will not be in the same ratio as their molar masses.

Design an Experiment

Propose an experiment to test your hypothesis. If resources are available and you have your teacher's permission, perform the experiment.

The experiment using Ar and CO_2 could be carried out as before, but the flask containing one of the gases could be heated briefly with the clamp open after filling.

13 EMPIRICAL FORMULA DETERMINATION

Text Reference
Section 10.3

Time Required
50 minutes

Objectives
- Convert magnesium metal to magnesium oxide by reacting Mg with O_2.
- Compute the empirical formula of magnesium oxide.
- Evaluate and compare the data to accepted values.

Advance Preparation
Magnesium ribbon
Cut a sufficient number of 25-cm-long Mg strips.

PURPOSE

To determine the empirical formula of magnesium oxide.

BACKGROUND

Carbon dioxide (CO_2), water (H_2O), and ammonia (NH_3) are three out of many chemical compounds that you are familiar with. Have you ever seen a compound with a formula such as $Na_{2.3}Cl_{3.9}$? In fact, such a formula is impossible. Only whole atoms, not fractions of atoms, react with each other to form products. Also, although elements may react in different proportions to form more than one compound, the proportions of atoms in those compounds will always be a ratio of small whole numbers.

An empirical formula gives the simplest whole-number ratio of the different atoms in a compound. For example, while the molecular formula for hydrogen peroxide is H_2O_2, the simplest whole-number ratio of hydrogen and oxygen atoms can be expressed as HO. Thus, the empirical formula of hydrogen peroxide is HO.

In this lab, you will experimentally determine the empirical formula of magnesium oxide, the compound formed when magnesium metal reacts with oxygen.

MATERIALS (PER PAIR)

safety goggles
crucible
crucible lid
clay triangle
ring stand
ring support
crucible tongs
gas burner
centigram balance
magnesium ribbon, Mg [F]
2 pieces of exposed film

SAFETY FIRST!

In this lab, the crucible you are using will become quite hot and could cause a severe burn if handled improperly. Observe all precautions, especially those listed below. If you see a safety icon beside a step in the Procedure, refer to the list below for its meaning.

Caution: Wear your safety goggles. (All steps.)

Caution: Do not look directly at burning magnesium. Do not inhale the smoke produced when the magnesium is burned. (Steps 3, 4.)

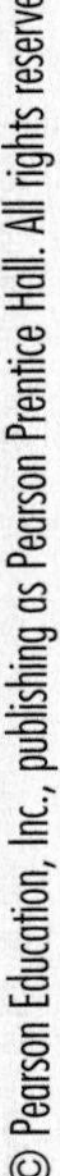

Name ______________________ Date ______________ Class ______________

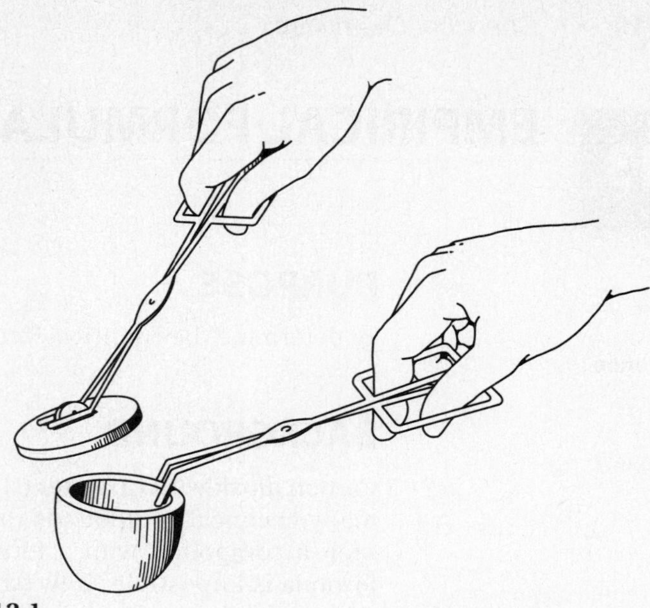

Figure 13.1

Emphasize the significance of the burn hazard associated with any hot crucible or crucible lid. Instruct students to handle these items only with crucible tongs.

 **Caution:** Always handle the crucible and crucible lid with crucible tongs, as shown in Figure 13.1. (Steps 3, 4.)

 **Note:** Return or dispose of all materials according to the instructions of your teacher. (Step 7.)

PROCEDURE

As you perform the experiment, record your data in Data Table 1.

1. Set up the equipment, as shown in Figure 13.2. Clean a crucible and its cover with water. Dry them by heating in the hottest part of the flame for 5 minutes. Allow them to cool for at least 10 minutes. Measure and record the combined mass of the crucible and lid to the nearest 0.01 g.
2. Place a coiled 25-cm length of magnesium ribbon in the crucible. Measure and record the combined mass of the crucible, lid, and magnesium.

Step 3.
Product will be lost as smoke if the lid is not put on the crucible as soon as burning begins. The smoke is MgO, which is toxic. The limit on air contamination with MgO is 10 mg/m^3 of air.
$2Mg(s) + O_2(g) \rightarrow 2MgO(s)$

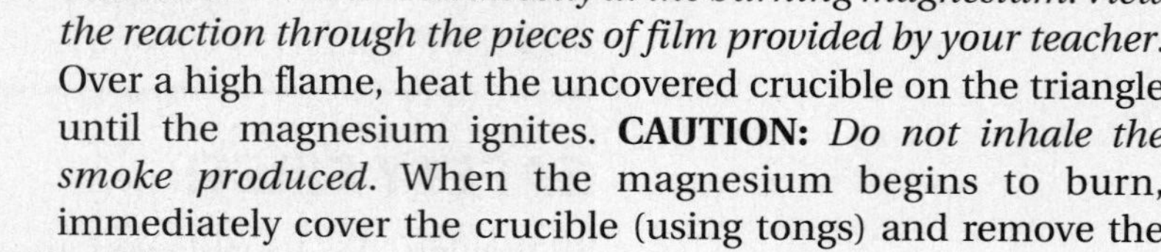

3. **CAUTION:** *Do not look directly at the burning magnesium. View the reaction through the pieces of film provided by your teacher.* Over a high flame, heat the uncovered crucible on the triangle until the magnesium ignites. **CAUTION:** *Do not inhale the smoke produced.* When the magnesium begins to burn, immediately cover the crucible (using tongs) and remove the burner.
4. After smoke production has ceased, replace the burner and continue heating the crucible. **CAUTION:** *Do not lean over the crucible.* Remove the burner and carefully lift the lid and check the reaction every 2 or 3 minutes. After heating for a total of 10 minutes, check to see if the reaction is complete. The magnesium should be wholly converted to a light gray powder, magnesium oxide. If ribbonlike material remains in the crucible, replace the burner and continue heating.

Name ____________________ Date ______________ Class ______________

Disposal 1: $MgO(s)$, the product, in Step 4.

5. Turn off and remove the burner. Allow the crucible to cool completely (at least 10 minutes).
6. Measure and record the combined mass of the crucible, crucible lid, and magnesium oxide.
7. Follow your teacher's instructions for proper disposal of the materials.

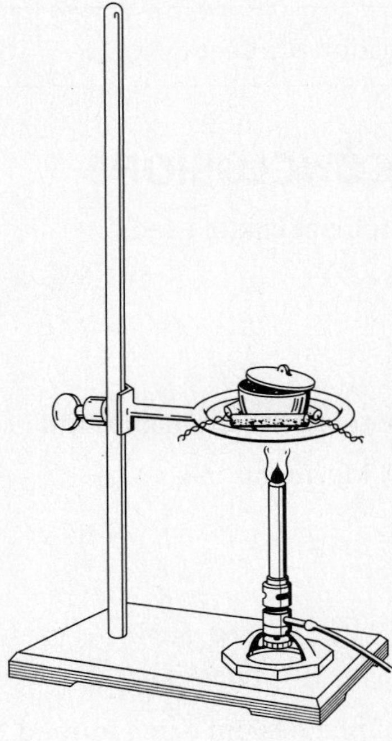

Figure 13.2

Name ______________________ Date ______________________ Class ______________________

OBSERVATIONS

DATA TABLE 1: MASS MEASUREMENTS	
Item	Mass
empty crucible and lid	38.73 g
crucible, lid, and Mg (before heating)	38.95 g
crucible, lid, and combustion product (Mg_xO_y)	39.08 g

ANALYSES AND CONCLUSIONS

1. Determine the mass of magnesium used.

$$\text{mass of Mg} = \text{mass of crucible, lid, and Mg} - \text{mass of crucible and lid}$$
$$= 38.95\text{ g} - 38.73\text{ g}$$
$$= 0.22\text{ g}$$

2. Determine the number of moles of magnesium used.

Hint: mol Mg = (mass Mg/molar mass Mg)

$$\text{number of moles Mg used} = \frac{\text{mass Mg used}}{\text{molar mass Mg}}$$
$$= \frac{0.22\text{ g}}{24.3\text{ g/mol}}$$
$$= 0.0091\text{ mol}$$

3. Determine the mass of magnesium oxide formed.

$$\text{Mass of MgO} = \text{mass of crucible, lid, and MgO} - \text{mass of crucible and lid}$$
$$= 39.08\text{ g} - 38.73\text{ g}$$
$$= 0.35\text{ g}$$

4. Determine the mass of oxygen that combined with the magnesium.

$$\text{mass of O} = \text{mass of MgO} - \text{mass of Mg}$$
$$= 0.35\text{ g} - 0.22\text{ g}$$
$$= 0.13\text{ g}$$

5. Calculate the number of moles of oxygen atoms that were used.

$$\text{mol O used} = \frac{\text{mass O used}}{\text{molar mass O}}$$
$$= \frac{0.13\text{ g}}{16.0\text{ g/mol}}$$
$$= 0.0081\text{ mol}$$

6. Calculate the ratio between moles of magnesium used and moles of oxygen used. Express this ratio in simplest whole-number form.

$$\frac{\text{mol Mg}}{\text{mol O}} = \frac{0.0091\text{ mol}}{0.0081\text{ mol}}$$
$$= 1.1$$
$$= 1:1\text{ ratio}$$

Name ______________________ Date ______________ Class ______________

7. Based on your experimental data, write the empirical formula for magnesium oxide.

MgO

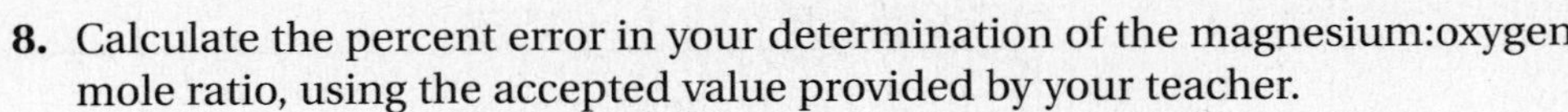

8. Calculate the percent error in your determination of the magnesium:oxygen mole ratio, using the accepted value provided by your teacher.

$$\text{Percent error} = \frac{|\text{accepted value} - \text{experimental value}|}{\text{accepted value}} \times 100 \text{ percent}$$

The accepted value for the Mg:O mole ratio is 1.0.

$$\text{Percent error in Mg:O ratio} = \frac{|1.0 - 1.1|}{1.0} \times 100 \text{ percent}$$
$$= 0.1 \times 100 \text{ percent}$$
$$= 10 \text{ percent}$$

9. Identify major sources of error in this experiment. Explain how the magnesium: oxygen ratio would be affected by each error you identify.

The major sources of error are incomplete combustion of Mg and loss of MgO as smoke. Both errors result in a mass gain upon heating that is less than would be predicted (stoichiometrically). With a measured mass of MgO that is less than expected, the experimentally obtained value for the Mg:O mole ratio would be greater than 1:1.

10. Is there agreement among the results obtained by others in the class? What does the class data tell you about the empirical formula of a compound?

There is usually large scatter in class data, with the Mg:O mole ratio greater than 1:1. Have the class average all of its results to possibly arrive at a Mg:O ratio of 1:1. It may be noted that an experiment designed to determine the empirical formula of a compound must be carried out with high accuracy and precision to yield a correct result. If the results are consistent, the students can conclude that the empirical formula of a compound represents a fixed ratio of atoms.

Name ____________ Date ____________ Class ____________

11. Interpret, in terms of atoms and in terms of moles, the subscripts in the chemical formula for ethane (C_2H_6).

The subscripts in a formula tell the numbers of each kind of atom in a molecule of the compound (2 carbon atoms and 6 hydrogen atoms in a molecule of ethane). The subscripts also tell the numbers of moles of each element in a mole of the compound (2 moles of carbon atoms and 6 moles of hydrogen atoms in each mole of ethane).

GOING FURTHER

Develop a Hypothesis

At the high temperature at which this reaction takes place, a green-yellow solid may also be formed. Propose a hypothesis about the chemical nature of this product.

The green-yellow solid may be magnesium nitride, which can form at high temperatures in the presence of atmospheric nitrogen.

$3Mg(s) + N_2(g) \rightarrow Mg_3N_2(s)$

Design an Experiment

Propose an experiment to test your hypothesis. If resources are available and you have your teacher's permission, perform the experiment.

Mg_3N_2 can react with water to form ammonia. Students can test for the presence of ammonia, using litmus paper.

Name ____________ Date ____________ Class ____________

14 TYPES OF CHEMICAL REACTIONS

Text Reference
Section 11.2

Time Required
50 minutes

Objectives
- Observe different types of chemical reactions.
- Define five general chemical reaction categories.
- Classify chemical reactions according to reaction categories.
- Write balanced chemical equations for each reaction.

Advance Preparation
0.1M copper(II) sulfate
5.0 g $CuSO_4 \cdot 5H_2O$/200 mL water

0.1M lead(II) nitrate
6.6 g $Pb(NO_3)_2$/200 mL water

0.1M potassium iodide
0.2 g KI/10 mL water

6.0M hydrochloric acid
Pour 50 mL concentrated HCl into 50 mL of water.

3% hydrogen peroxide
Use household hydrogen peroxide or dilute, with water, 5 mL of 30% H_2O_2 to 50 mL.

25 mL limewater, saturated solution of calcium oxide, CaO
The solubility of CaO in cold water is 0.131 g/100 mL. CaO dissolves in water to form $Ca(OH)_2$ with the production of a significant amount of heat. CaO is corrosive and can cause severe irritation and burning of skin and mucous membranes. Filter the CaO solution just before use.

PURPOSE

To identify and classify chemical reactions based on five general categories.

BACKGROUND

Although countless chemical reactions exist, nearly all of them can be classified into a few specific categories. In this experiment, you will learn to differentiate five general types of chemical reactions. Some of the reactions you will perform; others will be demonstrated by your teacher. From observations, you will identify the products of each reaction and determine the type of reaction that has taken place. You will consider the following reaction types: *combination reactions, decomposition reactions, single-replacement reactions, double-replacement reactions,* and *combustion reactions.* The majority of common chemical reactions can be classified as belonging to one of these categories.

MATERIALS (PER PAIR)

(Student Experiment)
safety goggles and apron
2 small test tubes
centigram balance
dropper pipet
2 medium test tubes
test-tube rack
crucible tongs
gas burner
ring stand
utility clamp
0.1*M* copper(II) sulfate, $CuSO_4$ [T]
iron filings, Fe
0.1*M* lead(II) nitrate, $Pb(NO_3)_2$ [T]
0.1*M* potassium iodide, KI [T]
6*M* hydrochloric acid, HCl [C] [T]
magnesium turnings, Mg [F]
2 wood splints
book of matches
3% hydrogen peroxide, H_2O_2

(Teacher Demonstration)
electrolysis apparatus
rubber stopper, one-holed
large test tube
glass tube, 25-cm length, bent at 90° angle in center
gas burner
ring stand
utility clamp
sodium hydrogen carbonate, $NaHCO_3$
wood splints
matches
limewater, saturated solution of calcium oxide, CaO [I] [C]

Name ______________________ Date ________________ Class ________________

SAFETY FIRST!

In this lab, observe all precautions, especially the ones listed below. If you see a safety icon beside a step in the Procedure, refer to the list below for its meaning.

Caution: Wear your safety goggles. (All steps.)

Caution: Hydrochloric acid is corrosive and can cause severe burns. (Step 3.)

Caution: Lead and copper compounds are toxic. Use as little of these compounds as practical. (Steps 1, 2.)

Caution: Exercise care when working with an open flame. Tie back hair and loose clothing. Do not use the burner near flammable materials. (Step 4.)

Note: Return or dispose of all materials according to the instructions of your teacher. (Step 7.)

Note: Wash your hands thoroughly after completing this experiment.

PROCEDURE

As you perform the experiment, record your observations in Data Table 1.

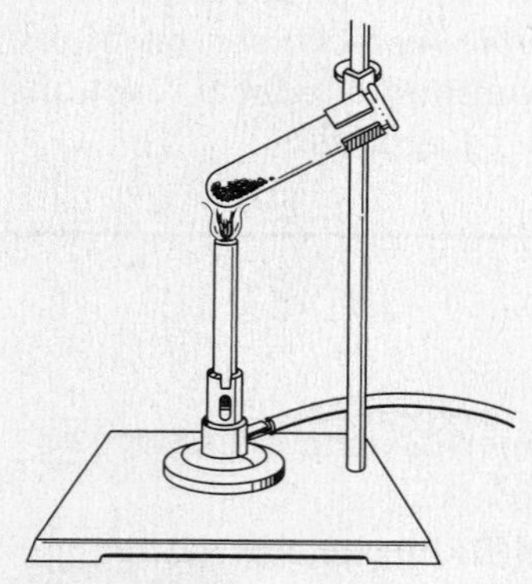

Figure 14.1

Step 4.
Tell students to allow sufficient time for the concentration of hydrogen gas to build up before inserting the glowing splint.

Part A. Student Experiments

1. **Iron metal and copper(II) sulfate solution.** Half-fill a small test tube with copper(II) sulfate solution. Add about 2 g of iron filings to the solution. After 5 minutes, record your observations.
2. **Lead(II) nitrate and potassium iodide solutions.** Put 2 mL of lead(II) nitrate solution into a small test tube. Add 5–10 drops of potassium iodide solution. Record your observations.

3. **Magnesium metal and hydrochloric acid. CAUTION:** *Hydrochloric acid is corrosive.* Half-fill a medium-sized test tube with 6*M* hydrochloric acid. Place the test tube in a test-tube rack and add several magnesium turnings. Identify any gas that forms by using crucible tongs to hold a *burning* wood splint at the mouth of the test tube. Record your observations.

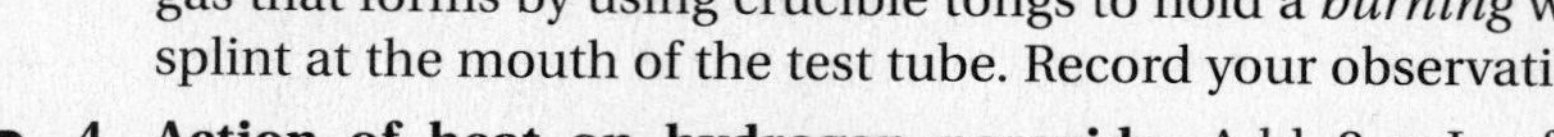

4. **Action of heat on hydrogen peroxide.** Add 2 mL of 3% hydrogen peroxide solution to a medium-sized test tube. Clamp the test tube to a ring stand, as shown in Figure 14.1. **CAUTION:** *Make sure that the mouth of the tube is pointed away from you and away from everyone else.* Heat the solution *very gently*. Identify any gas that forms by using crucible tongs to insert a *glowing* wood splint into the mouth of the test tube. Record your observations.

Name ______________________ Date ______________ Class ______________

Part B. Teacher Demonstrations

Step 5.

The gases collected during the electrolysis can be tested with a glowing splint (which will flame up in the presence of O_2) and a burning splint (which will ignite H_2, causing an audible pop). H_2 gas is produced at twice the rate of O_2 gas in this reaction:

$2H_2O(l) \rightarrow 2H_2(g) + O_2(g)$

Step 6.

The solution of CaO should be filtered immediately before use to remove the excess CaO and any precipitate of $CaCO_3$, which can form from CO_2 in the air.

Some students may know that they exhale CO_2. Using a straw, blow bubbles through a test tube one-third filled with freshly prepared limewater. The solution will turn milky white after 20–30 seconds of bubbling, as a precipitate of $CaCO_3$ is formed. Caution against swallowing the limewater. A solution of dilute methylene blue can be used as a substitute. The color changes from blue to lime green to yellow with exhalation, as the pH shifts from 6 or 7 to more acidic.

Use the following disposal methods for chemical waste.

Disposal 1: Fe(*s*) and Cu(*s*) in Step 1, and Mg(*s*) in Step 3.

Disposal 2: $CuSO_4(aq)$ in Step 1, $H_2O_2(aq)$ and $H_2O(l)$ in Step 4, and all the materials in Steps 5 and 6.

Disposal 3: The reaction solution in Step 3.

Disposal 7: The reaction solution in Step 2.

5. **Action of electricity on water (electrolysis).** Water can be broken down into its component elements by passing electricity through it. This process is called *electrolysis.* Your teacher will explain the apparatus shown in Figure 14.2. Make observations of the reaction during a 10-minute period.

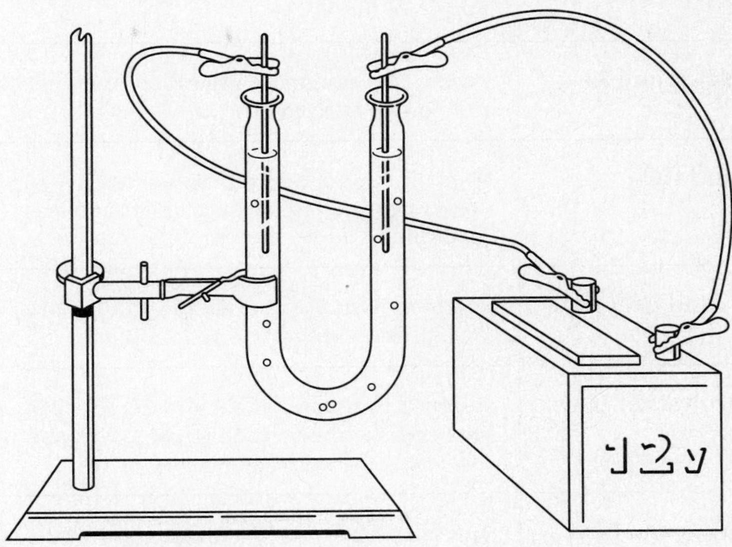

Figure 14.2

6. **Action of heat on sodium hydrogen carbonate.** Solid sodium hydrogen carbonate will be heated strongly in a large test tube for 2 minutes. The gas that is given off will be tested by exposing it to a burning splint and by bubbling it through limewater. Record your observations of these tests.

7. Follow your teacher's instructions for proper disposal of the materials.

Name ______________________ Date ________________ Class ________________

OBSERVATIONS

DATA TABLE 1: CHEMICAL REACTION TYPES		
Reaction	Observations	Reaction Type
Fe and $CuSO_4$	The blue color of the solution fades. A dark, solid material forms on the Fe.	single replacement
$Pb(NO_3)_2$ and KI	When the two colorless solutions are mixed, a yellow precipitate is formed.	double replacement
Mg and HCl	A gas is produced from the solution. The Mg metal "disappears." The burning splint causes a "bark" (explosion) in the mouth of the test tube.	single replacement
H_2O_2 and heat	Bubbles form in the solution (the solution is *not* boiling). The glowing splint bursts into flame.	decomposition
electrolysis of H_2O	A gas is produced at each electrode. The volume of gas (H_2) formed at one electrode is twice the volume of gas (O_2) formed at the other electrode.	decomposition
$NaHCO_3$ and heat	The burning splint is extinguished when placed in the gas. The limewater turns milky when the gas is bubbled through.	decomposition

Analyses and Conclusions
Ask students for evidence that each change was indeed a chemical change. Was there a color change? (reactions 1, 2) Was energy absorbed? (4, 5, 6) Was energy given off? (1, 3) Was a gas produced (3, 4, 5, 6) Was a precipitate formed? (2)

ANALYSES AND CONCLUSIONS

1. Classify each of the observed reactions as one of the five reaction types listed in the Background section. Record your answers in Data Table 1.

2. Write an equation for each reaction observed. Indicate the state (*s*, *l*, *g*, *aq*) for each reactant and product, then balance each equation.

   reaction 1 $Fe(s) + CuSO_4(aq) \rightarrow FeSO_4(aq) + C(s)$

   reaction 2 $Pb(NO_3)_2(aq) + 2KI(aq) \rightarrow PbI_2(s) + 2KNO_3(aq)$

   reaction 3 $Mg(s) + 2HCl(aq) \rightarrow MgCl_2(aq) + H_2(g)$

   reaction 4 $2H_2O_2(aq) \xrightarrow{heat} 2H_2O(l) + O_2(g)$

   reaction 5 $2H_2O(l) \xrightarrow{electricity} 2H_2(g) + O_2(g)$

   reaction 6 $2NaHCO_3(s) \xrightarrow{heat} Na_2CO_3(s) + CO_2(g) + H_2O(l)$

3. Although no combustion reactions were described in the Procedure section, two combustion reactions did occur in the course of this experiment. The reactants were H_2 and CH_4 (natural gas), respectively. Write a balanced equation for the combustion of each of these substances.

   $2H_2 + O_2 \rightarrow 2H_2O$

   $CH_4 + 2O_2 \rightarrow CO_2 + 2H_2O$

Name ______________________ Date ______________ Class ______________

4. Identify the combustion reaction in question 3 that is also a combination reaction.

$2H_2 + O_2 \rightarrow 2H_2O$

5. Describe in your own words the five types of chemical reactions listed in the Background section. Explain how to distinguish each of these types of reactions.

A combination reaction has a single product.

A decomposition reaction has a single reactant.

In a single-replacement reaction, one element displaces another element from an aqueous solution of a compound, to form a new compound and a free element.

In a double-replacement reaction, two new compounds are formed when aqueous solutions of two ionic compounds are mixed. One of the newly formed compounds is a precipitate, a gas, or a molecular compound.

In a combustion reaction, O_2 reacts with another chemical to produce an oxide and to generate heat and light. When O_2 reacts with a hydrocarbon, the products of the reaction are CO_2 and H_2O.

6. List the tests that were used to identify the three gases produced in this experiment.

Positive test for O_2: Glowing splint bursts into flames when inserted into test tube.

Positive test for H_2: Burning splint causes explosion when inserted into test tube containing H_2.

Positive test for CO_2: Limewater turns milky when CO_2 is bubbled through it. Burning splint is extinguished when inserted into test tube containing CO_2.

Name ______________________ Date ________________ Class ______________

7. Which type(s) of reactions are characterized by:

a. two products

double replacement, single replacement, decomposition, and combustion (sometimes)

b. a single reactant

decomposition

c. two reactants

combination, single replacement, double replacement, and combustion

d. a single product

combination

GOING FURTHER

Develop a Hypothesis

Based on the results of this lab, develop a hypothesis about the type of chemical reaction (and the predicted chemical equation) that occurs when iron filings are added to 6*M* hydrochloric acid.

Based on the observations made when magnesium reacted with hydrochloric acid, students may predict that iron will react in a similar fashion to produce hydrogen gas—a single-replacement reaction.

Design an Experiment

Propose an experiment to test your hypothesis. If resources are available and you have your teacher's permission, perform the experiment.

Students' experimental design should be similar to the procedure in Step 3.

Name ______________________ Date __________________ Class __________________

15 REACTIVITY OF METALS

Text Reference
Section 11.2

Time Required
40 minutes

Objectives

- Observe the reaction of metallic elements with metallic ions of other metals.
- Based on data, rank the metals according to their relative reactivities.

Advance Preparation
solutions, 5% w/v, in dropper bottles
Prepare each of the seven solutions by dissolving 5 g of the given substance in 100 mL of distilled water.

PURPOSE

To measure the relative reactivities of selected metallic elements.

BACKGROUND

The chemical reactivity of a metal determines how the metal is used. For example, gold, which is commonly used in jewelry, is highly resistant to chemical reactions. Sodium, however, is not used in jewelry because it is so reactive it will explode if it contacts water. The chemistry of the metals is based on their ability to lose electrons. Differences in chemical reactivity among metals depend on the relative ease with which they give up electrons.

You can measure the relative reactivity of two metals by placing a small pure sample of one metal in a solution containing the ions of the other metal. If the small metal sample is more reactive than the metal whose ions are in solution, electrons will move from the solid metal sample into the solution. For example, a piece of iron placed in a solution containing copper(II) ions will corrode, while fine copper particles deposit on the iron. However, no reaction occurs when a strip of copper metal is placed in a solution of iron(II) ions.

In this experiment, you will test the reactivities of a variety of metals with different metal ions. You will then use the results of your tests to construct a scale of relative reactivities of the metals.

MATERIALS (PER PAIR)

safety goggles and apron
gloves
glass-marking pencil
8 medium test tubes
steel wool
test-tube rack
3 dropper pipets
tweezers
thin metal strips, 0.25 mm thick, approximately 2.00 cm × 0.50 cm:
- 8 strips copper, Cu
- 8 strips zinc, Zn
- 8 strips magnesium, Mg [F]

solutions, 5% w/v, in dropper bottles:
- lead(II) nitrate, $Pb(NO_3)_2$ [T]
- silver nitrate, $AgNO_3$ [T] [I]
- copper(II) sulfate, $CuSO_4$ [T] [I]
- magnesium chloride, $MgCl_2$
- zinc chloride, $ZnCl_2$ [T]
- sodium chloride, NaCl
- potassium chloride, KCl

Name ______________________ Date ________________ Class ________________

SAFETY FIRST!

In this lab, observe all precautions, especially the ones listed below. If you see a safety icon beside a step in the Procedure, refer to the list below for its meaning.

Caution: Wear your safety goggles. (All steps.)

Caution: Wear your lab apron. (All steps.)

Caution: Wear plastic gloves. (All steps.)

Caution: Magnesium metal is flammable. Keep this material away from open flames. (Step 5.)

Caution: Solutions of lead and copper ions are toxic. (Steps 3–6.)

Caution: Silver nitrate is toxic and will leave dark brown stains on skin and clothing. (Steps 3–6.)

If $AgNO_3$ does get on the skin or clothing, staining can be prevented by dipping the affected area in "hypo" (0.5*M* sodium thiosulfate, $Na_2S_2O_3$), and then rinsing with water.

Note: Return or dispose of all materials according to the instructions of your teacher. (Step 6.)

PROCEDURE

As you perform this experiment, record your observations in Data Table 1.

Step 1. The metals must be polished to remove any oxide coating.

1. Polish metal strips of copper, zinc, and magnesium with steel wool until they are clean and shiny.
2. Using a glass-marking pencil, label eight test tubes with the numbers 1–8. Place the tubes in a test-tube rack.

3. To tube 1, add 5 drops of $Pb(NO_3)_2$ solution. To tube 2, add 5 drops of $AgNO_3$ solution. Using tweezers, add one strip of copper metal to each tube. Record your observations.
4. Add 5 drops of solution to each tube as follows: tube 3, $CuSO_4$; tube 4, $Pb(NO_3)_2$; tube 5, $MgCl_2$. Add a strip of zinc metal to each tube. Record your observations.

5. Add 5 drops of solution to each tube, as follows: tube 6, $ZnCl_2$; tube 7, NaCl; tube 8, KCl. Add a strip of polished magnesium metal to each tube. Record your observations.
6. Follow your teacher's instructions for proper disposal of the materials.

Use the following disposal methods for chemical waste.

Disposal 1: Cu(*s*), Zn(*s*), and Mg(*s*).

Disposal 2: All reaction solutions except those containing $Pb(NO_3)_2$ or $AgNO_3$.

Disposal 7: All reaction solutions containing $Pb(NO_3)_2$.

Disposal 8: All reaction solutions containing $AgNO_3$.

Name ______________ Date ______________ Class ______________

OBSERVATIONS

DATA TABLE 1: OBSERVATIONS OF METAL ACTIVITY			
Tube	Metal Ion	Metal	Observations
1	Pb^{2+}	Cu	no reaction
2	Ag^{+}	Cu	dark gray deposit on copper; solution turns blue
3	Cu^{2+}	Zn	dark copper-colored deposit on Zn, which corrodes
4	Pb^{2+}	Zn	black deposit on Zn, which corrodes
5	Mg^{2+}	Zn	no reaction
6	Zn^{2+}	Mg	dark gray deposit on Mg, which corrodes; may be evolution of gas
7	Na^{+}	Mg	no reaction
8	K^{+}	Mg	no reaction

ANALYSES AND CONCLUSIONS

1. Why is it necessary to polish the metal strips before doing the experiment?

Polishing will remove any oxide coat that may be present.

2. Write balanced chemical equations for those reactions that actually occurred.

$$Cu(s) + 2AgNO_3(aq) \rightarrow Cu(NO_3)_2(aq) + 2Ag(s)$$

$$Zn(s) + CuSO_4(aq) \rightarrow ZnSO_4(aq) + Cu(s)$$

$$Zn(s) + Pb(NO_3)_2(aq) \rightarrow Zn(NO_3)_2(aq) + Pb(s)$$

$$Mg(s) + ZnCl_2(aq) \rightarrow MgCl_2(aq) + Zn(s)$$

3. In which of the five general classifications of chemical reactions do the reactions in your answer for question 2 belong?

single-replacement reactions

Name ______________________ Date ________________ Class ________________

4. Using your experimental data, list the metals in order of increasing activity. Explain how you arrived at your list.

For each of the reactions tried, the activities are as follows.

1. Pb > Cu [$Pb(NO_3)_2$ + Cu produce no reaction]
2. Cu > Ag ($AgNO_3$ + Cu produce a reaction)
3. Zn > Cu ($CuSO_4$ + Zn produce a reaction)
4. Zn > Pb [$Pb(NO_3)_2$ + Zn produce a reaction]
5. Mg > Zn ($MgCl_2$ + Zn produce no reaction)
6. Mg > Zn ($ZnCl_2$ + Mg produce a reaction)
7. Na > Mg (NaCl + Mg produce no reaction)
8. K > Mg (KCl + Mg produce no reaction)

From 1 and 2, the relative activities are Pb > Cu > Ag.

From 3 and 4, Zn > Cu and Pb. Therefore, the order is Zn > Pb > Cu > Ag.

From 5–8, Na and K > Mg > Zn.

The final activity rankings are Na and K > Mg > Zn > Pb > Cu > Ag.

The experiment does not enable ranking of Na relative to K.

5. Using the results of problem 4, do you think there would be a reaction if strips of copper or zinc were placed in solutions of KCl or NaCl? Explain.

No, sodium and potassium are more active than zinc or copper.

GOING FURTHER

Develop a Hypothesis

Based on the results of this lab, develop a hypothesis about how the relative activities of the metals correspond to their arrangement in the periodic table.

Design an Experiment

Propose an experiment to test your hypothesis. If resources are available and you have your teacher's permission, perform the experiment.

Name ______________________ Date ______________ Class ______________

16 IDENTIFICATION OF ANIONS AND CATIONS IN SOLUTION

Text Reference
Section 11.3

Time Required
50 minutes for Part A
50 minutes for Part B

Objectives
- Perform simple chemical tests for common anions and cations in aqueous solutions.
- Draw conclusions and make predictions about the ions present in an unknown solution.

Advance Preparation
When the solvent is not specified, it is distilled water.

0.1M barium chloride
2.4 g $BaCl_2 \cdot 2H_2O$/100 mL

0.1M sodium hydrogen carbonate
0.84 g $NaHCO_3$/100 mL

0.1M sodium chloride
0.58 g NaCl/100 mL

0.05M sodium phosphate
1.9 g $Na_3PO_4 \cdot 12H_2O$/100 mL

0.1M sodium sulfate
1.4 g Na_2SO_4/100 mL

0.1M silver nitrate
1.7 g $AgNO_3$/100 mL

0.1M ammonium nitrate
0.80 g NH_4NO_3/100 mL

0.1M calcium nitrate
1.6 g $Ca(NO_3)_2$/100 mL

0.1M potassium chloride
0.74 g KCl/100 mL

0.1M potassium thiocyanate
0.97 g KSCN/100 mL

0.1M sodium oxalate
1.3 g $Na_2C_2O_4$/100 mL

0.1M iron(III) sulfate
4.0 g $Fe_2(SO_4)_3$/100 mL

PURPOSE

To identify the ions in an unknown solution through the application of chemical tests.

BACKGROUND

Detectives in mystery novels often rush evidence from the crime scene to the lab for analysis. In this experiment, you will become a chemical detective. You will conduct laboratory analysis to determine the ionic composition of an unknown solution. The process of determining the composition of a sample of matter by conducting chemical tests is called *qualitative analysis.* Solutions of unknown ions can be subjected to chemical tests, and the results can be compared to the results given by known ions in the same tests. By conducting the appropriate tests and applying logic, the identities of the ions present in an unknown solution can be determined.

The analyses you perform are based upon the idea that no two ions produce the same set of chemical reactions. Each ion reacts in its own characteristic way. In this experiment, you will observe several types of chemical reactions commonly used as tests in qualitative analysis. These reactions include a color change, the production of a gas, and the formation of a precipitate—a solid product. As you do this experiment, remember that careful observation and logical reasoning are the keys to being a good detective. Who knows what ions lurk in your unknown solution?

MATERIALS (PER PAIR)

safety goggles and apron
250-mL beaker
gas burner
ring stand
ring support
wire gauze
crucible tongs
9 small test tubes
test-tube rack
25-mL graduated cylinder
dropper pipet
nichrome wire (10-cm length)
cobalt-blue glass
test-tube holder
forceps
plastic wash bottle
distilled water
red litmus paper, 1 cm × 10 cm

Name ______________ Date ______________ Class ______________

0.1M ammonium molybdate
Dissolve 100 g of ammonium paramolybdate, $(NH_4)_6Mo_7O_{24}•4H_2O$, (or molybdic acid), in 145 mL of concentrated $NH_3(aq)$ and 270 mL of water. Slowly, and with constant stirring, pour this solution into a solution of nitric acid that has been prepared by dissolving 490 mL of concentrated HNO_3 in 1150 mL of water. Keep the mixture in a warm place for several days or until a portion heated to 40°C deposits no yellow precipitate. Decant the solution from any sediment and store in glass-stoppered bottles.

6M hydrochloric acid
Pour 150 mL of concentrated HCl slowly into 150 mL of water.

6M nitric acid
Pour 190 mL of concentrated HNO_3 slowly into 300 mL of water and dilute to 500 mL.

6M sodium hydroxide
Dissolve 24 g NaOH pellets in 80 mL of water, stirring; cool. Dilute to 100 mL. Store in a plastic bottle.

3M sulfuric acid
Pour 15 mL of concentrated H_2SO_4 into 80 mL of water and dilute to 100 mL.

red litmus paper
10-cm lengths

Place knowns and unknowns in dropper bottles. Assign the unknowns identification codes. Unknowns may be $NaHCO_3$, NaCl, Na_3PO_4, Na_2SO_4, KCl, $Fe_2(SO_4)_3$, NH_4NO_3, or $Ca(NO_3)_2$. Give each pair a single unknown to test along with the knowns and identity at the end of the procedure.

Part A. Anions

0.1*M* sodium chloride, NaCl
6*M* nitric acid, HNO_3 [C] [T]
0.1*M* silver nitrate, $AgNO_3$ [T] [I]
0.1*M* sodium sulfate, Na_2SO_4
6*M* hydrochloric acid, HCl [C] [T]
0.1*M* barium chloride, $BaCl_2$ [T]
0.1*M* sodium hydrogen carbonate, $NaHCO_3$
0.05*M* sodium phosphate, Na_3PO_4
0.1*M* ammonium molybdate, $(NH_4)_2MoO_4$
unknown solutions (anions) [T]

Part B. Cations

3*M* sulfuric acid, H_2SO_4 [C] [T]
0.1*M* iron(III) sulfate, $Fe_2(SO_4)_3$
0.1*M* potassium thiocyanate, KSCN [T]
0.1*M* sodium chloride, NaCl
6*M* hydrochloric acid, HCl [C] [T]
0.1*M* potassium chloride, KCl
0.1*M* calcium nitrate, $Ca(NO_3)_2$
0.1*M* sodium oxalate, $Na_2C_2O_4$ [T]
0.1*M* ammonium nitrate, NH_4NO_3
6*M* sodium hydroxide, NaOH [C] [T]
unknown solutions (cations)

SAFETY FIRST!

In this lab, observe all precautions, especially the ones listed below. If you see a safety icon beside a step in the Procedure, refer to the list below for its meaning.

Caution: Wear your safety goggles. (All steps.)

Caution: Nitric acid, hydrochloric acid, sulfuric acid, and sodium hydroxide are corrosive and can cause severe injury. Never cover the opening of a test tube with your finger when mixing chemicals in the tube. To mix the contents, "flick" the tube as demonstrated by your teacher. (Steps 3, 4, 5, 6, 9, 10, 11, 12, 13.)

Caution: Silver, barium, and oxalate compounds are poisonous. Avoid contact with these chemicals. (Steps 3, 4, 12.)

Caution: Silver nitrate will stain skin and clothing. (Step 3.)

Caution: Never pick up a dropper bottle by its cap. Always hold a dropper with the tip lower than the rubber bulb so that the liquid does not run into the bulb.

Caution: Exercise care when working with a hot water bath. (Steps 1, 6, 12.)

Note: Return or dispose of all materials according to the instructions of your teacher. (Steps 7, 14.)

Note: Wash your hands thoroughly after completing this experiment.

Name ______________________ Date ______________ Class ______________

Set up duplicates of the solutions for Part A and Part B in trays. Have half of the students do Part A first, half Part B. Use plastic dropper bottles with attached lids. Check manufacturer's guidelines to determine the appropriate plastic material for storing 6*M* HCl or 6*M* HNO_3. Be sure the material is chemically resistant.

Violent reactions can occur when thiocyanates are mixed with nitrates and nitric acid. Potassium thiocyanate must be kept away from nitric acid. Be sure that these chemicals are kept in separate trays in different areas of the laboratory.

Step 3.

$Ag^+ + Cl^- \rightarrow AgCl(s)$

The reaction is carried out in HNO_3 to prevent formation of the precipitate AgOH.

Step 4.

$Ba^{2+} + SO_4^{2-} \rightarrow BaSO_4(s)$

HCl is added to prevent formation of the precipitate $Ba(OH)_2$.

Step 5.

$HCO_3^- + H^+ \rightarrow H_2O + CO_2$

The presence of HCO_3^- is indicated by frothing of the test solution due to the production of CO_2 gas.

Step 6. A finely divided, canary-yellow precipitate of ammonium phosphomolybdate is formed.

$PO_4^{3-} + 12(NH_4)_2MoO_4 + 21HNO_3(aq) + 3H^+ \rightarrow$
$21NH_4NO_3(aq) + 12H_2O + (NH_4)_3PO_4\bullet12MoO_3(s)$

Step 9.

$Fe^{3+} + SCN^- \rightarrow FeSCN^{2+}$

HCl is added to prevent formation of iron hydroxide precipitates.

PROCEDURE

As you perform the experiment, record your observations in Data Table 1.

Procedure note: In testing for different ions in Steps 3–13, you will always begin with two test tubes. For each step, you must add 2 mL of the known solution to one test tube and 2 mL of your unknown solution to a second test tube. The name of the known solution is given in each step.

Note that 1 mL is approximately 20 drops. Count out 40 drops of water in a test tube and make note of the level of water in the tube. Throughout the experiment, fill a test tube to this same level whenever a 2-mL sample is called for. This practice will save you considerable time. Always clean the medicine dropper after each use.

Part A. Testing for Anions (Day 1)

1. Set up a boiling water bath for use in Step 6.
2. Thoroughly clean all the test tubes used in this experiment, rinsing them well with distilled water. Record the number of the unknown solution you will be testing.

3. Test for chloride ion, Cl^-. Known solution is sodium chloride. **CAUTION:** *Nitric acid is corrosive. Do not put your finger over the top of the tube to cover it.* Add 2 mL of 6*M* nitric acid to each tube and gently flick the tubes to mix. Add 10 drops of silver nitrate to each tube and flick to mix. Record your observations.

4. Test for sulfate ion, SO_4^{2-}. Known solution is sodium sulfate. **CAUTION:** *Hydrochloric acid is corrosive.* Add 2 mL of 6*M* hydrochloric acid to each tube and mix. Add 10 drops of barium chloride solution to each tube and mix. Record your observations.

5. Test for hydrogen carbonate ion, HCO_3^-. Known solution is sodium hydrogen carbonate. Carefully observe the test tubes as you add 2 mL of 6*M* hydrochloric acid to each tube. Record your observations.

6. Test for phosphate ion, PO_4^{3-}. Known solution is sodium phosphate. Add 1 mL of 6*M* nitric acid and 10 drops of ammonium molybdate solution to each tube and mix. Place the tubes in a boiling water bath and heat for 5 minutes. Allow tubes to cool in a test-tube rack for 10 minutes. Record your observations. (Retain the water bath for Part B, Step 12.)

7. Follow your teacher's instructions for proper disposal of the materials.

Part B. Testing For Cations (Day 2)

8. Review the general directions at the beginning of the Procedure section. Prepare your test tubes as in Part A, Step 2.

9. Test for iron(III) ion, Fe^{3+}. Known solution is iron (III) sulfate. **CAUTION:** *Sulfuric acid is corrosive.* Add 5 drops of 3*M* sulfuric acid and 5 drops of potassium thiocyanate solution to each tube. Flick gently to mix. Record your observations.

Name ______________________ Date ________________ Class ________________

The nichrome wire loop may be embedded in a glass rod. If it is, caution students to heat only the tip of the wire loop.

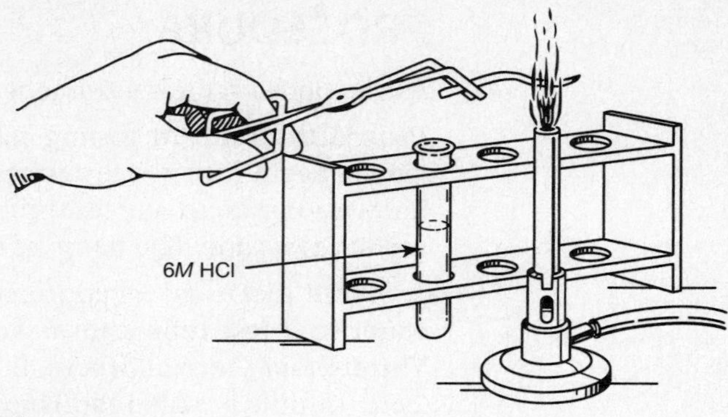

Figure 16.1

Step 10.
The sodium ion causes an intense yellow flame emission.

10. Flame-test for sodium ion, Na^{+}. Known solution is sodium chloride. Add 3 drops of 6*M* hydrochloric acid to each tube. Flick gently to mix.

Add 3–4 mL of 6*M* hydrochloric acid to a small test tube in a test-tube rack. Heat the end of a 10-cm length of nichrome wire in a hot burner flame, as shown in Figure 16.1. While it is still hot, dip the end of the wire into the hydrochloric acid in the test tube. Remove the wire from the acid and immediately reheat it in the burner flame. Repeat this acid cleaning of the wire until the flame remains unchanged when the wire is heated.

Dip the acid-cleaned wire into the sodium chloride solution. Immediately hold it in the hot burner flame. Observe the color of the flame. Acid-clean the wire and then test the unknown solution. Record the color of the flame. (A faintly colored flame is not considered a positive test for sodium.) Save the prepared unknown solution for the next test.

Step 11.
The potassium ion causes a violet flame emission. Cobalt glass absorbs the yellow color of the sodium flame emission, but transmits the violet color of the potassium flame emission.

11. Flame-test for potassium ion, K^{+}. Known solution is potassium chloride. Add 3 drops of 6*M* hydrochloric acid to each tube and flick gently to mix. Acid-clean the nichrome wire. Flame-test the potassium chloride solution. Acid-clean the wire and test your unknown. If your unknown contains sodium, the color of the sodium flame will mask the color that is characteristic of potassium. You will be able to see the potassium color, if it is there, by looking at the flame through a piece of cobalt-blue glass. Record your results.

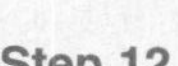

Step 12.
$Ca^{2+} + C_2O_4^{2-} \rightarrow CaC_2O_4(s)$

Calcium ions cause a brick-red flame emission.

12. Test for calcium ion, Ca^{2+}. Known solution is calcium nitrate. To each tube, add 10 drops of sodium oxalate solution. Warm the tubes in the boiling water bath for a few minutes. Record your observations.

Name ______________________ Date ______________ Class ______________

(Optional) You can also perform a flame test for calcium. Add 3 drops of 6*M* hydrochloric acid to fresh 2-mL samples of the calcium nitrate solution and the unknown solution. Perform flame tests as in Step 10. Record the color of the calcium flame and the results for your unknown.

Step 13.
$NH_4^+ + OH^- \rightarrow NH_3(aq) + H_2O$
Gentle heating drives the NH_3 from solution. The test paper is moistened so that, when the NH_3 contacts it, the above reaction is reversed. The OH^- ions produced thereby cause the litmus to change from red to blue.

13. Test for ammonium ion, NH_4^+. Known solution is ammonium nitrate. **CAUTION:** *Sodium hydroxide can cause burns.* To each tube, add 3 drops of 6*M* sodium hydroxide. Hold the tube containing the ammonium nitrate solution with a test-tube holder. *Gently* warm the tube along its sides using a back-and-forth motion through a burner flame. Do not allow the solution to boil. **CAUTION:** *At all times, make sure that the opening of the tube is pointed away from other people.* Hold a moistened piece of red litmus paper near the mouth of the test tube, as shown in Figure 16.2. The test will be spoiled if the solution contacts the litmus paper. Record the changes you observe. Fan the vapors coming out of the tube toward your nose with your hand. Cautiously sniff the vapors. Record your observations. Repeat the procedure for your unknown solution.

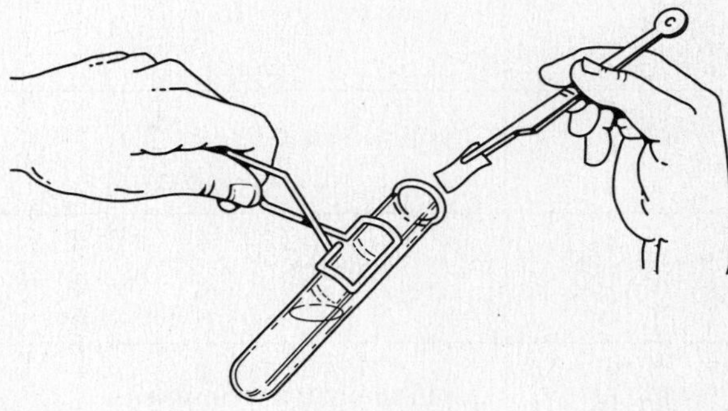

Figure 16.2

Use the following disposal methods for chemical waste.

Disposal 2: $NaCl(aq)$ in Step 10, and the materials in Step 12 (except materials required for optional flame test).

Disposal 3: Materials in Steps 5 and 6; $HCl(aq)$ in Step 10; and the materials in Steps 9, 11, and 13. (Also, the materials from the optional flame test in Step 12.)

Because only drops of $AgNO_3$ and $BaCl_2$ are used in Steps 3 and 4, realistically, these materials can be flushed with water down the drain—Disposal 2. Alternatively, use **Disposal Method 5** for the materials in Step 4 and **Disposal Method 8** for the materials in Step 3.

14. Follow your teacher's instructions for proper disposal of the materials.

Name ______________ Date ______________ Class ______________

OBSERVATIONS

DATA TABLE 1: OBSERVATIONS

Ion	Test Reagents/ Test Procedure	Test Results for Solution with Ion	Test Results for Unknown Solution No.___	Is Ion Present in Unknown?
Cl^-	HNO_3 $AgNO_3$	white ppt.		
SO_4^{2-}	HCl $BaCl_2$	white ppt.		
HCO_3^-	HCl	gas produced		
PO_3^{4-}	HNO_3 $(NH_4)_2MoO_4$	canary-yellow ppt.		
Fe^{3+}	H_2SO_4 KSCN	yellow solution turns deep red		
Na^+	flame test	yellow flame		
K^+	flame test	violet flame		
Ca^{2+}	$Na_2C_2O_4$	white ppt.; decomposes upon heating to produce another ppt. and a gas		
NH_4^+	NaOH	gas produced upon heating; wet litmus paper turns blue when exposed to the gas		

ANALYSES AND CONCLUSIONS

1. List the anions present in your unknown.
   Answers will vary, depending upon makeup of unknowns.

2. List the cations present in your unknown.
   Answers will vary, depending upon makeup of unknowns.

Name ______________________ Date ________________ Class ________________

3. Write the complete ionic equation and the net ionic equation for the reactions that occur in Steps 3, 4, 5, 12, and 13.

3. $Na^+(aq) + Cl^-(aq) + Ag^+(aq) + NO_3^-(aq) \rightarrow Na^+(aq) + NO_3^-(aq) + AgCl(s)$

$Ag^-(aq) + Cl^-(aq) \rightarrow AgCl(s)$

4. $2Na^+(aq) + SO_4^{2-}(aq) + Ba^{2+}(aq) + 2Cl^-(aq) \rightarrow 2Na^+(aq) + 2Cl^-(aq) + BaSO_4(s)$

$Ba^{2+}(aq) + SO_4^{2-}(aq) \rightarrow BaSO_4(s)$

5. $Na^+(aq) + HCO_3^-(aq) + H^+(aq) + Cl^-(aq) \rightarrow H_2O(l) + CO_2(g) + Na^+(aq) + Cl^-(aq)$

$HCO_3^-(aq) + H^+(aq) \rightarrow H_2O(l) + CO_2(g)$

12. $Ca^{2+}(aq) + NO_3^-(aq) + Na^+(aq) + C_2O_4^{2-}(aq) \rightarrow CaC_2O_4(s) + Na^+(aq) + NO_3^-(aq)$

$Ca^{2+}(aq) + C_2O_4^{2-}(aq) \rightarrow CaC_2O_4(s)$

13. $NH_4^+(aq) + NO_3^-(aq) + Na^+(aq) + OH^-(aq) \rightarrow NH_3(g) + H_2O(l) + NO_3^-(aq) + Na^+(aq)$

$NH_4^+(aq) + OH^-(aq) \rightarrow NH_3(g) + H_2O(l)$

4. It is possible to get a false-positive or a false-negative result when testing for ions. Propose a situation that could lead to a false positive for a particular ion. Choose a different ion and show how a false negative could result. Which do you think is more likely to happen—a false-positive or a false-negative result? Explain your reasoning.

A solution containing oxalate ions (but not chloride ions) could appear to test positive for chloride ions because silver oxalate is white and insoluble. A false negative could result because an ion is present in too low a concentration, from interference with another ion (for example, sodium ion interfering with the flame test for potassium), or from an improperly performed test. Both false-positive and false-negative results can occur, depending on the circumstances.

Name ____________________ Date ______________ Class ______________

GOING FURTHER

Develop a Hypothesis

In the test for the sulfate ion (Step 4), hydrochloric acid was added before the barium chloride solution was added. Propose a hypothesis to explain why the hydrochloric acid is needed.

The hydrochloric acid is added to prevent the formation of a precipitate of barium hydroxide, which could produce a false-positive result.

Design an Experiment

Propose an experiment to test your hypothesis. If resources are available and you have your teacher's permission, perform the experiment.

Test the hypothesis by adding barium chloride to aqueous solutions over a range of pH, and determine the approximate pH at which barium hydroxide will precipitate.

Name ______________________ Date ________________ Class ________________

17 PRECIPITATION REACTIONS

Text Reference
Section 11.3

Time Required
45 minutes

Objectives
- Observe which combinations of ionic solutions form precipitates.
- Identify the precipitate formed in each reaction.
- Write complete and net ionic equations for chemical reactions.
- Draw conclusions and make predictions about precipitation reactions.

Advance Preparation

0.1M aluminum chloride
2.4 g $AlCl_3 \cdot 6H_2O$/100 mL
0.1M aluminum sulfate
3.4 g $Al_2(SO_4)_3$/100 mL
0.1M barium nitrate
2.6 g $Ba(NO_3)_2$/100 mL
0.1M magnesium chloride
2.0 g $MgCl_2 \cdot 6H_2O$/100 mL
0.1M sodium sulfate
1.4 g Na_2SO_4/100 mL
0.1M magnesium nitrate
1.5 g $Mg(NO_3)_2$/100 mL
0.1M barium chloride
2.4 g $BaCl_2 \cdot 2H_2O$/100 mL
0.1M magnesium sulfate
2.5 g $MgSO_4 \cdot 7H_2O$/100 mL
0.1M potassium chloride
0.74 g KCl/100 mL
0.2M sodium hydroxide
0.80 g NaOH/100 mL
0.2M aluminum sulfate
6.8 g $Al_2(SO_4)_3$/100 mL
0.2M potassium chromate
3.9 g K_2CrO_4/100 mL
0.2M sodium chromate
3 g Na_2CrO_4/100 mL
0.2M silver nitrate
3.4 g $AgNO_3$/100 mL

PURPOSE

To determine which combinations of ions form water-insoluble precipitates.

BACKGROUND

Two colorless solutions, cadmium chloride ($CdCl_2$) and potassium sulfide (K_2S), are poured together. As the solutions mix, a bright yellow solid forms. This insoluble compound, cadmium sulfide (CdS), was once used as a yellow pigment for oil paint. The paint was called cadmium yellow.

An insoluble substance that "falls out" of a solution is called a *precipitate*. The formation of precipitates other than cadmium sulfide is often less dramatic. For example, the scum that forms a ring around the bathtub is, in part, a precipitate formed by the reaction of calcium ions in the bathwater with soap ions. Whenever you mix solutions containing ions, you may obtain new combinations of ions. If one or more of these new ion combinations happens to be insoluble in water, it falls out of the solution as a precipitate.

In this experiment, you will mix pairs of six different ionic solutions in all possible combinations to determine which pairs result in precipitate formation. Based upon your results, you will infer what reactions have occurred and write complete and net ionic equations for each reaction that has taken place.

MATERIALS (PER PAIR)

safety goggles
spot plate or 15 small test tubes
glass stirring rod
plastic wash bottle
6 dropper pipets
distilled water

Set 1

0.1*M* barium nitrate, $Ba(NO_3)_2$ [T] [C]
0.1*M* sodium sulfate, Na_2SO_4
0.1*M* aluminum sulfate, $Al_2(SO_4)_3$ [T] [I]
0.1*M* magnesium nitrate, $Mg(NO_3)_2$
0.1*M* magnesium chloride, $MgCl_2$ [T]
0.1*M* aluminum chloride, $AlCl_3$ [T] [I]

Set 2

0.1*M* potassium chloride, KCl
0.1*M* magnesium chloride, $MgCl_2$
0.1*M* sodium sulfate, Na_2SO_4
0.2*M* sodium hydroxide, NaOH [T] [C]
0.1*M* barium chloride, $BaCl_2$ [T] [C]
0.1*M* magnesium sulfate, $MgSO_4$

Name ______________________ Date ________________ Class ________________

Tips

1. Formation of insoluble metal hydroxides may interfere with some of the tests done here. Such interference can be prevented by adding one drop of 6*M* HNO_3 to a solution prior to testing. The HNO_3 should not be added for those tests in which sodium hydroxide (Set 2) is one of the test solutions.

2. The use of spot plates reduces the cleaning time involved in the lab and allows the experiment to be completed in a 45-minute period.

3. The $Mg(OH)_2$ precipitates formed in Set 2 may be faint and difficult to see. A transient precipitate may be observed with mixtures of $Al_2(SO_4)_3$ and for the two chromate solutions in Set 3.

Stains can be prevented by dipping fingers into "hypo" (a dilute solution of $Na_2S_2O_3$) immediately after touching $AgNO_3$, and then rinsing with water.

Disposal 2: Because only drops of NaOH, Na_2CrO_4, $Ba(NO_3)_2$, $AgNO_3$, $BaCl_2$, and K_2CrO_4 are used in this experiment, solutions containing these materials can realistically go down the drain. Alternatively, use the following disposal methods for chemical waste.

Disposal 3: All solutions containing NaOH(*aq*) unless solution also contains barium, silver, or chromium compounds.

Disposal 5: All solutions containing $Ba(NO_3)_2$ or $BaCl_2$.

Disposal 6: All solutions containing Na_2CrO_4 or K_2CrO_4.

Disposal 8: All solutions containing $AgNO_3$.

Set 3

0.1*M* barium chloride, $BaCl_2$ T C
0.1*M* magnesium nitrate, $Mg(NO_3)_2$
0.2*M* sodium chromate, Na_2CrO_4 T
0.2*M* aluminum sulfate, $Al_2(SO_4)_3$ T
0.2*M* potassium chromate, K_2CrO_4 C T
0.2*M* silver nitrate, $AgNO_3$ C T

SAFETY FIRST!

In this lab, the solutions you use may contain harmful materials. Never touch any of the chemicals. In the event of a spill, inform your teacher immediately. Observe all precautions, especially the ones listed below. If you see a safety icon beside a step in the Procedure, refer to the list below for its meaning.

Caution: Wear your safety goggles. (All steps.)

Caution: Potassium chromate, sodium chromate, and sodium hydroxide are toxic, corrosive substances that can cause severe skin and eye injury. (Steps 1, 2.)

Caution: Aluminum chloride is an irritant. Avoid skin contact.

Caution: Silver and barium compounds are poisonous. Silver nitrate will stain skin and clothing. Avoid contact with these chemicals and wash your hands thoroughly after use.

Note: Return or dispose of all materials according to the instructions of your teacher. (Step 3.)

Note: Wash your hands thoroughly after completing this experiment.

PROCEDURES

As you perform this experiment, record your observations in Data Table 1.

1. Obtain a spot plate and a set of chemicals in dropper bottles. (The tests may be done in small test tubes.)

2. Using Data Table 1 as a guide, mix every possible pair of solutions in a set in a separate spot plate depression or test tube. Use two drops of each solution. Do not contaminate the individual droppers with different solutions. Mix the solutions with a stirring rod. Rinse the rod with distilled water after each mixing. Observe each mixture carefully for signs of a precipitate. (Some precipitates are light in color and hard to see.) Note the color of any precipitate formed. Record the results in Data Table 1.

3. Follow your teacher's instructions for proper disposal of the materials.

Name ______________________ Date ________________ Class ________________

OBSERVATIONS

DATA TABLE 1: MIXING PAIRS OF IONIC SOLUTIONS TO TEST FOR PRECIPITATE FORMATION

Solution A	Solution B	Results of Mixing A and B
Set 1:		
1 $Ba(NO_3)_2$	2 Na_2SO_4	white ppt. $BaSO_4$
1 $Ba(NO_3)_2$	3 $Al_2(SO_4)_3$	white ppt. $BaSO_4$
1 $Ba(NO_3)_2$	4 $Mg(NO_3)_2$	no ppt. (can be predicted—no new ion pairs)
1 $Ba(NO_3)_2$	5 $MgCl_2$	no ppt.
1 $Ba(NO_3)_2$	6 $AlCl_3$	no ppt.
2 Na_2SO_4	3 $Al_2(SO_4)_3$	no ppt. (can be predicted—no new ion pairs)
2 Na_2SO_4	4 $Mg(NO_3)_2$	no ppt.
2 Na_2SO_4	5 $MgCl_2$	no ppt.
2 Na_2SO_4	6 $AlCl_3$	no ppt.
3 $Al_2(SO_4)_3$	4 $Mg(NO_3)_2$	no ppt.
3 $Al_2(SO_4)_3$	5 $MgCl_2$	no ppt.
3 $Al_2(SO_4)_3$	6 $AlCl_3$	no ppt. (can be predicted—no new ion pairs)
4 $Mg(NO_3)_2$	5 $MgCl_2$	no ppt. (can be predicted—no new ion pairs)
4 $Mg(NO_3)_2$	6 $AlCl_3$	no ppt.
5 $MgCl_2$	6 $AlCl_3$	no ppt. (can be predicted—no new ion pairs)
Set 2:		
1 KCl	2 $MgCl_2$	no ppt. (can be predicted—no new ion pairs)
1 KCl	3 Na_2SO_4	no ppt.
1 KCl	4 NaOH	no ppt.
1 KCl	5 $BaCl_2$	no ppt. (can be predicted—no new ion pairs)
1 KCl	6 $MgSO_4$	no ppt.
2 $MgCl_2$	3 Na_2SO_4	no ppt.
2 $MgCl_2$	4 NaOH	white flocculent ppt. $Mg(OH)_2$
2 $MgCl_2$	5 $BaCl_2$	no ppt. (can be predicted—no new ion pairs)
2 $MgCl_2$	6 $MgSO_4$	no ppt. (can be predicted—no new ion pairs)
3 Na_2SO_4	4 NaOH	no ppt. (can be predicted—no new ion pairs)
3 Na_2SO_4	5 $BaCl_2$	white ppt. $BaSO_4$
3 Na_2SO_4	6 $MgSO_4$	no ppt. (can be predicted—no new ion pairs)
4 NaOH	5 $BaCl_2$	no ppt.
4 NaOH	6 $MgSO_4$	white flocculent ppt. $Mg(OH)_2$
5 $BaCl_2$	6 $MgSO_4$	white ppt. $BaSO_4$
Set 3:		
1 $BaCl_2$	2 $Mg(NO_3)_2$	no ppt.
1 $BaCl_2$	3 Na_2CrO_4	yellow ppt. $BaCrO_4$
1 $BaCl_2$	4 $Al_2(SO_4)_3$	white ppt. $BaSO_4$
1 $BaCl_2$	5 K_2CrO_4	yellow ppt. $BaCrO_4$
1 $BaCl_2$	6 $AgNO_3$	white ppt. AgCl
2 $Mg(NO_3)_2$	3 Na_2CrO_4	no ppt.
2 $Mg(NO_3)_2$	4 $Al_2(SO_4)_3$	no ppt.
2 $Mg(NO_3)_2$	5 K_2CrO_4	no ppt.
2 $Mg(NO_3)_2$	6 $AgNO_3$	no ppt. (can be predicted—no new ion pairs)
3 Na_2CrO_4	4 $Al_2(SO_4)_3$	no ppt.
3 Na_2CrO_4	5 K_2CrO_4	no ppt. (can be predicted—no new ion pairs)
3 Na_2CrO_4	6 $AgNO_3$	red ppt. Ag_2CrO_4
4 $Al_2(SO_4)_3$	5 K_2CrO_4	no ppt.
4 $Al_2(SO_4)_3$	6 $AgNO_3$	no ppt. (transitory ppt. may be noticed here)
5 K_2CrO_4	6 $AgNO_3$	red ppt. Ag_2CrO_4

Name ______________________ Date ________________ Class ________________

ANALYSES AND CONCLUSIONS

1. For each combination of solutions that gave a precipitate, write correct formulas for the two new compounds that could form from the ions present. (Remember to balance the ionic charges!) Enter these formulas in Data Table 2.

DATA TABLE 2: PRECIPITATION RESULTS AND ANALYSIS

Solution Pairs Yielding Precipitates		Formulas of Possible Precipitates (Circle Choice)		Reason for Choice
Set 1: $Ba(NO_3)_2$	Na_2SO_4	$BaSO_4$ (circled)	$NaNO_3$	No ppt. in combination 2 and 4.
$Ba(NO_3)_2$	$Al_2(SO_4)_3$	$BaSO_4$ (circled)	$Al(NO_3)_3$	No ppt. in combination 3 and 4.
Set 2: $MgCl_2$	NaOH	$Mg(OH)_2$ (circled)	NaCl	No ppt. in Set 1 combination 2 and 5.
Na_2SO_4	$BaCl_2$	NaCl	$BaSO_4$ (circled)	$BaSO_4$ was a precipitate in Set 1.
NaOH	$MgSO_4$	Na_2SO_4	$Mg(OH)_2$ (circled)	Na_2SO_4 is one of original solutions.
$BaCl_2$	$MgSO_4$	$BaSO_4$ (circled)	$MgCl_2$	$MgCl_2$ is one of original solutions. $BaSO_4$ was a precipitate in Set 1.
Set 3: $BaCl_2$	Na_2CrO_4	$BaCrO_4$ (circled)	NaCl	No ppt. in Set 1 combination 2 and 5.
$BaCl_2$	$Al_2(SO_4)_3$	$BaSO_4$ (circled)	$AlCl_3$	$BaSO_4$ was a precipitate in Set 1. $AlCl_3$ is one of original solutions.
$BaCl_2$	K_2CrO_4	$BaCrO_4$ (circled)	KCl	$BaCrO_4$ always ppts. KCl is one of original solutions.
$BaCl_2$	$AgNO_3$	$Ba(NO_3)_2$	AgCl (circled)	No ppt. in Set 3 combination 1 and 2.
Na_2CrO_4	$AgNO_3$	$NaNO_3$	Ag_2CrO_4 (circled)	No ppt. in Set 1 combination 2 and 4.
K_2CrO_4	$AgNO_3$	KNO_3	Ag_2CrO_4 (circled)	Ag_2CrO_4 always ppts.

Name ____________________ Date ____________________ Class ____________________

2. For those combinations that produced a precipitate, decide which of the two new compounds is the precipitate by eliminating the other. Remember that all compounds in your sets are soluble, so they cannot be precipitates in any of the reactions. Also, a combination of ions will either always form a precipitate or never form one. Circle the formula of each compound you believe to be a precipitate, and record the reasons for your choices in Data Table 2.

3. Write complete ionic equations for the precipitation reactions that you observed. Show the reactants as ions, the precipitate as a solid, and the spectator ions as unchanged. Balance each equation for mass and charge. The total charge should be zero on each side of the equation.

Set 1 Solutions

(a) $Ba^{2+} + 2NO_3^- + 2Na^+ + SO_4^{2-} \rightarrow 2Na^+ + 2NO_3^- + BaSO_4(s)$

(b) $3Ba^{2+} + 6NO_3^- + 2Al^{3+} + 3SO_4^{2-} \rightarrow 2Al^{3+} + 6NO_3^- + 3BaSO_4(s)$

Set 2 Solutions

(a) $Mg^{2+} + 2Cl^- + 2Na^+ + 2OH^- \rightarrow 2Na^+ + 2Cl^- + Mg(OH)_2(s)$

(b) $2Na^+ + SO_4^{2-} + Ba^{2+} + 2Cl^- \rightarrow 2Na^+ + 2Cl^- + BaSO_4(s)$

(c) $2Na^+ + 2OH^- + Mg^{2+} + SO_4^{2-} \rightarrow 2Na^+ + SO_4^{2-} + Mg(OH)_2(s)$

(d) $Ba^{2+} + 2Cl^- + Mg^{2+} + SO_4^{2-} \rightarrow Mg^{2+} + 2Cl^- + BaSO_4(s)$

Set 3 Solutions

(a) $Ba^{2+} + 2Cl^- + 2Na^+ + CrO_4^{2-} \rightarrow 2Na^+ + 2Cl^- + BaCrO_4(s)$

(b) $3Ba^{2+} + 6Cl^- + 2Al^{3+} + 3SO_4^{2-} \rightarrow 2Al^{3+} + 6Cl^- + 3BaSO_4(s)$

(c) $Ba^{2+} + 2Cl^- + 2K^+ + CrO_4^{2-} \rightarrow 2K^+ + 2Cl^- + BaCrO_4(s)$

(d) $2Ag^+ + 2NO_3^- + Ba^{2+} + 2Cl^- \rightarrow Ba^{2+} + 2NO_3^- + 2AgCl(s)$

(e) $2Na^+ + CrO_4^{2-} + 2Ag^+ + 2NO_3^- \rightarrow 2Na^+ + 2NO_3^- + Ag_2CrO_4(s)$

(f) $2K^+ + CrO_4^{2-} + 2Ag^+ + 2NO_3^- \rightarrow 2K^+ + 2NO_3^- + Ag_2CrO_4(s)$

4. Write the net ionic equations for each reaction in the preceding question.

Set 1 Solutions

(a) $Ba^{2+} + SO_4^{2-} \rightarrow BaSO_4(s)$

(b) $Ba^{2+} + SO_4^{2-} \rightarrow BaSO_4(s)$

Set 2 Solutions

(a) $Mg^{2+} + 2OH^- \rightarrow Mg(OH)_2(s)$

(b) $Ba^{2+} + SO_4^{2-} \rightarrow BaSO_4(s)$

(c) $Mg^{2+} + 2OH^- \rightarrow Mg(OH)_2(s)$

(d) $Ba^{2+} + SO_4^{2-} \rightarrow BaSO_4(s)$

Name ______________ Date ______________ Class ______________

Set 3 Solutions

(a) $Ba^{2+} + CrO_4^{2-} \rightarrow BaCrO_4(s)$

(b) $Ba^{2+} + SO_4^{2-} \rightarrow BaSO_4(s)$

(c) $Ba^{2+} + CrO_4^{2-} \rightarrow BaCrO_4(s)$

(d) $Ag^{+} + Cl^{-} \rightarrow AgCl(s)$

(e) $2Ag^{+} + CrO_4^{2-} \rightarrow Ag_2CrO_4(s)$

(f) $2Ag^{+} + CrO_4^{2-} \rightarrow Ag_2CrO_4(s)$

5. What is the function of spectator ions in a precipitation reaction?

Spectator ions are not involved in precipitation reactions.

6. Explain in your own words why a precipitate forms.

Precipitates form when ions combine to form new substances that are not soluble in the reaction solution.

7. How does a complete ionic equation differ from a net ionic equation?

A complete ionic equation is a balanced equation that includes all the ions in the solution. A net ionic equation includes only those ions that participate in the reaction.

GOING FURTHER

Develop a Hypothesis

Suppose you are given three different solutions containing Na_3PO_4, $Ba(NO_3)_2$, and K_2CO_3, respectively. Based on the results of this lab, hypothesize about which combinations of these solutions will produce insoluble precipitates. (**Hint:** Use your observations of the behavior of the compounds studied in this lab to develop general statements about the solubility of ionic compounds containing Na^{+}, Ba^{2+}, K^{+}, NO_3^{-}, and CO_3^{2-}.)

Students may conclude that many barium-containing compounds are insoluble, suggesting that combining Na_3PO_4 and $Ba(NO_3)_2$ will lead to the formation of a precipitate. Group 1A and nitrate salts are generally soluble. Most carbonates are insoluble.

Name ______________________ Date ________________ Class ________________

Design an Experiment

Propose an experiment to test your hypothesis. If resources are available and you have your teacher's permission, perform the experiment.

Check students' experimental design for safety and to see that students have included the proper controls.

18 QUALITATIVE ANALYSIS

PURPOSE

To develop a systematic panel of chemical tests to identify an unknown solution.

Text Reference
Section 11.3

Time Required
50 minutes

Objectives

- Observe reactions between a set of reference solutions and a set of test reagents.
- Design an analytical scheme to identify an unknown solution, using the test reagents.
- Identify an unknown solution by comparing test results for reference and unknown solutions.

Advance Preparation
set of solutions (0.1M)

Solution 1:
2.4 g $BaCl_2 \cdot 2H_2O$/100 mL

Solution 2:
1.7 g $AgNO_3$/100 mL
Store in a brown bottle.

Solution 3:
3.3 g $Pb(NO_3)_2$/100 mL

Solution 4:
Dissolve 100 g of ammonium paramolybdate, $(NH_4)_6Mo_7O_{24} \cdot 4H_2O$, (or molybdic acid) in 145 mL of concentrated $NH_3(aq)$ and 270 mL of distilled water. Slowly, and with constant stirring, pour this solution into a solution of nitric acid that has been prepared by dissolving 490 mL of concentrated HNO_3 in 1150 mL of distilled water. Keep the mixture in a warm place for several days or until a portion heated to 40°C deposits no yellow precipitate. Decant the solution from any sediment and store in glass-stoppered bottles.

BACKGROUND

In Experiment 16, you learned how to identify the presence of common ions by conducting chemical tests, a process called qualitative analysis. But how do you test a solution containing mixtures of ions with similar chemical behavior? For example, both calcium and barium ions react with oxalate ions $C_2O_4^{2-}$ to form white precipitates. If you add oxalate ions to an unknown solution and a white precipitate forms, you cannot say conclusively whether the solution contains only calcium ions, only barium ions, or a combination of both. Additional tests are required to identify the unknown solution.

In this experiment, you will observe the reactions that occur when four solutions are mixed with each of three different reagents. Using these reactions as a reference, you will develop a systematic set of tests to identify an unknown solution. The solutions and reagents are deliberately unlabeled; knowledge of the chemicals used is not important. Instead, focus your attention on making careful observations and developing a logical, systematic approach for identifying the unknown solution.

MATERIALS (PER PAIR)

safety goggles
spot plate or 3–12 small test tubes
paper towels
plastic wash bottle
distilled water
set of reagents: A, B, C [T] [I]
set of solutions: 1, 2, 3, 4 [T] [I]
unknown solutions

SAFETY FIRST!

In this lab, the solutions you use may contain harmful materials. Treat all unknown solutions as if they were hazardous. Observe all precautions, especially the ones listed below. If you see a safety icon beside a step in the Procedure, refer to the list below for its meaning.

Caution: Wear your safety goggles. (All steps.)

Caution: Some of the chemicals used in this experiment are poisonous. Treat all chemicals with care. Do not mix any chemicals except as directed in the Procedure section. Avoid skin contact with these chemicals. (Steps 1, 3, 4.)

set of reagents (0.1M)
Reagent A: 1.9 g K_2CrO_4/100 mL
Reagent B: Add 10 mL of 1*M* HCl to 80 mL of distilled water and dilute to 100 mL.
Reagent C: 3.6 g $Na_2HPO_4 \cdot 12H_2O$/100 mL water

Unknown solutions
25 mL of solutions 1, 2, 3, and 4 in dropper bottles labeled only with code numbers.

Review the safety procedures before students begin to work. Impress upon students the need for exercising caution in handling unknowns. Most of the unknowns are toxic and reagent A, K_2CrO_4, is suspected to be a carcinogen. Students should exercise special care when working with this chemical.

Disposal 2: Because only drops of $BaCl_2$, $AgNO_3$, $Pb(NO_3)_2$, and K_2CrO_4 are used in this experiment, solutions containing these materials can realistically go down the drain. Alternatively, use the following disposal methods for chemical waste.

Disposal 3: All solutions containing HCl(*aq*), unless solution also contains barium, silver, lead, or chromium.

Disposal 5: All solutions containing $BaCl_2$.

Disposal 6: All solutions containing K_2CrO_4.

Disposal 7: All solutions containing $Pb(NO_3)_2$.

Disposal 8: All solutions containing $AgNO_3$.

Note: Return or dispose of all materials according to the instructions of your teacher. (Step 5.)

Note: Wash your hands thoroughly after completing this experiment.

PROCEDURE

As you perform the experiment, record your observations in Data Table 1.

1. Clean the spot plate or test tubes with distilled water. In separate depressions on the spot plate or in separate test tubes, mix solutions 1 through 4, one at a time, with each of the reagents. Use 1–2 drops of each solution. Record your observations.
2. Study your results and plan how to identify your unknown, using the fewest number of tests.

3. Obtain an unknown and identify it as solution 1, 2, 3, or 4 by testing it with the reagents. Record the tests done and the results obtained.
4. Repeat Step 3 with a second unknown solution. Record the tests done and the results obtained.

5. Follow your teacher's instructions for proper disposal of the materials.

Name ______________________ Date ______________ Class ______________

OBSERVATIONS

DATA TABLE 1: RESULTS OF MIXING SOLUTIONS AND REAGENTS

		Reagent A	Reagent B	Reagent C
Solution 1	$BaCl_2$	yellow ppt. $BaCrO_4$	no reaction	white ppt. $BaHPO_4$
Solution 2	$AgNO_3$	red ppt. Ag_2CrO_4	white ppt. $AgCl$	white ppt. Ag_2HPO_4
Solution 3	$Pb(NO_3)_2$	yellow ppt. $PbCrO_4$	white ppt. $PbCl_2$	white ppt. $PbHPO_4$
Solution 4	$(NH_4)_2MoO_4$	no reaction	no reaction	yellow ppt. $(NH_4)_3PO_4 \cdot 12MoO_3$
Unknown				
Unknown				

ANALYSES AND CONCLUSIONS

1. Without knowing the identity of the chemicals in the experiment, you identified an unknown solution. Explain how.

   Each solution (1–4) produced a unique set of results when tested with reagents A, B, and C. Having tested each unknown solution with each of the reagents, you can correctly identify an unknown as solution 1, 2, 3, or 4.

2. Based on your experimental results, how would you distinguish between solutions 1 and 3? Between solutions 2 and 3?

   Solution 3 produces a precipitate with reagent B; solution 1 does not produce a precipitate. Solution 2 produces a red precipitate with reagent A; solution 3 results in a yellow precipitate with solution A.

3. Suppose someone has randomly relabeled the solutions used in this experiment as I, II, III, and IV and the reagents as X, Y, and Z. Using the facts that follow, consult Data Table 1 and correctly identify the solutions and reagents by their original designations (1, 2, 3, 4, A, B, C).

When mixed:

I and Y produce a red precipitate.

II and Y produce no precipitate.

II and X produce a yellow precipitate.

III and Z produce a white precipitate.

I = 2, II = 4, III = 3, IV = 1

X = C, Y = A, Z = B

GOING FURTHER

Design an Experiment

Based on the results of this lab, develop a scheme of analysis for an unknown solution that contains more than one chemical species. For example, would it be possible to characterize a mixture of solutions 1, 3, and 4 by using the test reagents?

If resources are available and you have your teacher's permission, perform the experiment.

Students should construct a flowchart to show how the test reagents can be used in a certain sequence to analyze and separate a mixture of solutions 1, 3, and 4. Add Reagent B until no more white precipitate forms. Decant or filter the liquid layer. Add Reagent A to the liquid until no more yellow precipitate forms. Decant or filter the liquid layer. Add Reagent C to the remaining liquid until no more yellow precipitate forms.

Name ______________________ Date __________________ Class __________________

19 QUANTITATIVE ANALYSIS

Text Reference
Sections 12.1 and 12.2

Time Required
Two 50-minute lab periods

Objectives
- Measure the number of moles of iron consumed and copper produced in the reaction of iron with aqueous copper(II) chloride.
- Write a balanced equation for the reaction.

Advance Preparation
1M copper(II) chloride
170.5 g $CuCl_2 \cdot 2H_2O$/L distilled water

The addition of iron metal to a solution of Cu^{2+} ions results in the reduction of copper ions to copper metal and the oxidation of iron to Fe^{2+} ions. By measuring the mass of copper metal produced and the mass of iron lost, the molar ratios of the reacting metal species can be determined.
$Cu^{2+} + Fe(s) \rightarrow Cu(s) + Fe^{2+}$

PURPOSE

To determine the values for the coefficients used in a balanced chemical equation.

BACKGROUND

By now you are familiar with seeing and working with balanced chemical equations. But how do you know the coefficients in these equations are correct? Do the coefficients reflect how the chemical substances actually combine? In this experiment, you will determine the values for the coefficients used in the balanced chemical equation for the reaction of iron metal with a copper(II) chloride solution, which produces copper metal and an iron compound.

You will use the fact that the coefficients of the substances in a chemical equation represent the relative number of moles of each substance involved in the reaction. You will determine the relative numbers of moles of each reactant and product in the reaction you observe. From the mole ratios, you will derive the appropriate coefficients to be used in the chemical equation. If your experiment is successful, you should be able to determine the mole ratio of the *iron used* to the *copper produced.*

MATERIALS (PER PAIR)

safety goggles
gloves (optional)
glass-marking pencil
50-mL graduated cylinder
2 250-mL beakers
centigram balance
crucible tongs
plastic wash bottle
paper towels
glass stirring rod
drying oven or heat lamp
1*M* copper(II) chloride dihydrate, $CuCl_2 \cdot 2H_2O$ T
2 iron nails, Fe
steel wool
distilled water

SAFETY FIRST!

In this lab, observe all precautions, especially the ones listed below. If you see a safety icon beside a step in the Procedure, refer to the list below for its meaning.

Caution: Wear your safety goggles. (All steps.)

Caution: Copper(II) chloride solution is toxic. Avoid skin contact with this material. (Step 2.)

Name ______________________________ Date ____________________ Class ____________________

Caution: Copper(II) chloride is an irritant. Avoid skin contact with this chemical. (All steps.)

Note: Return or dispose of all materials according to the instructions of your teacher. (Steps 7, 8, 11.)

PROCEDURE

As you perform the experiment, record your data in Data Table 1 and your observations in Data Table 2.

Day 1

1. Using a glass-marking pencil, label a clean, dry 250-mL beaker with your name. Determine the mass of the beaker to the nearest 0.01 g, and record the measurement in Data Table 1.
2. Add 50 mL of copper(II) chloride solution to the beaker.

Step 4.
If possible, the heads of the nails should be kept out of the solution. If they are not, copper forms at the joint of the nail and the nail head and is difficult to remove.

3. Clean two iron nails with steel wool to remove any rust or protective coating. Determine the combined mass of the nails to the nearest 0.01 g and record the measurement.
4. Slide the nails carefully into the solution of copper(II) chloride. Let the beaker stand undisturbed for at least 20 minutes. Record any evidence of a chemical reaction in Data Table 2.
5. Using crucible tongs, remove one of the nails from the reaction solution. Hold the nail over the reaction beaker. Rinse the adherent reaction product off the nail and into the beaker, using a jet of distilled water from a wash bottle, as shown in Figure 19.1. Repeat this procedure for the second nail.
6. Allow the nails to dry on a paper towel in a safe place. (You will remeasure their mass later.)

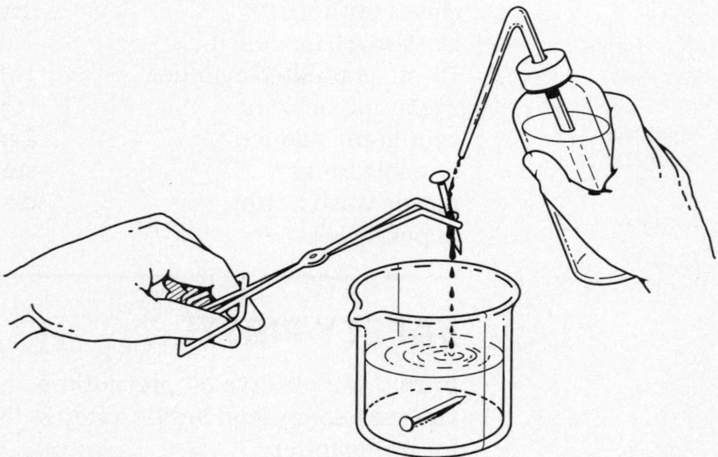

Figure 19.1

Name ____________________ Date ______________ Class ______________

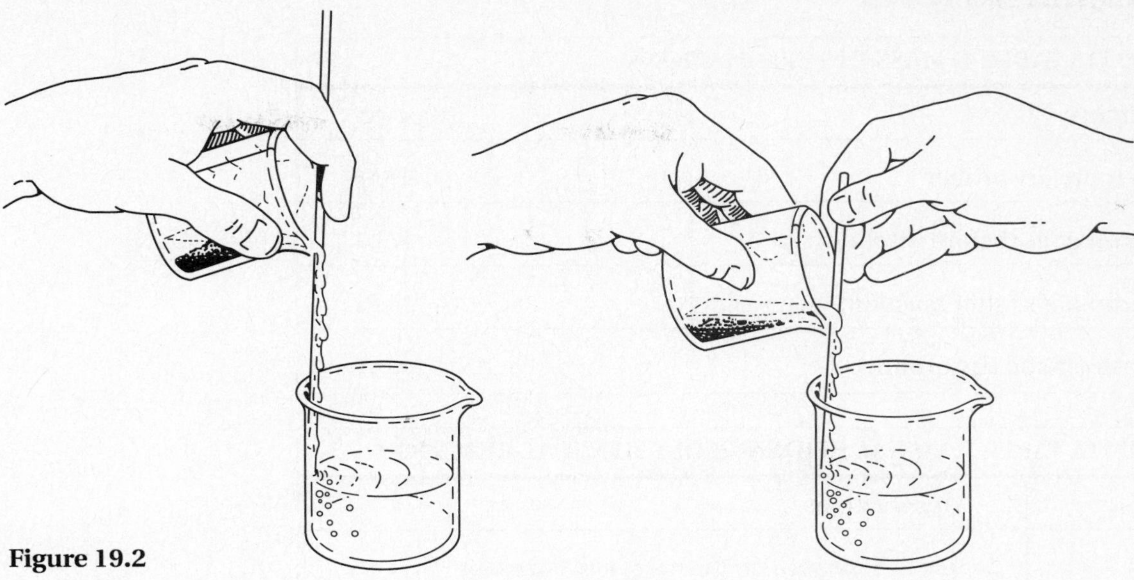

Figure 19.2

7. Carefully decant the liquid portion of the reaction solution into another 250-mL beaker, as shown in Figure 19.2. Leave the solid reaction product in the original beaker. Dispose of the decanted solution by pouring it into the sink.

Step 8.
Demonstrate the proper technique for washing the copper precipitate and decanting the supernatant.

8. Use 25 mL of distilled water to wash the reaction product contained in the beaker. Decant the wash water into the collection container. Repeat the washing and decanting procedures two more times, being careful to avoid losing any reaction product. Pour the contents of the collection container into the sink.

Step 9.
Ideally, the beaker and its contents should be dried overnight in an oven at 80°.

9. Give the reaction beaker containing the solid product to your teacher to be dried.

Day 2

10. Determine the combined mass of the dry nails to the nearest 0.01 g and record the measurement.

11. Determine the mass of the beaker and the dry reaction product to the nearest 0.01 g and record the measurement. When you are finished, dispose of the nails and the solid product in a waste container.

Use the following disposal methods for chemical waste.

Disposal 1: Fe(*s*) and Cu(*s*) in Step 11.

Disposal 2: The reaction solution in Step 7 and the decanting solution in Step 7.

Name ______________________ Date ________________ Class ________________

OBSERVATIONS

DATA TABLE 1: MASS DETERMINATIONS	
Items	Mass (g)
empty dry beaker	97.48
iron nails (before reaction)	17.07
iron nails (after reaction)	14.42
beaker and dry product	100.60

DATA TABLE 2: VISUAL EVIDENCE OF CHEMICAL REACTION	
Step	Observations
4	Copper is deposited on the nails, and the nails corrode. The blue color of the $CuCl_2$ solution fades as the reaction proceeds.

ANALYSES AND CONCLUSIONS

1. Determine the mass of iron lost by the nails.

mass of iron lost = mass of nails before reaction − mass of nails after reaction
= 17.07 g − 14.42 g
= 2.65 g

2. Calculate the number of moles of iron used.

$$\text{number of moles of iron used (mol)} = \frac{\text{mass of iron used (g)}}{\text{molar mass of iron (g/mol)}} = \frac{2.65\text{ g}}{55.8\text{ g/mol}} = 0.0475\text{ mol}$$

3. Determine the mass of the product.

mass of product (g) = mass of beaker and product (g) − mass of beaker (g)
= 100.60 g − 97.48 g
= 3.12 g

4. Assuming that one of the products is copper metal, calculate the number of moles of copper produced.

$$\text{number of moles of copper produced (mol)} = \frac{\text{mass of product (g)}}{\text{molar mass of copper (g/mol)}}$$

$$= \frac{3.12\ \text{g}}{63.5\ \text{g/mol}}$$

$$= 0.0491\ \text{mol}$$

5. Calculate the mole ratio of iron used to copper produced. Express this ratio as a simple whole-number ratio.

$$\frac{\text{mol (Fe)}}{\text{mol (Cu)}} = \frac{0.0475}{0.0491}$$

$$= 0.967$$

In simple whole numbers, the mole ratio is 1:1.

6. Calculate the percent error in your value for the mole ratio. Your teacher will give you the accepted value.

$$\text{percent error} = \frac{|\text{experimental value} - \text{accepted value}|}{\text{accepted value}} \times 100\%$$

The accepted value for the Fe:Cu mole ratio is 1.0.

$$\text{percent error} = \frac{|1.0 - 0.97|}{1.0} \times 100\%$$

$$= 0.03 \times 100\%$$

$$= 3\%$$

7. Assuming that one product is iron(II) chloride, write a balanced equation for the reaction. What type of reaction is this?

The accepted mole ratio of Fe:Cl in iron(II) chloride is 1:2.

$$Fe(s) + CuCl_2(aq) \rightarrow FeCl_2(aq) + Cu(s)$$

8. Copper could be lost in this experiment during the washing and decanting steps. How would this effect the iron:copper mole ratio? Explain.

If copper were lost, the whole number ratio, Fe:Cu, would increase. Chemically, it would appear that more Fe is required to reduce Cu^{2+} to metallic Cu than is actually needed. Mathematically, a reduction in the denominator of a ratio always increases the ratio.

Name ______________________ Date ________________ Class ______________

9. What other factors might account for any error in your mole ratio?

The iron/copper ratio can be less than 1:1 if some iron(III) ions are formed. If only iron(III) ions are formed, the limiting iron:copper ratio is only 2:3 (0.67).

$$3Cu^{2+}(aq) + Fe(s) \rightarrow 2Fe^{3+}(aq) + 3Cu(s)$$

Other possible errors that would affect the mole ratio are incorrect measurements of the beaker weight and of the weight of iron lost. A large error can result if the beaker and its contents are not completely dried. In drying overnight, Cu sometimes darkens as a layer of CuO forms on the metal surface. This CuO can cause the weight of Cu to appear higher than it really is.

10. Examine the data collected by other members of the class. Were the masses of iron and copper the same in all experiments? Were the mole ratios the same? Does the mole ratio of a substance in a chemical equation depend on the amounts of reactants used?

The masses of iron and copper are not the same for all students. Theoretically, the Fe:Cu mole ratio is the same. The mole ratio of species in a chemical equation does not depend upon the amount of reactants used. In the reaction investigated, the Fe:Cu mole ratio of 1:1 would be maintained regardless of the quantities of reactants used.

GOING FURTHER

Develop a Hypothesis

Based on the results of this lab, develop a hypothesis about other cations besides copper(II) ion that could be used in this experiment.

Aqueous solutions of other metal ions below iron on the activity series of metals (see Table 11.2 in the textbook) such as nickel or tin should also produce similar results.

Design an Experiment

Propose an experiment to test your hypothesis. If resources are available and you have your teacher's permission, perform the experiment.

The experiment would be similar, substituting the new metal cation.

20 BALANCED CHEMICAL EQUATIONS

Text Reference
Section 12.3

Time Required
45 minutes

Objectives

- Compute the mole ratio required for lead(II) nitrate and sodium iodide to be completely converted into reaction products.
- Observe what happens when either lead(II) nitrate or sodium iodide is present in excess.
- Classify reactants as either excess or limiting reactants.
- Prepare graphs comparing the actual and theoretical yields of lead(II) iodide.

Advance Preparation

0.5M lead(II) nitrate solution
Dissolve 165.6 g $Pb(NO_3)_2$ in 800 mL of water and dilute to 1 L.

0.5M sodium iodide solution
Dissolve 75.0 g NaI in 800 mL of water and dilute to 1 L.

PURPOSE

To examine the relationship between amounts of reactants and products in a chemical reaction.

BACKGROUND

Like a gymnast on a beam, the amounts of material involved in a chemical reaction must be properly balanced. An unbalanced gymnast will fall off the beam; an unbalanced equation will waste chemical reactants. In this experiment, you will examine the stoichiometry—the relationship between amounts of materials—of the reaction between lead(II) nitrate and sodium iodide. The balanced equation is:

$$Pb(NO_3)_2(aq) + 2NaI(aq) \rightarrow PbI_2(s) + 2NaNO_3(aq)$$

You will also explore the concepts of limiting and excess reagents. A *limiting reagent* is completely used up in a reaction. The amount of product that can be formed depends on the quantity of limiting reagent present. An *excess reagent* is so called because, after the reaction is complete, there is still an amount left unreacted. Finally, you will estimate the actual yield of one product, lead(II) iodide, and compare it with the theoretical yield predicted from the balanced equation.

MATERIALS (PER PAIR)

safety goggles
6 large test tubes
test-tube rack
2 50-mL burets
twin buret clamp
ring stand
glass-marking pencil
2 250-mL beakers
6 rubber stoppers
centimeter ruler
dropper pipet
spot plate
plastic wash bottle
0.5*M* lead(II) nitrate, $Pb(NO_3)_2$ [T]
0.5*M* sodium iodide, NaI [T]
distilled water

SAFETY FIRST!

In this lab, observe all precautions, especially the ones listed below. If you see a safety icon beside a step in the Procedure, refer to the list below for its meaning.

Caution: Wear your safety goggles. (All steps.)

Caution: Lead(II) nitrate is toxic. Wash your hands thoroughly after use. (Step 3.)

Note: Return or dispose of all materials according to the instructions of your teacher. (Step 12.)

Name ______________________ Date ________________ Class ________________

Aqueous solutions of $Pb(NO_3)_2$ and NaI will be mixed in different mole ratios. Students will determine the mole ratio at which the product yield is maximum and at which the reactants are completely consumed. They can then calculate the correct mole ratios for the balanced chemical equation.

PROCEDURE

As you perform the experiment, record your results in Data Tables 1 and 2.

Part A

1. Number, with the numerals 1–6, six large, clean, and dry test tubes.
2. Mount two 50-mL burets on a ring stand, using a twin buret clamp. Label one buret "NaI"; label the other "$Pb(NO_3)_2$."

3. Obtain, in separate labeled 250-mL beakers, about 50 mL of 0.5*M* $Pb(NO_3)_2$ and 75 mL of 0.5*M* NaI. Fill the labeled burets with these solutions.
4. Using the filled burets, add the solutions to the six test tubes, according to the following table. Place each tube in a test-tube rack.

	Tube 1	Tube 2	Tube 3	Tube 4	Tube 5	Tube 6
0.5*M* $Pb(NO_3)_2$ (mL)	2.0	4.0	6.0	8.0	10.0	12.0
0.5*M* NaI (mL)	16.0	14.0	12.0	10.0	8.0	6.0

Keep the remaining solutions in the burets for later use.

5. Seal each tube with a rubber stopper. Mix the contents by inverting each tube *three times*. Do not shake.
6. Leave the tubes undisturbed in the test-tube rack for at least 10 minutes.
7. Measure the height of the yellow precipitate [lead(II) iodide] in each tube to the nearest 0.1 cm and record the measurement.

Part B

8. **Testing the supernatant for excess reagent.** The liquid above a settled precipitate is called the *supernatant.* With a dropper pipet, remove a sample of supernatant from tube 1. Add *one* drop of supernatant to each of two adjacent depressions on a spot plate. Rinse the dropper with distilled water and repeat this procedure for tubes 2–6.
9. Add a drop of 0.5*M* $Pb(NO_3)_2$ to one set of samples from tubes 1–6.
10. Add a drop of 0.5*M* NaI to the other set of samples.
11. Record the results of these spot-plate tests in Data Table 2.

12. Follow your teacher's instructions for proper disposal of the materials.

Use the following disposal methods for chemical waste.

Disposal 7: All the solutions in this experiment.

Name ______________________ Date ________________ Class ________________

OBSERVATIONS

DATA TABLE 1: DATA FOR REACTION MIXTURES

Tube Number	$Pb(NO_3)_2$ (mL)	$Pb(NO_3)_2$ (mol)	NaI (mL)	NaI (mol)	Height Ppt. (cm)	Maximum Theoretical Yield Ppt. (mol)
1	2	0.001	16	0.008	2.0	0.0010
2	4	0.002	14	0.007	4.0	0.0020
3	6	0.003	12	0.006	6.0	0.0030
4	8	0.004	10	0.005	4.0	0.0025
5	10	0.005	8	0.004	2.0	0.0020
6	12	0.006	6	0.003	1.0	0.0015

DATA TABLE 2: SPOT TESTS OF SUPERNATANT SAMPLES FROM REACTION TUBES

Substance Added	Tube 1 Ppt.?	Tube 2 Ppt.?	Tube 3 Ppt.?	Tube 4 Ppt.?	Tube 5 Ppt.?	Tube 6 Ppt.?
$Pb(NO_3)_2$	yes	yes	no	no	no	no
NaI	no	no	no	yes	yes	yes
reagent present in excess	NaI	NaI	neither	$Pb(NO_3)_2$	$Pb(NO_3)_2$	$Pb(NO_3)_2$

ANALYSES AND CONCLUSIONS

1. Calculate the number of moles of $Pb(NO_3)_2$ and NaI added to each tube. (**Hint:** Calculate how many moles would be in 1 mL and then multiply by the number of milliliters in the sample.) Enter your result in Data Table 1.

$$\frac{0.5 \text{ mol } Pb(NO_3)_2}{1000 \text{ mL}} = \frac{x \text{ mol } Pb(NO_3)_2}{1 \text{ mL}}$$

$$x = \frac{0.0005 \text{ mol } Pb(NO_3)_2}{1 \text{ mL}}$$

$$\frac{0.5 \text{ mol NaI}}{1000 \text{ mL}} = \frac{x \text{ mol NaI}}{1 \text{ mL}}$$

$$x = \frac{0.0005 \text{ mol NaI}}{1 \text{ mL}}$$

tube 1: mol $Pb(NO_3)_2$ = 2 mL (0.0005 mol $Pb(NO_3)_2$/mL)
= 0.001 mol $Pb(NO_3)_2$

mol NaI = 16 mL (0.0005 mol NaI/mL) = 0.008 mol NaI

tube 2: mol $Pb(NO_3)_2$ = 4 mL (0.0005 mol $Pb(NO_3)_2$/mL)
= 0.002 mol $Pb(NO_3)_2$

mol NaI = 14 mL (0.0005 mol NaI/mL) = 0.007 mol NaI

tube 3: mol $Pb(NO_3)_2$ = 6 mL (0.0005 mol $Pb(NO_3)_2$/mL)
= 0.003 mol $Pb(NO_3)_2$
mol NaI = 12 mL (0.0005 mol NaI/mL) = 0.006 mol NaI

tube 4: mol $Pb(NO_3)_2$ = 8 mL (0.0005 mol $Pb(NO_3)_2$/mL)
= 0.004 mol $Pb(NO_3)_2$
mol NaI = 10 mL (0.0005 mol NaI/mL) = 0.005 mol NaI

tube 5: mol $Pb(NO_3)_2$ = 10 mL (0.0005 mol $Pb(NO_3)_2$/mL)
= 0.005 mol $Pb(NO_3)_2$
mol NaI = 8 mL (0.0005 mol NaI/mL) = 0.004 mol NaI

tube 6: mol $Pb(NO_3)_2$ = 12 mL (0.0005 mol $Pb(NO_3)_2$/mL)
= 0.006 mol $Pb(NO_3)_2$
mol NaI = 6 mL (0.0005 mol NaI/mL) = 0.003 mol NaI

2. For the tube with the greatest amount of precipitate, calculate the mole ratio between $Pb(NO_3)_2$ and NaI.

tube 3 $\frac{\text{mol } Pb(NO_3)_2}{\text{mol NaI}} = \frac{0.003}{0.006} = \frac{1}{2}$

3. Plot two *separate* bar graphs showing the height of lead(II) iodide (cm) versus tube number. One graph should show the height of lead(II) iodide actually obtained in each tube, and the other should show the maximum theoretical number of moles of lead(II) iodide in each tube. Number the tubes 1–6 from left to right.

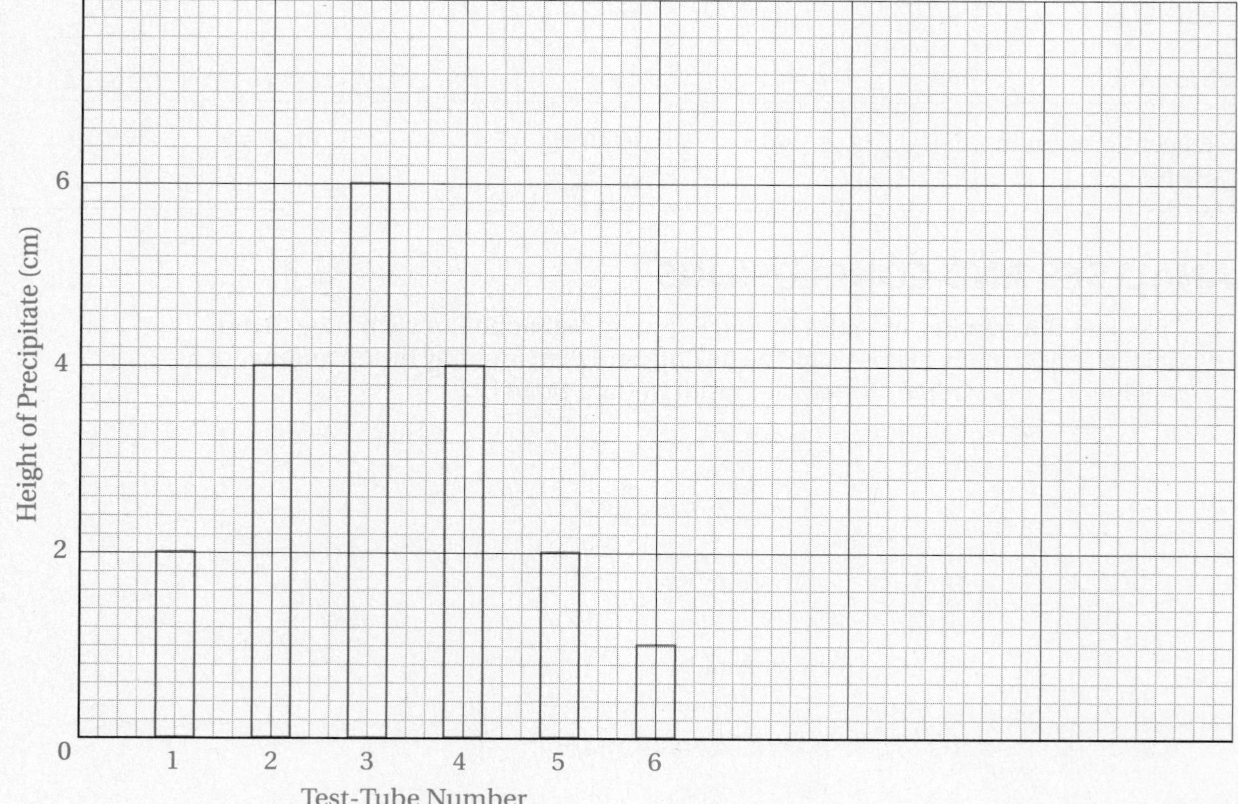

Name ______________________ Date ______________ Class ______________

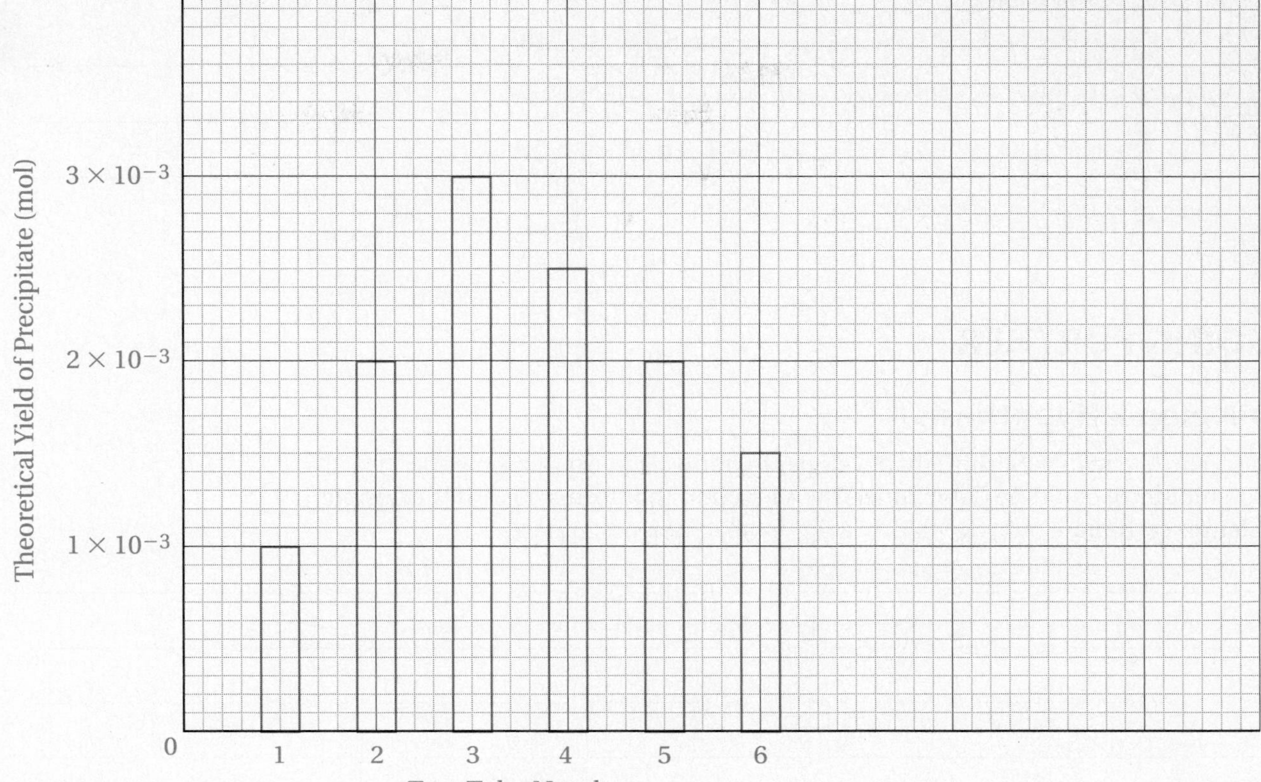

4. In which tube was there little or no reaction of the supernatant with either $Pb(NO_3)_2$ or NaI? What is the mole ratio of the reactants in this tube?

tube 3 **The mole ratio is 2 mol NaI to 1 mol $Pb(NO_3)_2$.**

5. How are your two graphs similar?

Their shapes are similar.

6. a. Write a complete ionic equation for the reaction observed in this experiment.

$Pb^{2+} + 2NO_3^- + 2Na^+ + 2I^- \rightarrow PbI_2(s) + 2Na^+ + 2NO_3^-$

b. Indicate which ions are spectator ions in this reaction.

Na^+, NO_3^-

c. Write a net ionic equation for this reaction.

$Pb^{2+}(aq) + 2I^-(aq) \rightarrow PbI_2(s)$

Name ______________________ Date ________________ Class ______________

7. Examine the class data, especially for tube 3. Explain any inconsistency you observe in the results.

Inconsistency is possible because any slight error is still very close to the exact stoichiometric ratios—a bit one way gives excess sodium iodide, a bit the other way gives excess lead nitrate. It is analogous to a titration endpoint.

GOING FURTHER

Develop a Hypothesis

Based on the results of this lab, develop a hypothesis to explain how the stoichiometry could be determined for a reaction that forms a gas (for example, calcium carbonate + hydrochloric acid) instead of a precipitate.

An apparatus could be designed to capture and measure the volume of carbon dioxide gas produced using varying whole-number ratios of moles of each reactant.

Design an Experiment

Propose an experiment to test your hypothesis. If resources are available and you have your teacher's permission, perform the experiment.

Experimental design will most likely include an inverted buret to capture and measure the gas produced by water displacement. Students should correct for the solubility of CO_2 in water.

21 ALLOTROPIC FORMS OF SULFUR

Text Reference
Section 13.3

Time Required
40 minutes

Objectives
- Observe the allotropic forms of sulfur.
- Compare the physical properties of these allotropes.
- Based on the data, draw conclusions about the relative stabilities of these allotropes.

PURPOSE

To observe and describe the allotropes of sulfur.

BACKGROUND

Some elements can have several different molecular forms while in the same physical state. These differing forms are called *allotropes*. Environmental conditions, such as temperature and pressure, determine which allotrope will form. Carbon is an element with several allotropes. The allotropes of carbon have very different physical properties. Diamond is hard, clear, and shiny. Graphite is black, with a slippery, greasy feel. Buckminsterfullerenes contain 60 carbon atoms arranged in a hollow sphere resembling a soccer ball. Sulfur is another element with several allotropes. Unlike carbon's allotropes, however, sulfur's allotropes can be easily produced in the lab.

In this experiment, you will observe the allotropes of sulfur.

MATERIALS

safety goggles
50-mL beaker
dropper pipet
2 watch glasses
100-mL beaker
250-mL beaker
medium test tube
test-tube holder
tweezers
magnifying glass or microscope
ring stand
ring support
wire gauze
gas burner
vegetable oil [F]
powdered sulfur, S [F] [T]
filter paper circles
distilled water
paper towels

SAFETY FIRST!

Caution: This experiment must be done in a fume hood. If a fume hood is not available, the experiment must not be carried out. The experiment is to be done only as a teacher demonstration.

This lab is intended to be done as a teacher demonstration. Observe all precautions, especially the ones listed below. If you see a safety icon beside a step in the Procedure, refer to the list below for its meaning.

Caution: Wear your safety goggles. (All steps.)

Caution: This experiment must be conducted in a fume hood. Use a low flame to heat the sulfur. Sulfur is flammable and can be ignited. (Steps 3, 7, and 10.)

Caution: Exercise care when working with an open flame. Tie back hair and loose clothing. (Steps 3, 7, 10.)

Name ______________________ Date ________________ Class ________________

Caution: Avoid breathing fumes from heated sulfur. Individuals with asthma or allergies to sulfur compounds should not be present when this experiment is conducted. (Steps 3, 7, 10.)

Caution: Molten sulfur can cause severe burns. (Steps 8, 10.)

Note: Your teacher will properly dispose of the materials. (Step 12.)

PROCEDURE

Your teacher will conduct this experiment in a fume hood as a demonstration. During the demonstration, record your observations and draw sketches in Data Table 1. Note that the instructions in the Procedure are written for the teacher.

Part A. Orthorhombic Sulfur

1. Pour vegetable oil to a depth of about 0.5 cm into a 50-mL beaker.
2. Add a pea-sized sample of sulfur to the oil.

3. Using a gas burner, heat the oil-sulfur mixture over a low flame for a few seconds. **CAUTION:** *Excessive heating may cause the sulfur-oil mixture to ignite, producing toxic fumes.*
4. Using a dropper pipet, place a few drops of the warm oil-sulfur mixture on a watch glass. Put the watch glass and beaker aside. After about 20 minutes, examine the product under a magnifying glass or a microscope. Record your observations and sketch the shapes of any crystals that have formed.

Part B. Monoclinic Sulfur

5. Fold a circle of filter paper into the conical shape used for filtering, and place it in a 100-mL beaker for support, as shown in Figure 21.1.
6. Fill a medium test tube about one-third full with powdered sulfur.

7. Heat the test tube over a low flame. **CAUTION:** *Slow heating is recommended.* Continue heating until all the sulfur has melted to an orange-yellow liquid.

Name ______________________ Date ________________ Class ________________

8. **CAUTION:** *Molten sulfur can cause painful burns.* Pour the liquid sulfur rapidly into the filter paper cone. As soon as the sulfur begins to solidify, carefully use tweezers to remove the filter paper from the beaker. Place the open filter paper on a watch glass. Examine the product with a magnifying glass or a microscope. Record your observations and sketch any crystals that have formed.

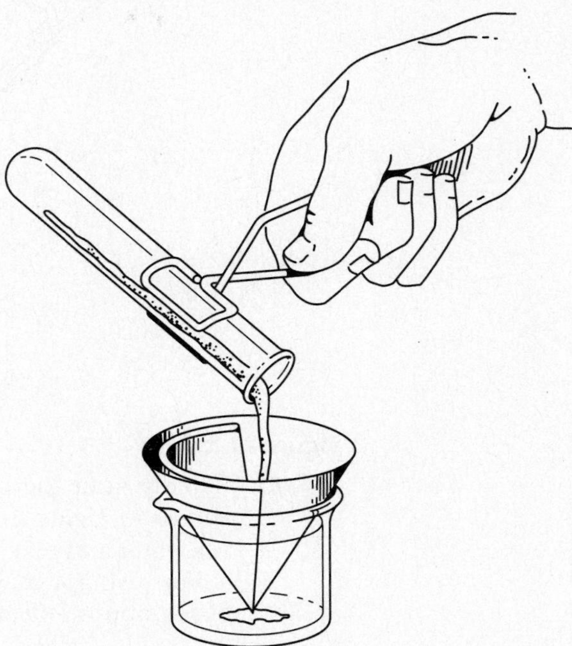

Figure 21.1

Part C. Plastic Sulfur

9. Add 150 mL of water to a 250-mL beaker. Fill the test tube used in Part B about one-third full with sulfur.

10. Heat the test tube in a burner flame until the sulfur just begins to boil. The sulfur should be dark red at the boiling point. **CAUTION:** *Sulfur has a boiling point of 444°C!*

Name ______________________ Date ______________ Class ______________

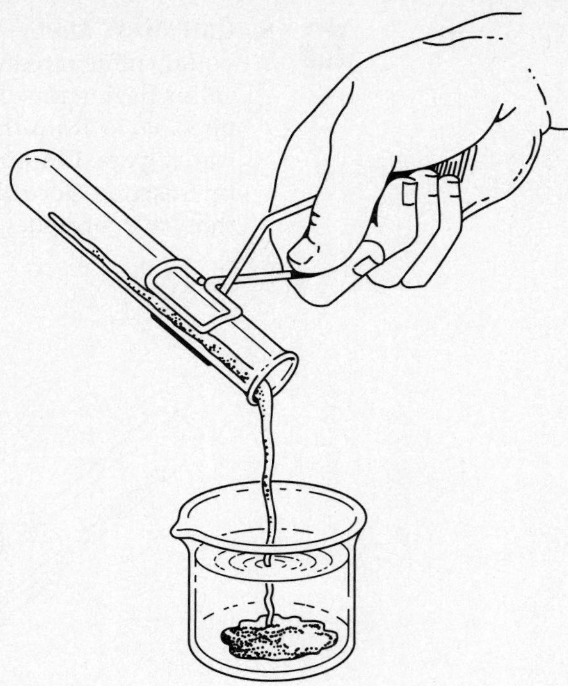

Figure 21.2

11. Rapidly pour the hot sulfur into the beaker of cold water, as shown in Figure 21.2. When the sulfur is cool, remove it from the water and place it on a paper towel to dry. Examine the dry sulfur, using a magnifying glass or microscope. Record your observations and sketch this form of the sulfur.

12. Your teacher will properly dispose of the materials.

Use the following methods to dispose of chemical waste.

Disposal 1: S(*s*), all forms.

Disposal 2: $H_2O(l)$ in Step 11.

Name ______________ Date ______________ Class ______________

OBSERVATIONS

DATA TABLE 1: OBSERVATIONS OF ALLOTROPIC SULFUR		
Allotrope	Description	Drawing of sample
orthorhombic sulfur	blocky crystals	
monoclinic sulfur	small needles	
plastic sulfur	amorphous	

ANALYSES AND CONCLUSIONS

1. Which allotropes of sulfur are crystalline? Compare the structure of any crystals formed.

Orthorhombic sulfur forms blocklike crystals. Monoclinic sulfur forms needlelike crystals.

2. What happened to the plastic sulfur upon standing for a time? What does this suggest about the relative stabilities of the allotropes of sulfur?

The plastic sulfur changes from having no crystalline form (amorphous) to having orthorhombic and monoclinic crystals embedded in the solid. This suggests that the crystalline forms are the more stable forms of sulfur.

Name ______________________ Date ________________ Class ________________

3. Design an experiment to determine which of the crystalline forms of sulfur is the most stable at room temperature and 1 atm pressure.

Store the crystalline products under these conditions. Observe any changes in crystalline structure over time. Monoclinic sulfur is less stable than the rhombic form and reverts back to orthorhombic sulfur after some weeks.

GOING FURTHER

Do Research

Sulfur is not the only element that can exist in more than one allotropic form. Do research on the allotropes of phosphorus. Describe their physical and chemical properties and any important industrial applications.

Elemental phosphorus has three forms that differ in appearance and properties: white, red, and black. White phosphorus is the most common form and the most commercially important. It is soft, waxy, and comprised of individual P_4 molecules. The white form is the most reactive of the three and must be stored under water because it will react when exposed to air. Heating the white form in the absence of air produces the red form, which is used in safety matches. When a match is struck, the heat from the friction changes the red form into the white, which ignites. The red form is an amorphous polymer comprised of interconnected P_4 units. The black form is polymeric and is the most dense and the least reactive of the three forms. It is produced by heating white phosphorus with mercury. Some common uses of red and white phosphorus are phosphoric acid, pesticides, fertilizers, fireworks, detergents, and flame retardants. The black form is industrially useless.

22 CHANGES OF PHYSICAL STATE

Text Reference
Section 13.4

Time Required
45 minutes

Objectives

- Observe the behavior of lauric acid during melting and freezing.
- Prepare a graph of the heating and cooling curves for lauric acid.
- Interpret the freezing and melting point of lauric acid.
- Hypothesize about what happens to the energy that is put into or removed from lauric acid during melting and freezing.

Advance Preparation
The tubes and wire loops can be prepared ahead of time (or by the first hour's students) and used by subsequent classes.

The lab can be simplified if tubes of lauric acid are warmed to 60°C before class so that students can use the first part of the period to obtain data for the cooling curve.

Lauric acid, $CH_3(CH_2)_{10}COOH$, has a molar mass of 200.3 g/mol and a density of 0.87 g/cm^3. This compound melts at 44.0°C and boils at 131.0°C.

PURPOSE

To investigate the melting and freezing behavior of a compound.

BACKGROUND

If you have ever cooled a glass of water with ice cubes and watched water vapor condense on the outside of the glass, you know water can exist in distinct physical states—the solid state (ice), the liquid state (water), and the gaseous state (water vapor). In any pure substance, changes of physical state occur at constant, discrete temperatures that are uniquely characteristic of the substance. Changes in physical state include solids melting, liquids freezing or boiling, and gases condensing.

In this experiment, you will closely examine what happens when a substance undergoes a change in physical state. Specifically, you will investigate the melting and freezing behavior of a sample of an organic compound called lauric acid, $CH_3(CH_2)_{10}COOH$. You are chiefly concerned with two questions. First, does liquid lauric acid begin to freeze at the same temperature that solid lauric acid begins to melt? Second, what happens to the temperature of the lauric acid between the time freezing or melting begins and the time it is complete? You will also consider what happens to the energy that is put into or removed from the lauric acid system during melting or freezing.

MATERIALS (PER PAIR)

safety goggles	2 ring stands
2 400-mL beakers	2 ring supports
2 thermometers	pliers
rubber stopper	beaker tongs or insulated glove
large test tube	timer with second hand
2 wire gauzes	tap water
2 utility clamps	lauric acid, $CH_3(CH_2)_{10}COOH$
2 gas burners	20-cm copper wire, Cu

SAFETY FIRST!

In this lab, observe all precautions, especially the ones listed below. If you see a safety icon beside a step in the Procedure, refer to the list below for its meaning.

Caution: Wear your safety goggles. (All steps.)

Name ______________________ Date ________________ Class ________________

Caution: Exercise care when working with hot water baths to prevent a thermal burn. Do not touch the beaker containing hot water with your bare hands. (Steps 2, 4, 5.)

Caution: Never use a thermometer as a stirrer. (Steps 3, 5, 6.)

Note: Return or dispose of all materials according to the instructions of your teacher. (Step 7.)

PROCEDURE

As you perform the experiment, record your data in Data Table 1.

Part A. The Change From Liquid to Solid

1. Heat about 250 mL of water in a 400-mL beaker to 30°C. Separately, heat 250 mL of water in another 400-mL beaker to 60°C.

2. Use a utility clamp to support a large test tube containing approximately 20 g of acid in the hot (60°C) water, as shown in Figure 22.1. Make sure that the lauric acid is totally beneath the water in the beaker and that the test tube does not touch the bottom of the beaker.

CAUTION: Teach students the proper technique for inserting a thermometer in a rubber stopper. See p. 16.

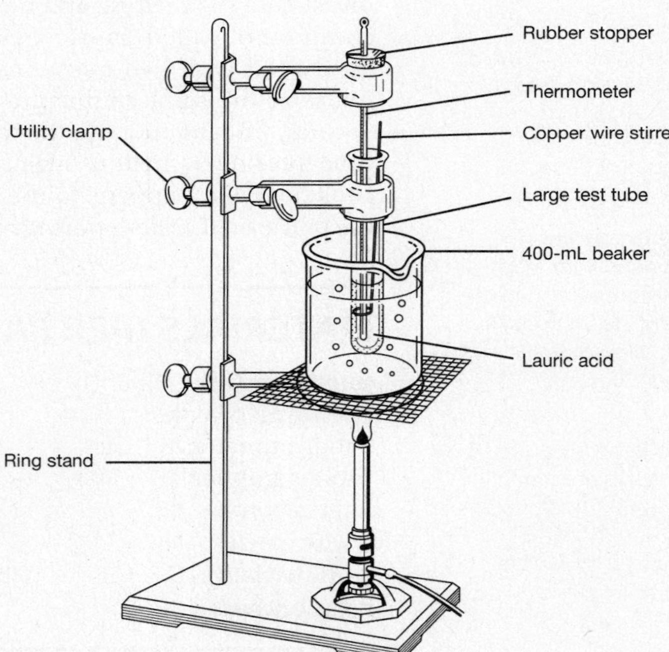

Figure 22.1

Name ______________________ Date ______________ Class ______________

3. While the sample is heating, use the pliers to construct a stirrer from a piece of stiff copper wire, as shown in Figure 22.2. When the crystals have melted, slip the loop of the wire stirrer around a thermometer fitted with a rubber stopper. Referring to Figure 22.1, place the stirrer-thermometer assembly in the test tube so that the thermometer bulb is at the center of the molten lauric acid and the stirrer moves easily up and down. The bulb of the thermometer should not touch the bottom of the test tube. Make certain that the markings on the thermometer can be easily read.

Figure 22.2

4. Carefully replace the beaker containing the 60°C water with the beaker containing the 30°C water. Do this by removing the gas burner and lowering the ring support while holding the beaker with tongs or insulated gloves. Return the ring support to its previous position.

5. Gently stir the lauric acid. When its temperature has fallen to about 55°C, take a temperature reading every 30 seconds. Record the temperature to the nearest 0.1°C. Continue stirring the lauric acid and recording temperature readings until the temperature of the material has fallen to 40°C or lower. (**Note:** When most of the lauric acid has solidified, you will no longer be able to stir the contents. Continue taking temperature readings during this period.)

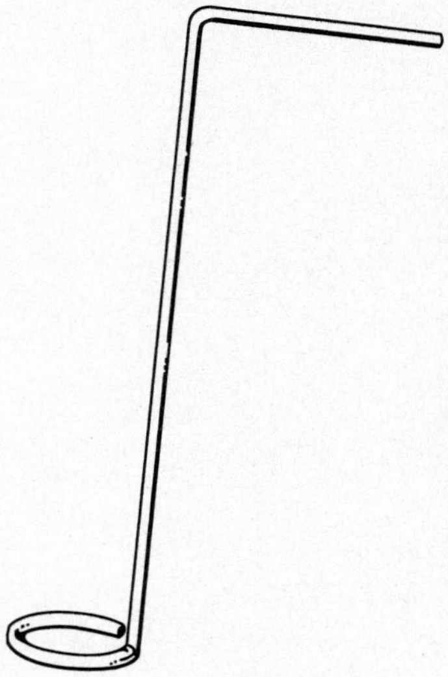

Part B. The Change From Solid to Liquid

6. Replace the beaker containing 30°C water with one that contains water at approximately 55°C. Begin to collect temperature data immediately. Record temperature measurements of the test-tube contents every 30 seconds until the lauric acid is completely melted. Begin stirring as soon as you are able to move the copper stirrer freely. **CAUTION:** *Do not force the stirrer.*

Use the following disposal method for chemical waste.

Disposal 1: lauric acid.

7. Carefully disassemble the apparatus and dispose of the lauric acid as directed by your teacher.

Name ______________________ Date ________________ Class ________________

OBSERVATIONS

DATA TABLE 1: HEATING AND COOLING DATA			
Part A		Part B	
Time (min)	Temperature (°C)	Time (min)	Temperature (°C)
0	55.0	0	30.0
0.5	52.6	0.5	33.2
1.0	49.5	1.0	35.5
1.5	45.5	1.5	37.5
2.0	44.3	2.0	39.0
2.5	44.1	2.5	41.0
3.0	44.0	3.0	42.0
3.5	44.0	3.5	42.6
4.0	44.0	4.0	43.0
4.5	44.0	4.5	43.3
5.0	44.0	5.0	43.6
5.5	44.0	5.5	43.7
6.0	44.0	6.0	43.8
6.5	44.0	6.5	44.0
7.0	44.0	7.0	44.0
7.5	43.7	7.5	44.1
8.0	43.5	8.0	44.2
8.5	43.3	8.5	44.5
9.0	43.0	9.0	45.2
9.5	42.6	9.5	46.0
10.0	42.3	10.0	47.5
10.5	41.9	10.5	49.0
11.0	41.5	11.0	51.4

Name ______________________ Date ______________ Class ______________

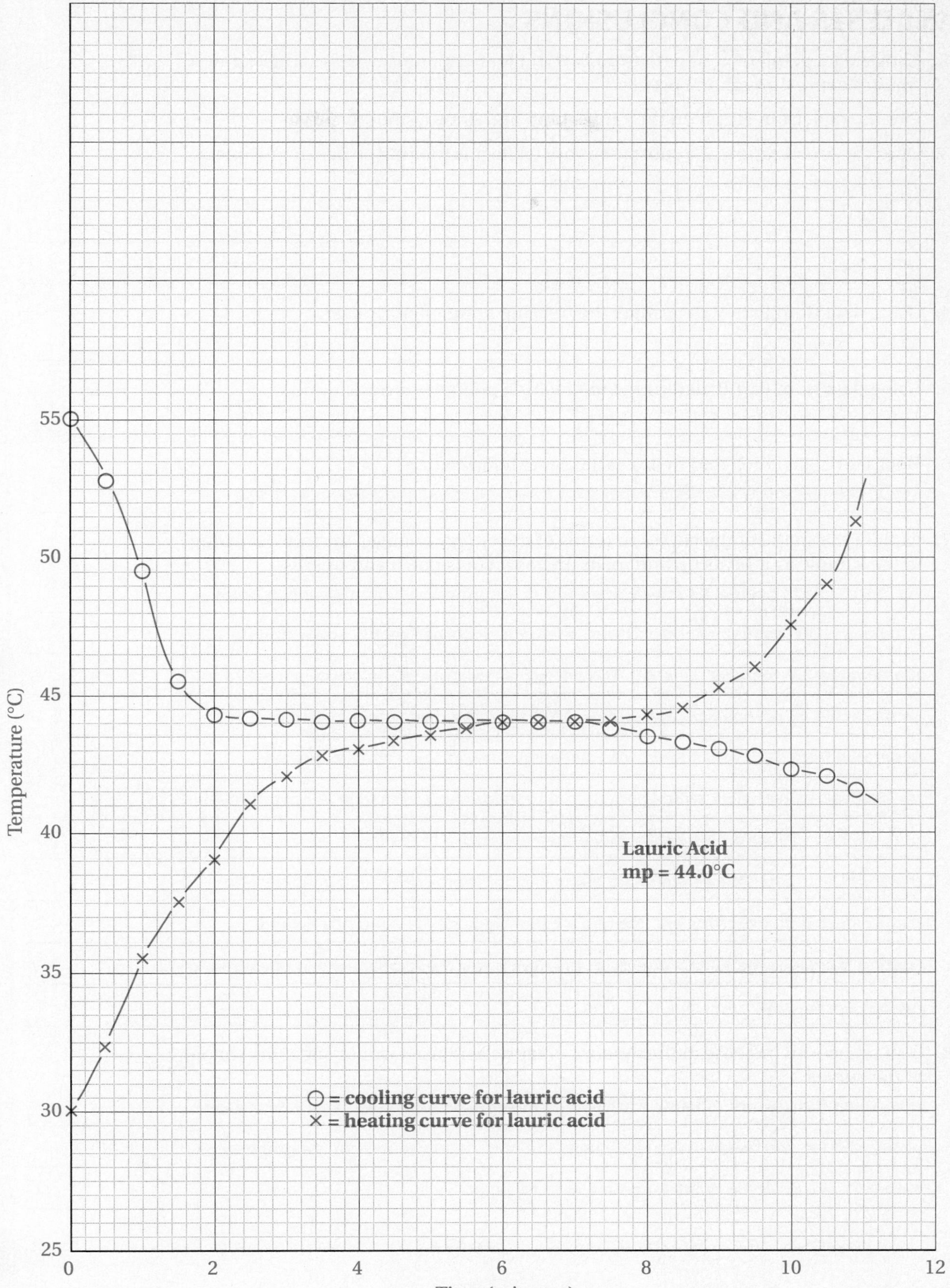

Name ______________________ Date __________________ Class ________________

ANALYSES AND CONCLUSIONS

1. Construct a graph of your data from Part A. Plot temperature versus time. Draw a smooth curve through the points.

2. Plot the data from Part B on the same graph and draw a smooth curve.

3. Does the temperature of a substance vary while it is melting or freezing? Explain.

   The temperature tends to remain constant.

4. Using data from Part A, determine the freezing point of lauric acid.

   44.0°C

5. Using data from Part B, determine the melting point of lauric acid.

   44.0°C

6. Does lauric acid melt and freeze at the same temperature?

   Yes, within the limits of experimental error (theoretical melting point is 44.0°C).

7. Explain the shape of the curves in terms of the energy changes that are occurring in the sample as it heats up and melts and as it cools down and freezes.

   As lauric acid is heated, its temperature increases gradually until its melting point is reached. During the melting process, energy is absorbed by the solid, although the temperature remains constant. The energy added during this stage is used to separate the closely packed molecules of the solid. As these molecules are separated from each other, their potential energy increases. There is, however, no increase in average kinetic energy—and therefore no increase in temperature—until all the molecules of the solid have been separated to the intermolecular distances characteristic of the liquid state. In other words, there is no increase in temperature until the entire sample has melted. Once all the solid has melted, heating increases the kinetic energy of the liquid, and the temperature is observed to increase gradually.

8. Explain how an increase in the amount of lauric acid used would affect the shape of the curves.

   Increasing the amount of lauric acid would increase the total time required for each phase change and would, therefore, cause the horizontal sections of the graph to be longer. There would be no effect on the melting point.

Name ______________________ Date ________________ Class ________________

9. Explain in your own words what is going on at the molecular level as liquid lauric acid cools and freezes.

The cooling curve of lauric acid is the opposite of its heating curve. As the liquid is cooled, the kinetic energy of the lauric acid molecules gradually decreases until the freezing point is reached. At the freezing point, the liquid begins to solidify. At this point, the average kinetic energy of the molecules remains constant while their potential energy decreases as the molecules are pulled closer together by attractive intermolecular forces. Energy is still being removed from the system, but all in the form of potential energy, not kinetic energy. For this reason, no temperature change is observed. Once all the molecules have attained the close intermolecular distances characteristic of the solid state—that is, when all the liquid has solidified—kinetic energy can again be removed from the system. Continued cooling of the solid after the phase change is complete will cause a decrease in the average kinetic energy of the molecules in the solid, and the temperature of the solid will be observed to decrease.

GOING FURTHER

Develop a Hypothesis

Based on what you have learned about the melting behavior of lauric acid, develop a hypothesis about how the melting behavior of lauric acid would change if an impurity was introduced into the sample.

Hypotheses will vary. In general, the melting point of a compound is depressed (decreases) when impurities are present in a sample of the compound. The actual change in the freezing point will depend on the amount of impurities in the sample. Chemists often use melting points to evaluate the purity of a sample.

Do Research

If resources are available, read textbooks or articles about the melting behaviors of solids that will support or disprove your hypothesis.

PRESSURE–VOLUME RELATIONSHIPS FOR GASES

Text Reference
Section 14.2

Time Required
45 minutes

Objectives
- Discover the quantitative relationship between the pressure and volume of a gas (air).
- Based on data, infer the relationship between pressure and volume for all gases, and express this relationship in a mathematical formula.

Advance Preparation
Assemble one-holed stoppers fitted with capillary tubes prior to class. The capillary tubes should be cut and fire-polished prior to use. Insertion in the rubber stopper is difficult and more hazardous if the tubes are not fire-polished. Use a glass-marking pencil to mark the tube at 1-cm intervals. Select one-holed stoppers to fit the 500-mL filter flasks. Lubricate one end of the tube with a drop of glycerin and, using a towel, gently twist the tube into the stopper. Adjust the capillary tube so that its lower end will extend about 5 mm below the surface of the dibutyl phthalate (50 mL) in the 500–mL flask.

PURPOSE

To investigate the relationship between the pressure and volume of a gas.

BACKGROUND

When you squeeze a tennis ball, the ball compresses easily at first. But as you squeeze harder, the ball becomes harder and harder to compress. You can explain these qualitative observations simply. For example, you know that the gas contained inside the tennis ball is being compressed into a smaller volume. As a result, the harder you squeeze, the smaller the volume and the greater the pressure exerted by the gas pushing outward against the ball. Therefore, the harder you squeeze the ball, the more resistance you encounter. This example suggests a relationship between the volume and pressure of a gas. In this experiment, you will measure the pressure of a gas sample as its volume is changed. You will then analyze your data to determine the relationship that exists between the volume and pressure of a gas.

MATERIALS (PER PAIR)

safety goggles
plastic tubing, 1-cm × 5-cm length
50-cm glass capillary tube, fire polished
500-mL filter flask
one-holed rubber stopper, to fit filter flask
30-mL plastic syringe
2 ring stands
2 utility clamps
centimeter ruler
50-mL graduated cylinder
glass-marking pencil
500-mL graduated cylinder
pinch clamp
barometer
dibutyl phthalate (DBP), $C_6H_4(CO_2C_4H_9)_2$ T
silicone grease

SAFETY FIRST!

In this lab, observe all precautions, especially the ones listed below. If you see a safety icon beside a step in the Procedure, refer to the list below for its meaning.

 **Caution:** Wear your safety goggles. (All steps.)

 **Caution:** Exercise care when handling the glass capillary tube. It is easy to break. (Step 3.)

Name ____________________ Date ______________ Class ______________

The dibutyl phthalate may be colored with a few drops of methyl red to aid visibility. Dibutyl phthalate may be reused. The DBP, if wet, may be dried overnight with anhydrous sodium sulfate. Use vermiculite, diatomaceous earth, or similar material to absorb any spills of DBP.

Caution: Dibutyl phthalate (DBP) is toxic. Do not come in contact with this chemical. Contact your teacher immediately in the event of a spill. (Steps 4–12.)

Note: Return or dispose of all materials according to the instructions of your teacher. (Step 12.)

PROCEDURE

As you perform the experiment, record your data in Data Tables 1 and 2.

1. Your teacher will have a partial lab set up prepared for you. You need to carefully finish assembling the apparatus. Refer to Figure 23.1.
2. Fit a 5-cm length of plastic tubing over the sidearm of the flask.

3. Take the capillary tube-stopper assembly out of the flask. Carefully measure the outside diameter of the capillary tube.

4. Carefully measure 50 mL of dibutyl phthalate (DBP) in a *dry* 50-mL graduated cylinder. Pour this volume into the *dry* flask. Replace the capillary tube-stopper assembly. The lower end of the capillary tube should be about 5 mm below the surface of the dibutyl phthalate.
5. Measure and record the length of the tube that is inside the flask and below the stopper.
6. Apply a *thin film* of silicone grease to the 30-mL syringe if the plunger does not operate smoothly. Depress the plunger to the 30-mL mark. Refer to Figure 23.1. Insert the end of the syringe into the plastic tubing attached to the sidearm of the flask. Use a utility clamp attached to a ring stand to support the syringe.

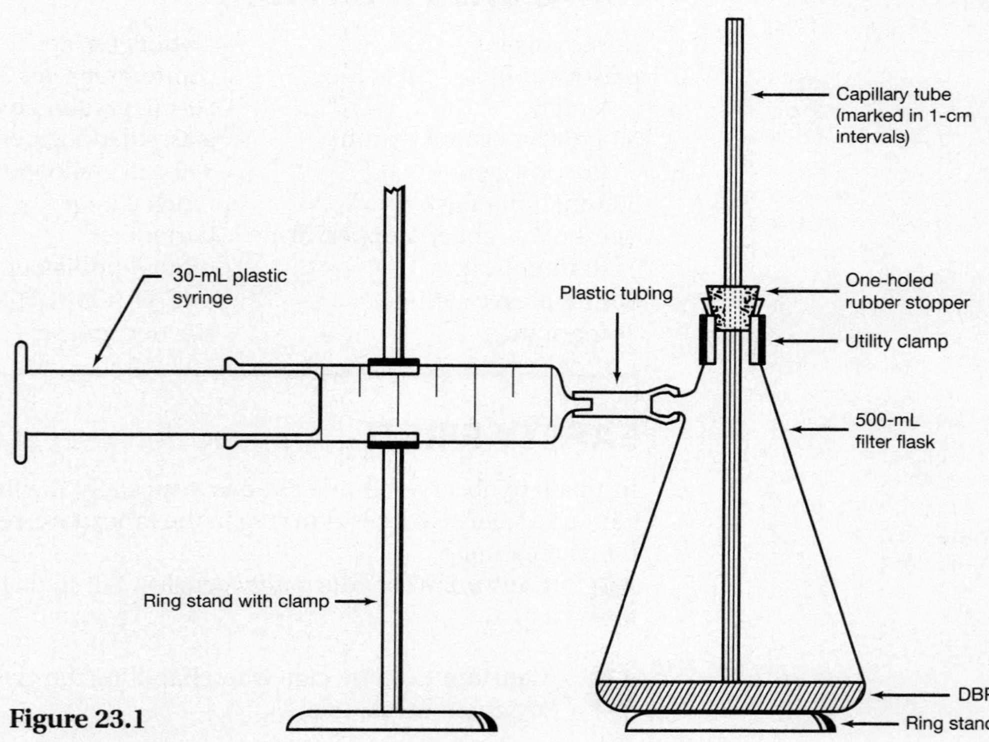

Figure 23.1

Name ______________________ Date __________________ Class __________________

7. Make sure that all connections are tight and your setup matches Figure 23.1.
8. Make sure that the plunger reads 30 mL. Record this reading and the height of the DBP in the capillary tube.
9. Now depress the plunger to the 25-mL mark. Record this reading. Wait until the DBP comes to rest in the capillary tube. Then measure and record this height.

Step 10.
Depending on the tightness of the system and the volume of the filter flask, students may not be able to expel all the air from the syringe.

10. Repeat this process at 5-mL intervals until as much air as possible has been pushed out of the syringe and into the flask.
11. Remove the syringe from the plastic tubing. Set the plunger at the 30-mL mark and reattach the syringe to the flask. Repeat Steps 8–10 and record your data in Data Table 2.

No disposal is required if the DBP is reused. Otherwise, use **Disposal Method 4b** for dibutyl phthalate.

12. Mark the neck of the flask at the bottom of the rubber stopper. Remove the stopper assembly and the syringe, leaving the plastic tubing in place on the sidearm. Dispose of the DBP and rinse the flask as directed by your teacher.
13. Use a pinch clamp to close the end of the plastic tubing, as shown in Figure 23.2. Fill the flask with water to the mark on the neck. Pour this water into a 500-mL graduated cylinder. Record the volume to the nearest milliliter. This is the volume of your flask.
14. Record atmospheric pressure and room temperature in Data Table 1.

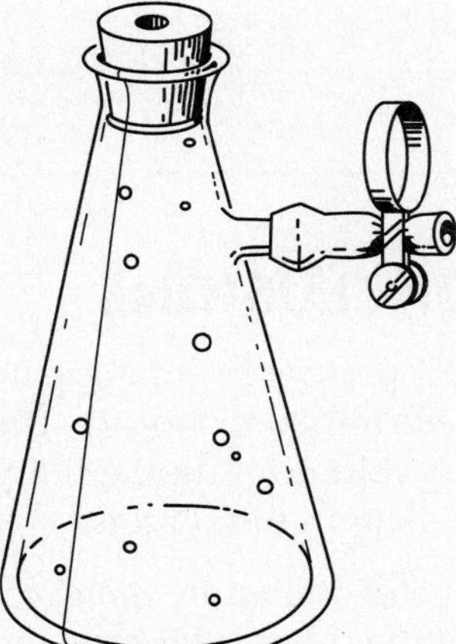

Figure 23.2

Name ______________________ Date ______________ Class ______________

OBSERVATIONS

DATA TABLE 1: PRELIMINARY MEASUREMENTS	
diameter of capillary tube:	0.4 cm
length of capillary tube in flask:	17 cm
barometric pressure:	758 mm Hg
room temperature:	23°C
volume of flask:	546 cm^3

DATA TABLE 2: SYRINGE VOLUME AND DBP HEIGHT READINGS

Trial 1		Trial 2	
Syringe Volume (mL)	DBP Height (cm)	Syringe Volume (mL)	DBP Height (cm)
30	0	30	0
25	9.0	25	8.6
20	17.4	20	17.1
15	25.8	15	25.4
10	33.6	10	32.8
5	41.0	5	40.2

ANALYSES AND CONCLUSIONS

1. Calculate the volume of air present in your apparatus during the experiment. You must correct the value determined in Step 13 (the volume of the flask) to include the following volumes: the volume of the capillary tube in the flask, the volume of the DBP, and the volume of air in the syringe.

First, calculate the volume occupied by the capillary tube, using your measurements for the diameter of the tube and for the length of that part of the tube that was within the flask.

$$\text{volume of capillary tube} = \pi \times \text{radius}^2 \times \text{length}$$
$$= 3.14 \times (\text{diameter}/2)^2 \times \text{length}$$
$$= 3.14 \times \left(\frac{0.4\ \text{cm}}{2}\right)^2 \times 17\ \text{cm}$$
$$= 2\ \text{cm}^3$$

Next, calculate the volume of air in the flask, without the capillary tube or the DBP.

$$\text{volume of air} = \text{volume of flask} - \text{volume of DBP} - \text{volume of tube}$$

$$\text{volume of air in flask} = 546\ \text{cm}^3 - 50\ \text{cm}^3 - 2\ \text{cm}^3$$
$$= 494\ \text{cm}^3$$
$$= 494\ \text{mL}$$

Name ______________________ Date ________________ Class ________________

Finally, for each trial, calculate the total volume of the air in the apparatus by adding the volume of the air in the syringe to the volume of air in the flask. Record this volume in Data Table 3.

DATA TABLE 3: VOLUME AND PRESSURE CALCULATIONS FOR AIR ENCLOSED IN FLASK					
Trial 1			Trial 2		
P (mm Hg)	V (mL)	$P \times V$ (mm Hg $\times$ mL)	P (mm Hg)	V (mL)	$P \times V$ (mm Hg $\times$ mL)
758	524	3.97×10^5	758	524	3.97×10^5
765	519	3.97×10^5	765	519	3.97×10^5
771	514	3.96×10^5	771	514	3.96×10^5
778	509	3.96×10^5	778	509	3.96×10^5
784	504	3.95×10^5	783	504	3.95×10^5
790	499	3.94×10^5	789	499	3.94×10^5

2. For each trial, calculate the pressure exerted by the air enclosed within the flask. Use millimeters of mercury (mm Hg) as the units of pressure. You have already read the pressure directly in centimeters of DBP (cm DBP), but now you must convert this figure to millimeters of mercury (mm Hg). DBP has a density of 1.05 g/cm^3; the density of mercury is 13.6 g/cm^3. This means that a pressure that supports a 1-mm column of DBP will support a column of mercury (1.05/13.6 = 0.0772 mm) high.

Calculate the pressure of the volume of enclosed air in millimeters of mercury, using this equation:

$$\text{pressure of enclosed air in mm Hg} = \left(\text{height of DBP in mm} \times \frac{0.077 \text{ mm Hg}}{\text{mm DBP}}\right) + \text{room pressure in mm Hg}$$

Record the pressure for each trial in Data Table 3.

Sample calculation for a syringe reading of 25 mL (height of 9.0 cm DBP):

$$\text{height of DBP (mm)} = 9.0 \text{ cm DBP} \times \frac{10 \text{ mm}}{1 \text{ cm}} = 90 \text{ mm DBP}$$

$$\text{pressure of enclosed air in mm Hg} = 90 \text{ mm DBP} \times \frac{0.077 \text{ mm Hg}}{\text{mm DBP}} + 758 \text{ mm Hg}$$
$$= 6.9 \text{ mm Hg} + 758 \text{ mm Hg}$$
$$= 765 \text{ mm Hg}$$

3. Calculate the product of the pressure of the enclosed air (see problem 2) and the volume of the enclosed air (see problem 1) for each trial. Record the results in Data Table 3.

Sample calculation:

$$P \times V = 519 \text{ mL} \times 765 \text{ mm Hg}$$
$$= 3.97 \times 10^5 \text{ (mL} \times \text{mm Hg)}$$

Name ______________________ Date ______________ Class ______________

4. Make a graph of pressure versus volume. Draw a best-fit smooth line for your data points. Title and label your graph.

5. Based on your data, what relationship exists between the pressure and volume of a gas (assuming constant temperature)?

Pressure varies inversely with volume. $P \times V$ = constant. Students may be concerned that their graphs are linear. Explain that the curve covers a small portion of a typical pressure–volume curve.

6. Look up a statement of Boyle's law in your textbook. Are your results consistent with Boyle's law? Examine the class data. Is it consistent with the law? Explain.

Yes to both questions. $P \times V$ product is (approximately) a constant.

7. Would your results have been affected if the room temperature had changed during the experiment? Explain.

An increase in temperature would have caused the subsequent pressure reading to be too high; a decrease in temperature would have had the opposite effect.

8. How would your results have been affected if you had used a different gas in the flask? Explain.

The results of the experiment would have been exactly the same if a different gas had been used. Boyle's law applies to all gases at ordinary conditions of temperature and pressure.

GOING FURTHER

Develop a Hypothesis

Based on the results of this lab, develop a hypothesis to explain why weather balloons are only partially filled up before they are released into the atmosphere. (These balloons can reach altitudes of 40,000 feet.)

As the weather balloons rise, the gas inside the balloon responds to the decrease in atmospheric pressure by expanding to fill a greater volume.

Design an Experiment

Propose an experiment to test your hypothesis.

Name ______________________ Date __________________ Class __________________

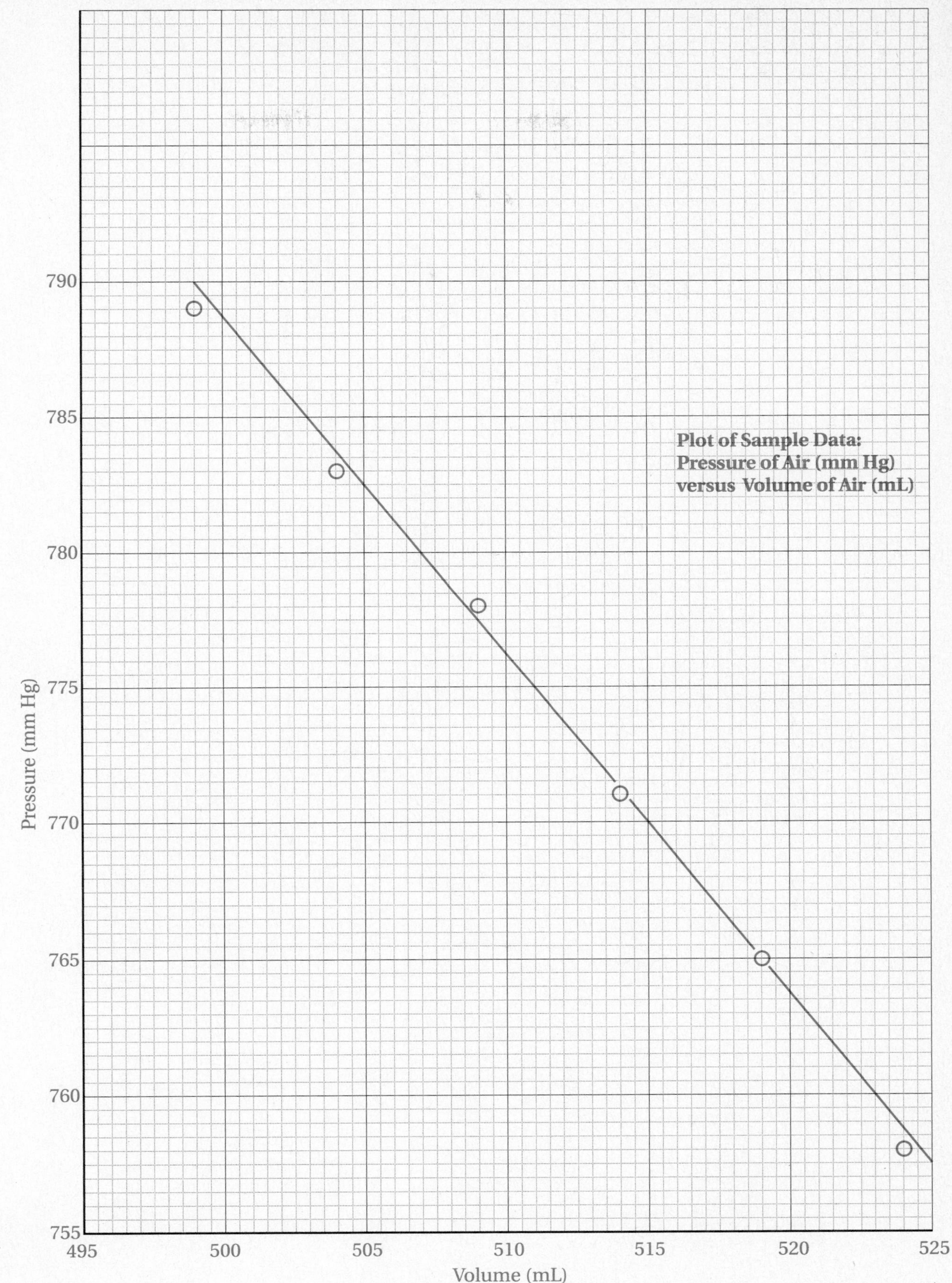

Name ______________________ Date __________________ Class ______________

24 TEMPERATURE–VOLUME RELATIONSHIPS FOR GASES

Text Reference
Section 14.2

Time Required
45 minutes

Objectives
- Collect data relating the volume and temperature of a gas.
- Make a graph of volume versus temperature for a gas.
- Interpret the relationship between volume and temperature based on the graph.
- Determine the value of absolute zero by extrapolation based on the graph.

Students will verify Charles's law concerning the direct relationship between the temperature and volume of a gas. A sample of air will be placed in a capillary tube and sealed on top with a layer of DBP. The tube will then be heated and the change in volume determined by noting the change in position of the DBP layer. Students will prepare a graph of volume versus temperature to illustrate the linear relationship.

The molar mass of DBP is 278 g/mol; its boiling point is 335°C; its vapor pressure at 20°C is less that 0.01 mm Hg.

PURPOSE

To investigate the relationship of the volume of a gas and its temperature.

BACKGROUND

Have you noticed that the tires on automobiles appear to be a little flat on a cold winter's day or that a balloon inflated in a cold room will expand when taken to a warm room. These observations suggest that there is a relationship between the temperature and volume of a gas. If a gas is heated, its volume increases. If a gas is cooled, its volume decreases. In this experiment, you will measure the volume of a sample of air at different temperatures and analyze the data to determine the relationship between the temperature and the volume of a gas. You will also extrapolate from your experimental data to determine absolute zero—the temperature at a which a gas theoretically has no volume.

MATERIALS (PER PAIR)

- safety goggles
- glass capillary tube, 2 mm × 20 cm
- gas burner
- dropper pipet
- watch glass
- test-tube holder
- ring stand
- ring support
- 2 utility clamps
- wire gauze
- small rubber band
- thermometer
- 2 400-mL beakers
- forceps
- centimeter ruler
- dibutyl phthalate, $C_6H_4(CO_2C_4H_9)_2$ T
- ice and water

SAFETY FIRST!

In this lab, observe all precautions, especially the ones listed below. If you see a safety icon beside a step in the Procedure, refer to the list below for its meaning.

Caution: Wear your safety goggles. (All steps.)

Caution: Dibutyl phthalate is toxic. Do not come in contact with this chemical. (All steps.)

Name ______________________ Date ______________ Class ______________

Any small spill of DBP should be absorbed in vermiculite, diatomaceous earth, or a similar material and placed in a chemical waste container. Large spills of DBP should also be absorbed as described, but disposal must be handled by a professional.

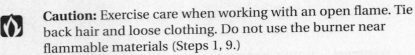

Caution: Exercise care when working with an open flame. Tie back hair and loose clothing. Do not use the burner near flammable materials (Steps 1, 9.)

Caution: Exercise care when working with hot water. Hot glass tubing can cause burns. Make certain that any glass you use is cool before you handle it. Remember that hot glass looks the same as cold glass. If you should be burned, hold the burned area under cold running water until the burning sensation stops. Notify your teacher immediately. (Steps 1, 9.)

Note: Return or dispose of all materials according to the instructions of your teacher. (Step 10.)

Step 1.
The capillary tubes with DBP can be used by subsequent classes to save time and to reduce the amount of DBP that must be disposed of. The DBP may be colored with a few drops of methyl red.

Step 2.
If a watch glass is used, excess DBP can be drawn up in a dropper pipet and returned to the dropper bottle. DBP samples may be obtained without the need of a watch glass. Remove the lid of the DBP dropper bottle. Touch the warm capillary tube to the surface of the DBP and then remove. The only waste involved in this procedure is the very small amount of DBP in the capillary tube. This quantity can be safely disposed of in a conventional manner.

PROCEDURE

As you perform the experiment, record your observations in Data Table 1.

1. Seal one end of the capillary tube by rotating it in a hot burner flame. Fire-polish the open end. **CAUTION:** *Place all hot glassware on a heat-resistant ceramic square to cool.*

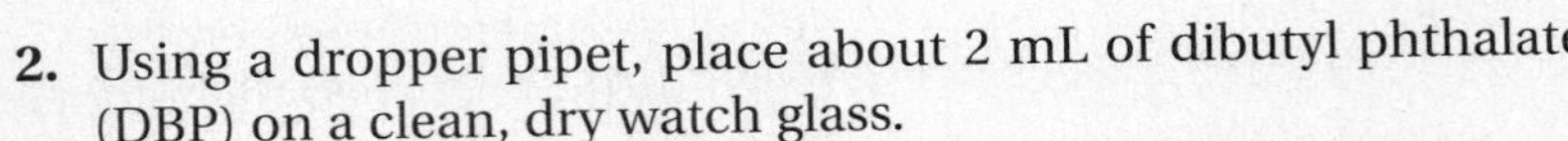

2. Using a dropper pipet, place about 2 mL of dibutyl phthalate (DBP) on a clean, dry watch glass.

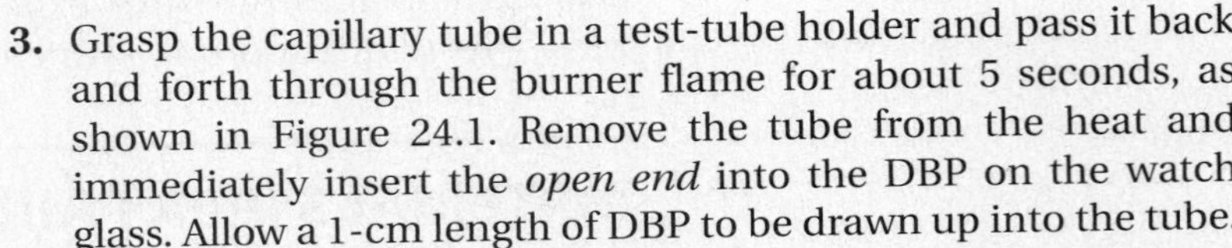

3. Grasp the capillary tube in a test-tube holder and pass it back and forth through the burner flame for about 5 seconds, as shown in Figure 24.1. Remove the tube from the heat and immediately insert the *open end* into the DBP on the watch glass. Allow a 1-cm length of DBP to be drawn up into the tube.
4. On a ring stand, clamp the tube vertically, with its *open end up*, and allow the tube to cool to room temperature. The column of trapped air should be between 5 and 10 cm long.
5. Push a small rubber band over the capillary tube until it is about halfway up the tube. This rubber band will serve as a distance marker.
6. Lower the clamped capillary tube, *open end up*, and a thermometer into ice water in a 400-mL beaker so that the entire column of trapped air is submerged. Refer to Figure 24.2. Wait several minutes. Without removing the tube from the ice water, use forceps to slide the rubber band to mark the top of the air column. Wait another minute and readjust the band if necessary.

Name ______________________ Date ________________ Class ________________

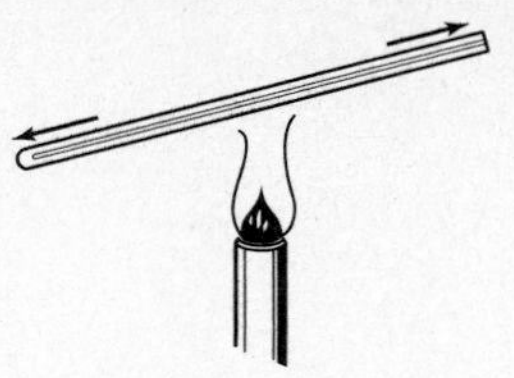

Fanning the capillary tube in flame

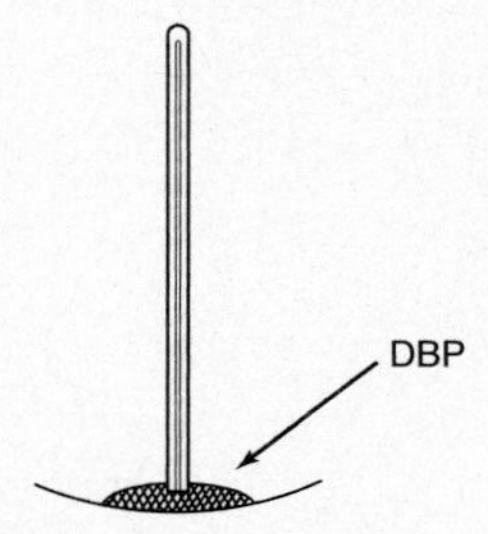

Trapping a volume of air

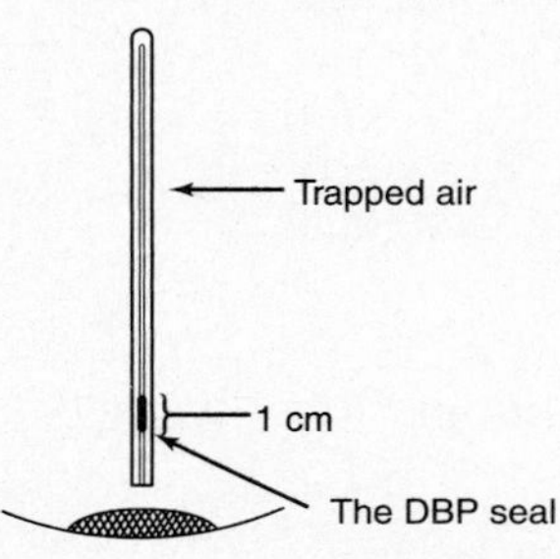

Figure 24.1

7. Measure and record the height of the column of trapped air inside the capillary tube. Measure and record the temperature of the ice water bath to the nearest 0.1°C.

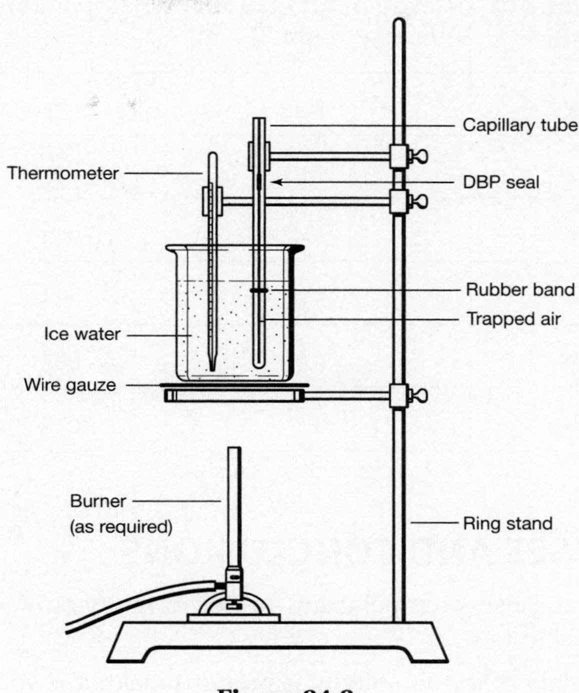

Figure 24.2

8. Repeat Steps 6 and 7, using a 400-mL beaker filled with water at room temperature.

9. Use a gas burner to heat the water in the beaker to about 40°C. Measure and record the new water temperature and the length of the air column. Repeat this procedure at 20°C intervals, up to 100°C, time permitting.

10. Save the DBP for reuse, or dispose of it as directed by your teacher.

Use the following disposal method for chemical waste.

Disposal 4b: Dibutyl phthalate.

Note: No disposal is required if the DBP is reused. Return the used DBP to the stock bottle, mark the bottle as used, and save until DBP is needed again.

If the DBP is wet, it can be dried by storing it over anhydrous sodium sulfate.

Name ______________________ Date ______________ Class ______________

OBSERVATIONS

DATA TABLE 1: DATA AND CALCULATIONS			
Temperature of Water Bath (°C)	Height of Air Column (relative volume) (cm)	Temperature (K)	V/T (cm/K)
1.1	4.8	274	0.018
23.2	5.2	296	0.018
40.1	5.4	313	0.017
61.4	5.8	334	0.017
79.0	6.2	352	0.018
99.9	6.5	373	0.017

ANALYSES AND CONCLUSIONS

1. Convert Celsius temperatures to Kelvin temperatures and record the results in Data Table 1.
2. The height of the air column is proportional to the volume of air contained in the capillary tube. Therefore, use the height of the air column as the value for the volume of the gas, and calculate the volume/temperature ratio for each trial. Enter your results in Data Table 1.
3. Plot a graph of relative volume (measured in centimeters) versus temperature (in kelvins). Draw a best-fit straight line through the data points. Should the point (0, 0) be on the line?
4. Plot a second graph using the same data, but using degrees Celsius as the unit of temperature. Begin the volume scale at 0 cm, but start the temperature scale at −300°C. Again, draw a best-fit straight line through the data points. Use dashes to extend the straight line from the lowest data point to the horizontal axis. According to your graph, what is the Celsius temperature at which the volume would be equal to 0? How does this value compare with the actual value for absolute zero, in degrees Celsius?

   The graph indicates that absolute zero occurs at −275°C; the actual value for absolute zero is −273°C.

Name ______________________ Date ________________ Class ________________

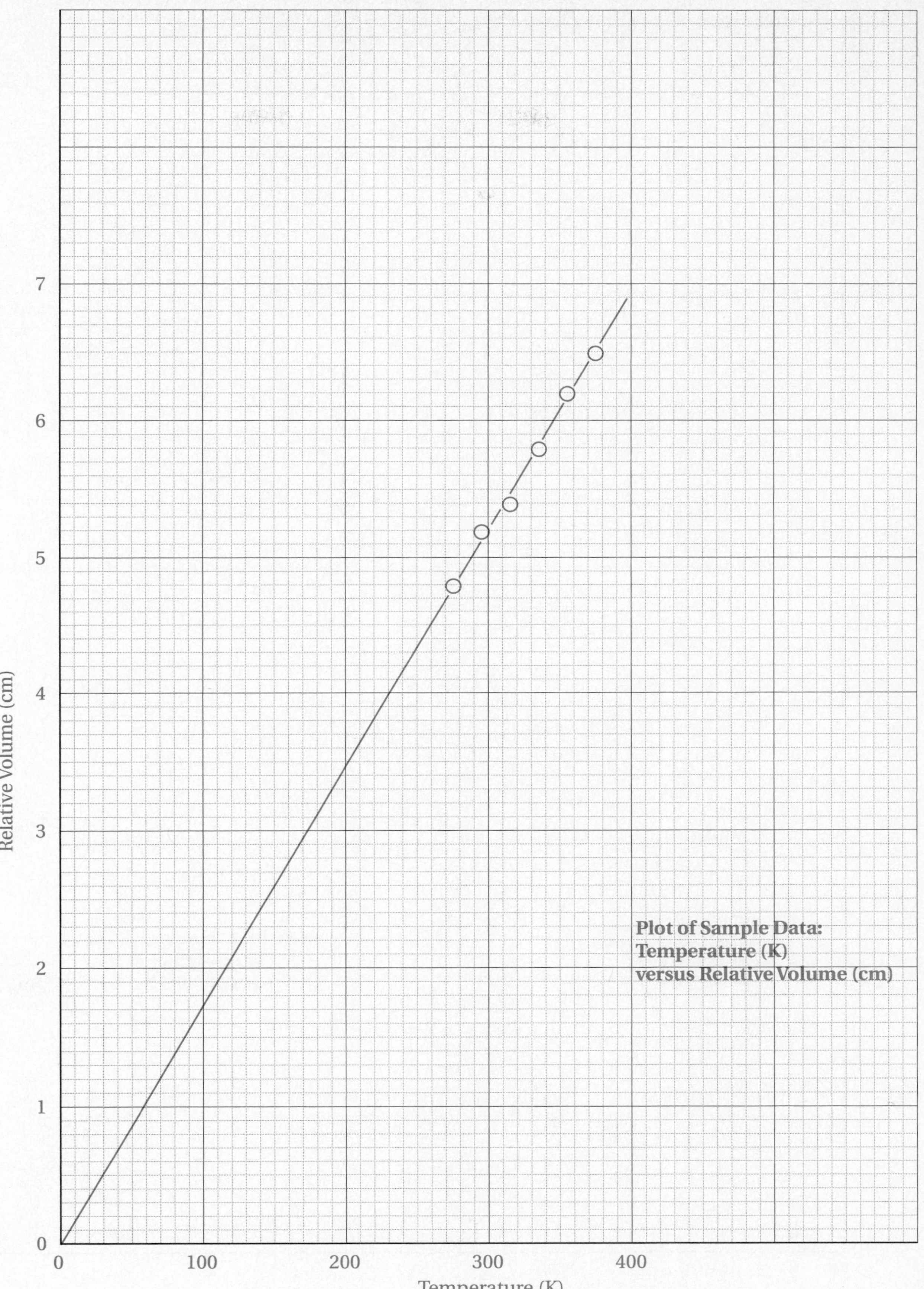

Name ____________________ Date ______________ Class ______________

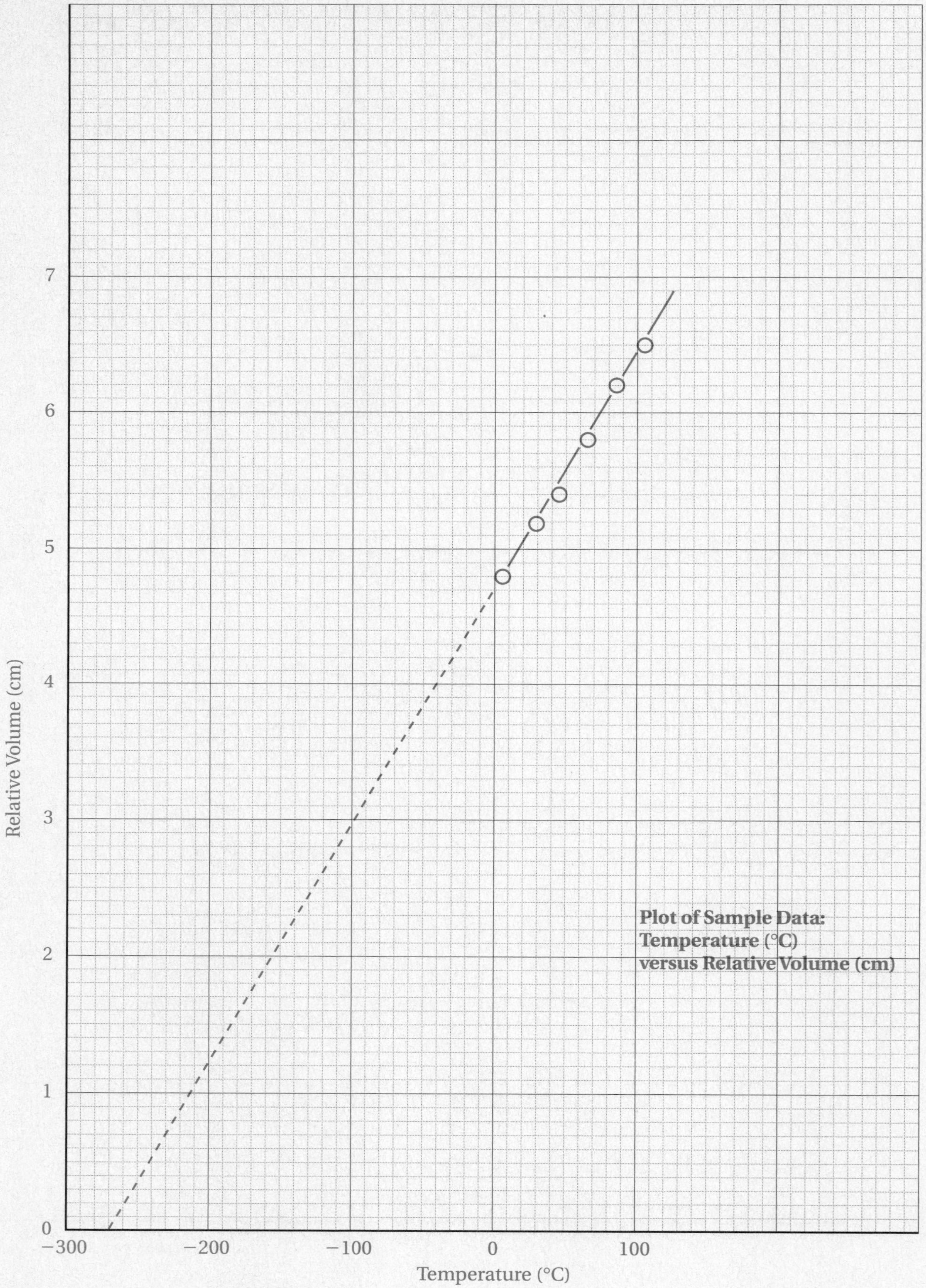

Plot of Sample Data: Temperature (°C) versus Relative Volume (cm)

Relative Volume (cm)

7

6

5

4

3

2

1

0

−300 −200 −100 0 100

Temperature (°C)

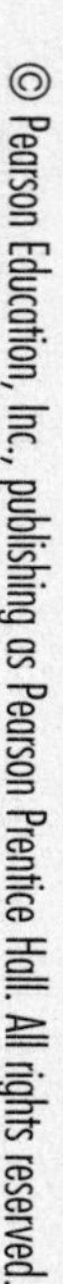

Name ______________________ Date ________________ Class ________________

5. Does your data show a volume-temperature relationship for a gas? Explain.

Yes. Within the limits of experimental error, the ratio of volume to temperature is a constant (0.17 to 0.18), as Charles's law would predict.

6. The pressure did not vary during the experiment, because all trials were performed at constant room (atmospheric) pressure. If the pressure had varied, how would it have affected your results? Explain.

A change in pressure would cause a change in volume. This would interfere with determining the temperature-volume relationship.

7. What are some possible sources of error in this experiment?

1. inability to measure the height of the air column accurately
2. expansion of the glass tube, giving a varying volume
3. not allowing enough time for the gas to achieve a temperature equilibrium with the water bath

8. How do the class results for the value of absolute zero compare with the actual value? What factors (besides those mentioned in problem 7) could be responsible for any error noted in the class results?

Variations in the way points were plotted and lines were drawn can contribute to any error observed in the class results.

GOING FURTHER

Develop a Hypothesis

Interpret the results of this lab in terms of the kinetic theory of matter as it applies to gases.

The average kinetic energy of a population of gas particles is directly proportional to the Kelvin temperature. Consequently, heating an enclosed gas causes the particles in a gas to strike the container walls more frequently and with greater force. If the pressure of the gas is kept constant, the volume of the gas must increase.

Design an Experiment

To verify your ideas, do research on the kinetic theory of gases. What are some of the predictions made by this theory, and how has it been tested? What other types of experiments could be designed to test this theory?

Name ______________ Date ______________ Class ______________

25 DIFFUSION OF GASES

Text Reference
Section 14.4

Time Required
30 minutes

Objectives
- Measure the relative rates of diffusion of ammonia gas and hydrogen chloride gas.
- Examine the relationship between diffusion rate and molar mass.
- Compare the results to those predicted by Graham's law of diffusion.

Students should not handle concentrated acids and bases. You may want to conduct this experiment as a demonstration or to use a wash bottle to dispense the HCl and NH_3.

PURPOSE

To verify Graham's law of diffusion.

BACKGROUND

Have you noticed that, if someone enters a room and sits near you, it can take several minutes before you are aware of his or her cologne? You become aware of the scent because molecules in the cologne diffuse through the surrounding air. *Diffusion* is the process in which particles in a system move from an area of high concentration to an area of low concentration. Diffusion continues until a uniform concentration of particles is reached throughout the system. The rate at which molecules of a gas diffuse, at constant temperature, decreases as the molar mass of the gas increases. In fact, the rate of gas diffusion at constant temperature is inversely proportional to the square root of the molar mass of the gas. This proportionality is called Graham's law of diffusion.

$$\text{rate of diffusion} \propto \frac{1}{\sqrt{\text{molar mass}}}$$

In this experiment, you will determine the relative rates of diffusion for two gases with significantly different molar masses. The gases that you will study are ammonia, NH_3, and hydrogen chloride, HCl.

MATERIALS

- safety goggles and apron
- 2 ring stands
- 2 utility clamps
- glass tube, 1 cm × 70 cm
- cotton wads
- 2 medicine droppers
- 2 rubber stoppers
- timer, with second hand
- meter stick
- tweezers
- concentrated hydrochloric acid, 12*M* HCl(*aq*) C T I
- concentrated ammonia, 15*M* NH_3(*aq*) C T I

SAFETY FIRST!

In this lab, observe all precautions, especially the ones listed below. If you see a safety icon beside a step in the Procedure, refer to the list below for its meaning.

Caution: Wear your safety goggles. (All steps.)

Caution: Concentrated hydrochloric acid is highly corrosive and can cause severe burns. (Step 2.)

Name ______________________ Date ________________ Class ________________

Caution: Concentrated ammonia solution is corrosive. Avoid skin contact. Avoid the inhalation of ammonia fumes. Use a fume hood for this demonstration. (Step 2.)

Note: Your teacher will dispose of all materials. (Step 4.)

PROCEDURE

Your teacher will perform this experiment in a fume hood as a teacher demonstration. The instructions in the Procedure are written for your teacher. During the demonstration, record your observations in Data Table 1.

1. Use two ring stands and two utility clamps to hold a clean, dry glass tube in a level position, as shown in Figure 25.1. Fit a cotton plug snugly into each end of the tube.
2. Use medicine droppers to simultaneously add 5 drops of concentrated HCl to the cotton plug at one end of the tube and 5 drops of concentrated NH_3 solution to the cotton plug at the other end. Close the ends with rubber stoppers. Note and record the start time in Data Table 1.
3. Record the time it takes to see a white deposit form in the tube. Measure the distances (in centimeters) from the inside end of each cotton plug to the center of the white deposit. Record these measurements in Data Table 1.

4. Your teacher will dispose of the materials.

Step 1.
Drying the diffusion tube between classes may be a problem. A quick acetone rinse may be appropriate.

Step 3.
Holding a dark piece of paper behind the tube makes it easier to see the white deposit of NH_4Cl.

Use the following disposal methods for chemical waste.

Disposal 2: $NH_4Cl(s)$, the reaction product.

Disposal 3: Required if excess $HCl(aq)$ and $NH_3(aq)$ are wastes.

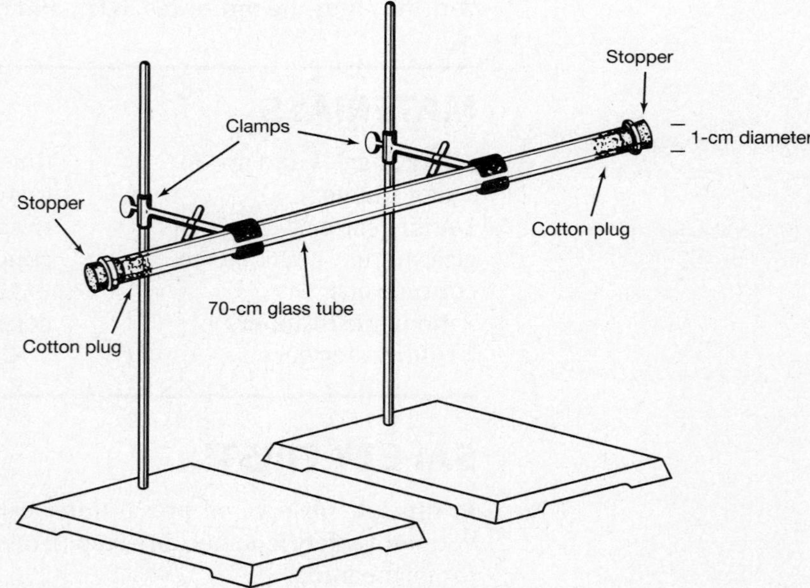

Figure 25.1

Name ______________________ Date ________________ Class ________________

OBSERVATIONS

DATA TABLE 1: DATA AND CALCULATIONS	
start time:	12:10:00
time when deposit forms:	12:14:10
elapsed time:	4 min 10 s (250 s)
distance from HCl to product:	26.4 cm
distance from NH_3 to product:	39.6 cm
rate of diffusion HCl (distance/time):	0.106 cm/s
rate of diffusion NH_3 (distance/time):	0.158 cm/s
experimental ratio of rates (NH_3/HCl):	1.49
theoretical ratio of rates (NH_3/HCl):	1.46

ANALYSES AND CONCLUSIONS

1. Calculate the rate of diffusion for each gas by dividing the distance (centimeters) each gas traveled by the time (seconds) required for the appearance of the white deposit. Enter the calculated rates in Data Table 1.

$$\text{rate of diffusion} = \frac{\text{distance traveled by gas}}{\text{time required for product formation}}$$

2. Find the ratio of the rate of diffusion of NH_3 and the rate of diffusion of HCl. (Use the rates calculated in Step 1.) Record this ratio in Data Table 1.

3. Calculate the theoretical ratio of the rates of diffusion of these gases, using the following equation.

$$\frac{\text{diffusion rate of } NH_3}{\text{diffusion rate of HCl}} = \frac{\sqrt{\text{molar mass HCl}}}{\sqrt{\text{molar mass } NH_3}}$$

Enter the value for the theoretical ratio in Data Table 1.

4. Would a change in temperature affect the diffusion rates you calculated? Explain.

Yes. An increase in temperature would cause both rates to increase by the same factor.

5. Would a change in temperature affect the ratio of diffusion rates? Explain.

No. The ratio of the rates would remain the same.

6. Are the results of this experiment consistent with Graham's law of diffusion? Explain.

Yes. The ratio of diffusion rates is very close to the theoretical value.

7. The white substance in the tube is ammonium chloride, NH_4Cl. It is the only product in the reaction. Write a balanced equation for this reaction. What type of chemical reaction is this?

$$NH_3(g) + HCl(g) \rightarrow NH_4Cl(s)$$

This is a combination reaction.

8. Calculate the percent error in your experimentally determined value for the ratio of diffusion rates of NH_3 and HCl. Use the theoretical ratio calculated in problem 3 as the accepted value for the ratio.

$$\text{percent error} = \frac{|\text{experimental ratio} - \text{theoretical ratio}|}{\text{theoretical ratio}} \times 100\%$$

$$\text{experimental ratio} = 1.49$$

$$\text{theoretical ratio} = 1.46$$

$$\text{percent error} = \frac{|1.49 - 1.46|}{1.46} \times 100\%$$

$$= \frac{|0.03|}{1.46} \times 100\%$$

$$= 0.0205 \times 100\%$$

$$= 2.05\%$$

GOING FURTHER

Develop a Hypothesis

Suppose an opened bottle of vinegar containing acetic acid (CH_3COOH) was placed next to an opened bottle of pentylamine ($C_5H_{13}N$). Which would you smell first? What is the diffusion ratio?

Acetic acid should diffuse about 1.2 times faster than pentylamine.

Design an Experiment

Propose an experiment to test your hypothesis. If resources are available and you have your teacher's permission, perform the experiment.

Moistened litmus paper suspended from the top of an inverted buret that is positioned over a beaker of each substance could be used to measure the rate of diffusion.

Name ____________ Date ____________ Class ____________

26 DISTILLATION

Text Reference
Section 15.2

Time Required
50 minutes

Objective
- Observe the use of distillation to separate the volatile and nonvolatile components of a homogeneous mixture.

Advance Preparation

6M ammonia
Add 40 mL concentrated aqueous NH_3 to 50 mL of water and dilute to 100 mL.

0.1M silver nitrate
Dissolve 0.17 g of $AgNO_3$ in 10 mL of distilled water.

3M nitric acid
Add 20 mL concentrated HNO_3 to 50 mL of distilled water and dilute to 100 mL.

PURPOSE

To investigate the use of distillation as a method for separating the volatile and nonvolatile components of a liquid solution.

BACKGROUND

Pure water is a valuable commodity, as anyone who has experienced flooding and a contaminated water supply knows. Because water is an excellent solvent, it never exists in its pure state in nature. Even water purified for drinking contains a number of dissolved substances. However, pure water can be obtained from aqueous solutions through a process called *distillation*. In distillation a solution is boiled, vaporizing the water and leaving behind any dissolved solid material. The vapor is directed through a condenser consisting of a straight glass tube encased by an outer glass jacket. Cold water circulates through the outer jacket, causing the water vapor in the inner tube to condense on the cold walls. The purified condensed liquid, called the *distillate*, can then be collected.

In this experiment, you will distill a solution of water that contains one volatile and one nonvolatile impurity. A volatile substance is one that easily evaporates from a solution.

MATERIALS (PER GROUP)

safety goggles and apron
condenser
2 utility clamps
ring stand
2 rubber hoses for condenser
thermometer
2 one-holed rubber stoppers
250-mL distillation flask
ring support
wire gauze
gas burner
250-mL beaker
2 100-mL beakers
spatula
100-mL graduated cylinder
long-stemmed funnel
3 medium test tubes
dropper pipet
towel
glycerin
sodium chloride, NaCl
distilled water
1% phenolphthalein solution [I]
6*M* ammonia, NH_3 [T] [I]
boiling chips
3*M* nitric acid, HNO_3 [C] [T]
0.1*M* silver nitrate, $AgNO_3$ [T] [I]

Name ______________________ Date ________________ Class ________________

SAFETY FIRST!

In this lab, observe all precautions, especially the ones listed below. If you see a safety icon beside a step in the Procedure, refer to the list below for its meaning.

Caution: Wear your safety goggles. (All steps.)

Caution: Nitric acid is corrosive and can cause severe burns. Silver nitrate can stain skin and clothing. (Step 6.)

$AgNO_3$ stains on the hands can be prevented by rinsing with 0.1*M* sodium thiosulfate, $Na_2S_2O_3$, immediately after contact.

Caution: Ammonia is an irritant. Avoid inhaling the fumes of this chemical. (Step 2.)

Caution: Be careful when putting glass tubing or a thermometer into a rubber stopper. Wrap the glassware in a towel to prevent cutting yourself in case of breakage. Grasp the thermometer close to the rubber stopper and twist gently when inserting. (Step 1.)

Caution: Exercise care when working with an open flame. Tie back hair and loose clothing. Do not use the burner near flammable materials. (Step 4.)

Note: Return or dispose of all materials according to the instructions of your teacher. (Step 9.)

Name ______________________ Date ______________ Class ______________

PROCEDURE

As you perform the experiment, record your observations in Data Table 1.

Step 1.
Note that the cold water must enter the bottom of the condenser and leave at the top so that the condenser is kept filled with slowly flowing water.

1. Study the distillation apparatus shown in Figure 26.1. First, support the condenser with a utility clamp and ring stand. Connect a length of rubber hose from the cold water tap to the "Cold water in" connection on the condenser. Connect another length of rubber hose to the "Cold water out" connection on the condenser, and run the hose into the sink. Turn on the cold water and check for leaks. The water should flow steadily through the outer tube of the condenser and into the sink. Turn off the water.

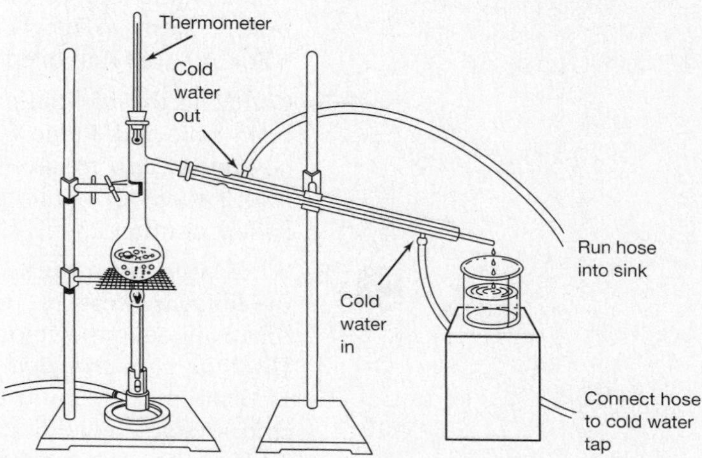

Figure 26.1

Demonstrate the technique for insertion and removal of the thermometer. Emphasize that little force is required. If a thermometer becomes stuck in a stopper, cut away the stopper by making a lengthwise slit with a scalpel or sharp knife.

CAUTION: *Use glycerin or water to lubricate the thermometer.* Insert the thermometer into a one-holed rubber stopper that securely fits the neck of the round-bottomed 250-mL flask. Insert the thermometer into the stopper by twisting the thermometer and stopper in opposite directions. Adjust the position of the thermometer so the thermometer bulb reaches just to the sidearm of the flask when the stopper is in position. *Wait until the entire distillation apparatus is assembled before inserting the stopper and thermometer into the flask.*

CAUTION: *Use glycerin or water to lubricate the sidearm.* Insert the sidearm of the flask into a one-holed rubber stopper that fits the neck of the condenser. The stopper should be positioned far enough in so that the sidearm extends into the straight portion of the inner condenser tube.

Finish assembling the distillation apparatus. Tighten the utility clamps on the condenser and the flask only enough to gently support the apparatus. **CAUTION:** *Do not tighten the clamp too tightly; otherwise, the glass will break.* The apparatus should be *secure,* but *not rigid.* Insert the rubber stopper and thermometer into the flask.

2. Dissolve about 1 g of NaCl in 100 mL of water in a 250-mL beaker. Add 2 drops of phenolphthalein solution and 2 drops of 6*M* NH_3 to the solution. Note the color of the solution. **CAUTION:** *Aqueous ammonia is an irritant. Do not inhale its vapors.*

Step 3.
Point out that boiling chips aid boiling by providing a rough surface on which small bubbles of gas can form.

3. Remove the thermometer and stopper from the flask and pour the colored solution through a long-stemmed funnel into the flask. Add three or four boiling chips to the solution.

Steps 4 and 5.
At first, the ammonia will distill over the water, and the solution in the distillation flask will become a lighter pink. At a later point in the distillation, the solution will become darker pink again as water continues to distill off, but ammonia remains in solution.

4. Turn on the cold water. Add 2 drops of phenolphthalein solution to a clean 100-mL beaker and position it at the end of the condenser to catch the distillate. Use the gas burner to gently heat the contents of the flask. Record the temperature at which liquid begins to drip from the condenser. Adjust the burner flame to keep the solution boiling steadily. Note any color changes that occur during the distillation.

5. Continue the distillation until about 25 mL of distillate has been collected. Remove the collection beaker from under the condenser and replace it with another clean 100-mL beaker. Add 2 drops of phenolphthalein solution to this beaker and collect another 25 mL of distillate.

Step 6.
The distillate should be colorless, but may be colored if the solution was bumped during heating.

The test for chloride ions is based on the formation of insoluble silver chloride upon addition of silver ions. The nitric acid prevents possible interference from formation of insoluble silver hydroxide, AgOH.

$Ag^+(aq) + Cl^-(aq) \rightarrow AgCl(s)$

6. While waiting for the second distillate to accumulate, perform the following tests on the first distillate. Compare the color of the distillate to the color of the mixture in the flask. **CAUTION:** *HNO_3 is corrosive and can cause burns.* Add 3 mL of this distillate to a medium test tube and test for the presence of chloride ions by adding 10 drops of 3*M* HNO_3 and 5 drops of 0.1*M* $AgNO_3$. Test for the presence of ammonia in the distillate by using the technique described in Step 11 of Experiment 2 on page 28 to detect ammonia fumes. Record your results and observations in Data Table 1.

7. When the second 25 mL of distillate has been collected, turn off the gas burner. Repeat the procedure in Step 6 for the second distillate; record your results and observations in Data Table 1.

8. Allow the apparatus to cool completely before carefully taking it apart. If time permits, perform the tests in Step 6 on the solution that remains in the flask.

9. Discard the solutions as directed by your teacher. Save the boiling chips for future use.

Use the following disposal methods for chemical waste.

Disposal 2: $NaCl(aq)$, $NH_3(aq)$, and phenolphthalein.

Disposal 8: The distillate from Steps 6, 7, and 8 to which $AgNO_3$ was added.

Name ______________________ Date ________________ Class ________________

OBSERVATIONS

DATA TABLE 1: DISTILLATION DATA FOR AQUEOUS SOLUTION OF NaCl, NH_3, AND PHENOLPHTHALEIN

Test	Solution Before Distillation	Solution After First Distillation	Solution After Second Distillation	First Distillate	Second Distillate
color	pink	pale pink	pink	pink	pale pink
Cl^-	yes	not tested	yes	no	no
NH_3 fumes	yes	not tested	no	yes	no

ANALYSES AND CONCLUSIONS

1. For each of the solutes used in this experiment, state whether it is volatile or nonvolatile. Give evidence for your answer.

   NaCl is an ionic compound. It is nonvolatile and does not appear in the distillate. NH_3 is volatile and does appear in the distillate.

2. Should you have tested for sodium ion in the distillate? Explain.

   There is no need to test for sodium ions because the distillate will not contain any nonvolatile solutes.

Name ______________________ Date __________________ Class __________________

GOING FURTHER

Develop a Hypothesis

Based on the results of this lab, propose a hypothesis about whether or not distillation could be used to separate a mixture of volatile liquids.

____

____

____

Design an Experiment

Propose an experiment to test your hypothesis. If resources are available and you have your teacher's permission, perform the experiment.

____

____

____

Name ______________________ Date ________________ Class ________________

27 THE SOLVENT PROPERTIES OF WATER

Text Reference
Section 15.2

Time Required
30 minutes

Objective
- Compare the solubility, in water, of compounds having different polarities.

PURPOSE

To examine the relationship between a compound's polarity and its solubility in water.

BACKGROUND

"Oil and water don't mix!" You've probably heard this phrase before. Though this phrase is true, there are plenty of substances that do dissolve in water. The polar nature of the water molecule is largely responsible for its remarkable solvent action. Because of its polarity, water is able to dissolve ionic compounds, such as sodium chloride and copper sulfate, and polar covalent compounds, such as sugar and ammonia. Many chemical reactions and most biochemical reactions take place in water.

Similarly, many substances dissolve in oily, nonpolar solvents, such as gasoline and kerosene. In general, only nonpolar molecules will dissolve in nonpolar solvents.

In this experiment, you will examine the relationship between a compound's polarity and its solubility in water.

Advance Preparation
Glycerin (also called glycerol), hexane, ethanol, and kerosene are liquids that should be placed in dropper bottles for class use. Normal hexane is more expensive than mixed hexanes, which can be used as a substitute.

Provide solids in small, labeled jars with screw tops. There should be one set of solids for each group of four students.

MATERIALS (PER PAIR)

safety goggles
10 small test tubes
test-tube rack
plastic wash bottle
spatula
dropper pipet
sodium chloride, NaCl
glycerin, $C_3H_8O_3$
sucrose, $C_{12}H_{22}O_{11}$
sodium thiosulfate, $Na_2S_2O_3$
calcium carbonate, $CaCO_3$
hexane, C_6H_{14} F T
potassium sulfate, K_2SO_4 T
ethanol, C_2H_5OH F T
kerosene, C_{12}–C_{15} F T
distilled water

SAFETY FIRST!

In this lab, observe all precautions, especially the ones listed below. If you see a safety icon beside a step in the Procedure, refer to the list below for its meaning.

Caution: Wear your safety goggles. (All steps.)

Caution: Ethanol, hexane, and kerosene are flammable. Do not use these substances near open flames. (All steps.)

Caution: Avoid skin contact with these chemicals. Many of them are toxic. (Step 2.)

Note: Return or dispose of all materials according to the instructions of your teacher. (Step 3.)

Note: Wash your hands thoroughly after completing this experiment.

PROCEDURE

As you perform the experiment, record your results and observations in Data Table 1.

1. Record the chemical formula, physical state, and color of each of the substances in the Materials section, with the exception of distilled water.

Step 2.
Compounds such as glycerin and ethanol contain an OH group, which can form hydrogen bonds with water. These compounds are soluble in water. Hexane does not form hydrogen bonds and is insoluble or slightly soluble in water.

2. Test each of the substances for water solubility. Add 3–4 mL of distilled water to each small test tube. Add a very small quantity of the substance to be tested to an individual test tube. For solids, use a sample about the size of a match head. For liquids, use one drop. Be careful not to contaminate the chemicals with one another.

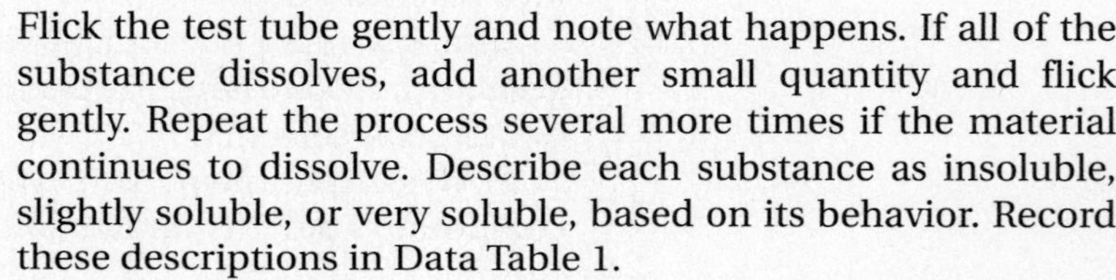

Flick the test tube gently and note what happens. If all of the substance dissolves, add another small quantity and flick gently. Repeat the process several more times if the material continues to dissolve. Describe each substance as insoluble, slightly soluble, or very soluble, based on its behavior. Record these descriptions in Data Table 1.

Use the following disposal methods for chemical waste.

Disposal 1: $CaCO_3(s)$.

Disposal 2: All materials except $CaCO_3$, C_6H_{14}, and kerosene.

Disposal 4a: C_6H_{14}, hexane.

Disposal 4b: Kerosene.

3. Dispose of the hexane and kerosene samples as directed by your teacher. Dispose of all other samples by flushing them, with water, down the drain. Rinse the test tubes.

Name ______________________ Date ________________ Class ________________

OBSERVATIONS

DATA TABLE 1: RESULTS AND OBSERVATIONS			
Substance	Formula	Physical State	Solubility in Water
sodium chloride	$NaCl$	white solid	very soluble
glycerin	$C_3H_8O_3$	colorless syrupy liquid	very soluble
sucrose	$C_{12}H_{22}O_{11}$	white solid	very soluble
sodium thiosulfate	$Na_2S_2O_3$	white crystalline solid	very soluble
calcium carbonate	$CaCO_3$	white solid	insoluble
hexane	C_6H_{14}	colorless liquid	insoluble
potassium sulfate	K_2SO_4	white solid	very soluble
ethanol	C_2H_5OH	colorless liquid	very soluble
kerosene*	C_{12}–C_{15}	colorless liquid	insoluble

*mixture of hydrocarbons

ANALYSES AND CONCLUSIONS

1. Polar and ionic substances generally dissolve in water; nonpolar substances do not. Explain.

The rule is that "like dissolves like." By the word *like* scientists mean compounds of similar polarities. A strongly polar solvent, such as water, dissolves most ionic compounds and many polar molecules. Ionic compounds will not dissolve in nonpolar solvents, such as gasoline. Nonpolar or weakly polar compounds will dissolve in nonpolar solvents.

2. Based on the fact that calcium carbonate is an ionic compound, you may be puzzled by your experimental results for this compound. Propose an explanation for the solubility of calcium carbonate.

Calcium carbonate is insoluble in water. The attractive forces between the ions (Ca^{2+} and CO_3^{2-}) within the crystal are stronger than the attractive forces between the water molecules and the ions.

Name ______________________ Date ________________ Class ________________

3. What basis can you use to decide whether the liquids tested are polar or nonpolar? Which of the liquid substances tested are polar? Which are nonpolar?

Polar liquids are soluble in water; nonpolar liquids are insoluble in water.

polar: glycerin, ethanol

nonpolar: hexane, kerosene

4. The structural formulas of the four liquids other than kerosene that were tested in this experiment are shown. Do these structural formulas support the solubility data obtained? Explain.

```
 Glycerin                   Hexane                         Ethanol

    H              H   H   H   H   H   H                    H   H
    |              |   |   |   |   |   |                    |   |
H — C — O — H  H — C — C — C — C — C — C — H            H — C — C — O — H
    |              |   |   |   |   |   |                    |   |
H — C — O — H      H   H   H   H   H   H                    H   H
    |
H — C — O — H
    |
    H
```

Both glycerin and ethanol contain polar bonds (O—H bonds) and are very polar molecules; they are water soluble. Hexane is nonpolar and is insoluble in water.

GOING FURTHER

Develop a Hypothesis

Based on the results of this lab, develop a hypothesis about how soaps and detergents are able to *emulsify* oils and greases in a solution of water.

Name ______________________ Date ______________ Class ______________

Do Research

To test your hypothesis, look up the chemical structures of some soaps and detergents. What do they all have in common, and how are their emulsifying properties related to their chemical structures?

Soaps are composed of molecules that have long nonpolar tails attached to a polar head group. As a result, they are able to interact with both nonpolar and polar substances simultaneously in a way that helps disperse nonpolar substances, such as grease, in a polar solvent.

Name ______________________ Date ________________ Class ______________

28 WATER OF HYDRATION

Text Reference
Section 15.2

Time Required
30 minutes

Objective
- To observe the effect of heat on several hydrates.

PURPOSE

To investigate the effect of heat on several hydrates.

BACKGROUND

Have you ever had your arm put in a plaster cast? If you have, then you already know something about hydrates. Plaster of Paris is the semihydrate of calcium sulfate, $CaSO_4 \cdot \frac{1}{2}H_2O$. When you add water to plaster of Paris and allow it to set, it is gradually transformed into a hard crystalline compound, calcium sulfate dihydrate, $CaSO_4 \cdot 2H_2O$. Water is an integral part of many ionic solids, and such ionic solids are called *hydrates*. The water in these solids is called *water of hydration*.

The water of hydration is more loosely bound in the hydrated crystal than the ions are. Thus, you can usually drive off the water by heating the crystals. The material that remains after the water is gone is called the *anhydrous salt*.

In this experiment, you will heat several hydrates and observe the appearance of the reactants and products involved. You will also heat a nonhydrated compound as a basis for comparison.

Advance Preparation
$MgSO_4 \cdot 7H_2O$ is Epsom salts.

MATERIALS (PER PAIR)

- safety goggles
- glass-marking pencil
- 4 medium test tubes
- spatula
- test-tube holder
- gas burner
- copper(II) sulfate pentahydrate, $CuSO_4 \cdot 5H_2O$ [T] [I]
- sodium chloride, NaCl
- magnesium sulfate heptahydrate, $MgSO_4 \cdot 7H_2O$
- sodium carbonate decahydrate, $Na_2CO_3 \cdot 10H_2O$ [I]

SAFETY FIRST!

In this lab, observe all precautions, especially the ones listed below. If you see a safety icon beside a step in the Procedure, refer to the list below for its meaning.

Caution: Wear your safety goggles. (All steps.)

Caution: Copper compounds are toxic. Avoid contact with copper(II) sulfate pentahydrate. (All steps.)

Caution: Exercise care when heating a test tube over a flame. Use a test-tube holder. (Step 2.)

Remind students that hot glass looks like cool glass.

Name ______________________ Date ________________ Class ________________

A semiquantitative experiment can be carried out by having students add one hydrate to a tared test tube and obtain the mass of the hydrate to 0.01 g by difference. The mass is again determined after heating.

Caution: Exercise care when working with an open flame. Tie back hair and loose clothing. Do not use the burner near flammable materials. (Step 2.)

Note: Return or dispose of all materials according to the instructions of your teacher. (Step 4.)

PROCEDURE

As you perform the experiment, record your observations in Data Table 1.

1. Label four clean, dry test tubes with the numbers 1–4. To separate test tubes add about 1 g of each of the following substances.

tube 1	$CuSO_4 \cdot 5H_2O$
tube 2	$NaCl$
tube 3	$MgSO_4 \cdot 7H_2O$
tube 4	$Na_2CO_3 \cdot 10H_2O$

Step 2. Wrap a wet paper towel around the upper part of the test tube to keep it cool. This will aid condensation of the water that is lost from the crystals.

2. Grasp tube 1 in a test-tube holder. Hold the tube almost horizontally and heat it *gently* in a burner flame, as shown in Figure 28.1. **CAUTION**: *Never point the mouth of the tube at yourself or anyone else.* Record what you observe near the mouth of the test tube, and note any change in the appearance of the crystals.

3. Repeat Step 2 for tubes 2, 3, and 4. Record your observations.

4. Follow your teacher's instructions for proper disposal of the materials.

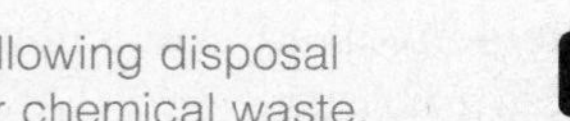

Use the following disposal method for chemical waste.

Disposal 1: All materials in this experiment.

You can collect $CuSO_4$ after heating and use it for growing crystals or for making solutions.

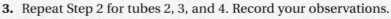

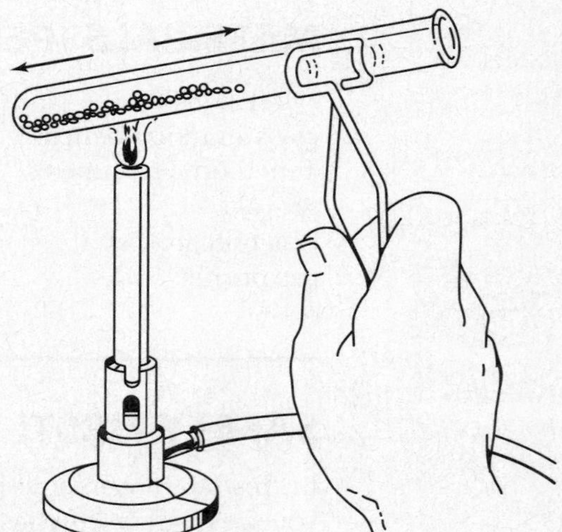

Figure 28.1

Name ______________________ Date ______________ Class ______________

OBSERVATIONS

DATA TABLE 1: OBSERVATIONS		
Tube	Substance	Observations
1		
2		
3		
4		

ANALYSES AND CONCLUSIONS

1. In which tubes did you observe a change near the test tube's mouth?

____

2. In which tubes did the appearance of the crystals change?

____

3. Write a general statement to describe what you would expect to observe when a hydrate is heated.

____

____

Name ______________ Date ______________ Class ______________

4. For any substance that was a hydrate, write a balanced equation for the change that took place when the substance was heated. In each case, assume that the anhydrous salt was formed.

$CuSO_4 \cdot 5H_2O + \text{heat} \rightarrow CuSO_4 + 5H_2O$

$MgSO_4 \cdot 7H_2O + \text{heat} \rightarrow MgSO_4 + 7H_2O$

$Na_2CO_3 \cdot 10H_2O + \text{heat} \rightarrow Na_2CO_3 + 10H_2O$

5. Design and carry out an experiment for determining the number of moles of water per mole of anhydrous salt in a $BaSO_4$ hydrate.

Given that the formula mass of the anhydrous salt is 208.0 g/mol, determine the mass of the unknown hydrate to the nearest 0.01 g. Heat the hydrate to drive off the water of hydration. Reheat the substance to constant mass and report the mass to the nearest 0.01 g. The calculation is as follows:

$$\text{mass of unknown hydrate} = 16.26\text{ g}$$

$$\text{mass of anhydrous salt} = 13.87\text{ g}$$

$$\text{mass of water} = 2.39\text{ g}$$

$$\text{moles of anhydrous salt} = \frac{\text{mass of anhydrous salt}}{\text{molar mass of anhydrous salt}} = \frac{13.87\text{ g}}{208.00\text{ g/mol}} = 0.06668\text{ mol}$$

$$\text{moles of water} = \frac{\text{mass of water}}{\text{molar mass of water}} = \frac{2.39\text{ g}}{18.00\text{ g/mol}} = 0.133\text{ mol}$$

Ratio of anhydrous salt to water of hydration

= 0.06668 mol anhydrous salt: 0.133 mol water

= 1 mol anhydrous salt: 1.99 mol water

≈ 1 mol anhydrous salt: 2 mol water

The hydrate was barium sulfate dihydrate, $BaSO_4 \cdot 2H_2O$.

GOING FURTHER

Do Research

Over time, a bottle of anhydrous salt gradually becomes hydrated from exposure to humidity in the air. As a result, the mass of a given quantity of the sample does not accurately reflect the amount of salt in the sample. To control for this "partial" hydration process, chemists often determine the amount of salt in a particular hydrated sample by dissolving it in a known volume of distilled water and measuring other physical properties. What other physical properties could be measured to determine the amount of salt in an aqueous solution?

density, colligative properties of solutions

Name ______________ Date ______________ Class ______________

29 ELECTROLYTES AND NONELECTROLYTES

Text Reference
Section 15.2

Time Required
40 minutes

Objective
- Classify aqueous solutes as strong electrolytes, weak electrolytes, or nonelectrolytes.

Advance Preparation

6M ethanoic acid
Add 17 mL glacial CH_3COOH to 20 mL of distilled water and dilute to 50 mL.

1M ammonia
Add 7 mL concentrated NH_3 to 90 mL of distilled water and dilute to 100 mL.

6M ammonia
Add 40 mL concentrated NH_3 to 50 mL of water and dilute to 100 mL.

1M hydrochloric acid
Add 8 mL concentrated HCl to 40 mL of distilled water and dilute to 100 mL.

5% sodium chloride
Dissolve 5 g NaCl in 100 mL of distilled water.

1M sodium hydroxide
Add 4.0 g NaOH to 70 mL of chilled distilled water while stirring; then dilute to 100 mL.

5% sucrose
Dissolve 5 g of sucrose in 100 mL of distilled water.

PURPOSE

To investigate the electrical properties of aqueous solutions of ionic and molecular substances.

BACKGROUND

If an electrical device accidentally falls into water in which you're standing, you could receive a severe or even fatal shock. This is possible because small amounts of dissolved ions in the water allow it to conduct electricity. Thus, in the case of an electrical device accidentally dropped into water, the electricity normally conducted to the device is instead conducted into you. Substances that dissolve in water to produce electrically conductive solutions are called *electrolytes*. If, when dissolved, the substance is a good conductor of electricity, it is called a *strong electrolyte*. In general, strong electrolytes are almost completely ionized when dissolved in solution. If, when dissolved, the substance is a poor conductor of electricity, it is called a *weak electrolyte*. In general, weak electrolytes are only slightly ionized when dissolved in solution. Substances that dissolve in water without ionizing will not conduct electricity and are called *nonelectrolytes*.

In this experiment, you will observe as your teacher tests several solutions for conductivity. You will classify the solute in each solution as a strong electrolyte, a weak electrolyte, or a nonelectrolyte.

MATERIALS

(Teacher Demonstration)
safety goggles and apron
conductivity apparatus, including light bulbs
100-mL beaker
plastic wash bottle
paper towels
5% sodium chloride solution, NaCl(*aq*)
sodium chloride , NaCl
5% sucrose solution, $C_{12}H_{22}O_{11}(aq)$
1*M* hydrochloric acid, HCl [T] [I]
glacial ethanoic acid, CH_3COOH [C] [T] [F]
ethanol, C_2H_5OH [F] [T]
kerosene, C_{12}–C_{15} [F] [T] [I]
1*M* sodium hydroxide, NaOH [C] [T]
6*M* ethanoic acid, CH_3COOH [C]
6*M* ammonia, $NH_3(aq)$ [T] [I]
1*M* ammonia, $NH_3(aq)$ [T] [I]
distilled water and tap water

SAFETY FIRST!

This lab should be done as a teacher demonstration. Observe all precautions, especially the ones listed below. If you see a safety icon beside a step in the Procedure, refer to the list below for its meaning.

 **Caution:** Wear your safety goggles. (All steps.)

Name ______________________ Date ________________ Class ________________

Safety
Always be sure that the switch is turned off and the plug is removed from the socket before handling the conductivity apparatus. Otherwise, a severe electrical shock can result. Do not allow students to use a conductivity apparatus connected to 110 V (AC). This experiment should only be done as a teacher demonstration.

Caution: Hydrochloric and ethanoic acids are irritating and corrosive and can cause severe injury, depending on concentration. Sodium hydroxide is corrosive and can cause severe burns. (Step 3.)

Caution: Ammonia is an irritant and has a choking smell. Avoid inhalation and skin contact with this chemical. (Step 3.)

Caution: Note that your teacher will always be sure that the switch is turned off and the plug is removed from the outlet before handling the conductivity apparatus. This is done to prevent electric shock. (Steps 1–4.)

Note: Properly dispose of all materials. (Step 4.)

PROCEDURE

As this demonstration is conducted by your teacher, record your observations in Data Table 1.

1. The apparatus commonly used in determining electrical conductivity is shown in Figure 29.1. **CAUTION:** *The plug of the conductivity apparatus should be removed from the outlet, and the switch should be turned off except when making a test.*
2. Your teacher will put about 20 mL of the 5% sodium chloride solution into a 100-mL beaker. The beaker will be positioned so that the electrodes are immersed to a depth of 0.5–1.0 cm in the solution. The apparatus will then be plugged in and the switch turned on. Record your observations in Data Table 1. The apparatus will then be turned off and unplugged.

3. Your teacher will clean and dry the electrodes and repeat Step 2, testing each of the substances listed in the Materials section. For liquids, a 20-mL sample will be used; for solids, a depth of 1 cm, in a *dry* beaker, will be used.

4. Your teacher will properly dispose of the materials.

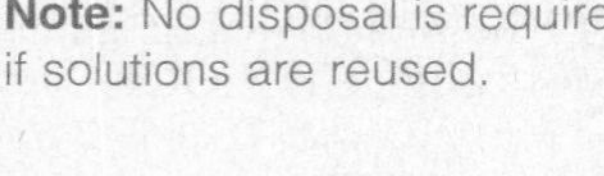

Note: No disposal is required if solutions are reused.

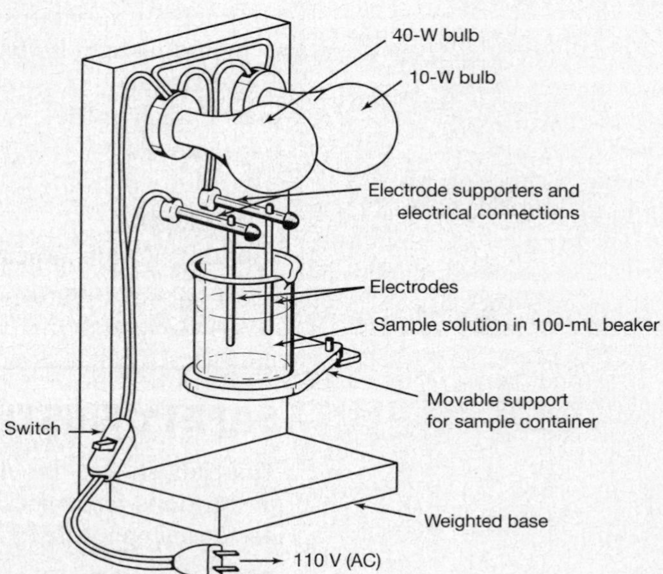

Figure 29.1

Name ______________________ Date ________________ Class ________________

OBSERVATIONS

DATA TABLE 1: CONDUCTIVITY DATA

Substance	Observation	Comments
5% NaCl solution		
distilled water		
tap water		
NaCl crystals		
5% sucrose solution		
kerosene		
1*M* HCl		
1*M* NaOH		
glacial CH_3COOH		
6*M* CH_3COOH		
6*M* NH_3		
1*M* NH_3		
ethanol, C_2H_5OH		

Name ______________________ Date ______________ Class ______________

ANALYSES AND CONCLUSIONS

1. In Data Table 1, identify each substance tested as a strong electrolyte, a weak electrolyte, or a nonelectrolyte.

$HCl(aq)$ is essentially 100% ionized in solution.

Ethanoic acid is less than 1% ionized in solution.

$CH_3COOH(aq) + H_2O \rightleftharpoons CH_3COO^-(aq) + H_3O^+(aq)$

The K_a of a solution of ethanoic acid is 1.7×10^{-5}.

An aqueous solution of ammonia is a weak base.

$NH_3 + H_2O \rightleftharpoons NH_4^+(aq) + OH^-(aq)$

The K_b is 1.8×10^{-5}.

2. For each strong or weak electrolyte, write the formulas of the ions that are present in a solution of the substance.

5% NaCl	**$Na^+ Cl^-$**
6*M* HCl	**$H_3O^+ Cl^-$**
6*M* NaOH	**$Na^+ OH^-$**
6*M* CH_3COOH	**$H_3O^+ CH_3COO^-$**
6*M* NH_3	**$NH_4^+ OH^-$**
1*M* NH_3	**$NH_4^+ OH^-$**

3. Based on the type of bonding present in hydrochloric acid, the results of the conductivity test may have been unexpected. Explain.

Hydrogen chloride, $HCl(g)$, is a polar covalent compound. It will not conduct an electric current. However, when $HCl(g)$ is dissolved in water, the following reaction occurs:

$$HCl(g) + H_2O(l) \rightarrow H_3O^+(aq) + Cl^-(aq)$$

Hydrochloric acid exists as dissociated hydronium and chloride ions. It is a strong electrolyte and a good conductor of electricity.

4. Compare the conductivity of solid sodium chloride and a 5% solution of sodium chloride. Explain any difference.

Solid NaCl is composed of Na^+ and Cl^- ions, but they are not free to move because they are fixed in the crystal lattice. Solid NaCl does not conduct an electric current. When NaCl is dissolved in water, its ions are free to move. Consequently, a 5% solution of NaCl will conduct an electric current.

Name ______________________ Date ______________ Class ______________

5. Glacial ethanoic acid is ethanoic acid that is at least 99.8% pure—that is, it contains no more than 0.2% water. Compare the conductivity of glacial ethanoic acid with that of 6*M* ethanoic acid and explain the difference.

Glacial ethanoic acid does not exist as ions. It is therefore a nonelectrolyte and does not conduct an electric current. However, 6*M* ethanoic acid is a water solution of glacial ethanoic acid. It ionizes partially in water as follows:

$$CH_3COOH + H_2O \rightarrow CH_3COO^- + H_3O^+$$

However, it does not fully dissociate in water, so it is a poor conductor of electricity. 6*M* ethanoic acid is a weak electrolyte.

6. Compare the conductivity of 6*M* ammonia and 1*M* ammonia. Explain any difference.

Ammonia, NH_3, ionizes in water as follows:

$$NH_3 + H_2O \rightarrow NH_4^+ + OH^-$$

Aqueous solutions of NH_3 contain ions and therefore will conduct an electric current. They are weak electrolytes. The 6*M* NH_3 solution contains more ions per unit volume that the 1*M* NH_3 solution and is, therefore, the better conductor of electricity.

7. What types of bonding do compounds that are electrolytes have?

Strong electrolytes have ionic bonds. Weak electrolytes are molecular compounds with covalent bonds.

GOING FURTHER

Develop a Hypothesis

Based on the results of this lab, propose a hypothesis about the electrical behavior of other molecular and ionic substances.

____

____

____

Design an Experiment

Propose an experiment to test your idea(s). If resources are available and you have your teacher's permission, perform the experiment.

____

____

Name ______________________ Date __________________ Class __________________

30 FACTORS AFFECTING SOLUTION FORMATION

Text Reference
Section 16.1

Time Required
25 minutes

Objective
- Observe the effect of particle size, degree of mixing, and temperature on the rate of dissolution.

PURPOSE

To investigate factors that influence the rate of solution formation.

BACKGROUND

When you put a spoonful of sugar into a glass of iced tea, you probably begin to stir it up immediately. Why? If your reply is that the sugar will sink to the bottom and not easily dissolve if it is not stirred, you already understand an important fact about solution formation. Stirring is one factor that determines how fast a substance will dissolve, forming a solution.

A solution consists of a *solute*, the material that is dissolved, and a *solvent*, the material that the solute is dissolved in. In this experiment, you will investigate the effects of stirring, temperature, and particle size on the rate of dissolution.

MATERIALS (PER PAIR)

Rock salt may be substituted for $CuSO_4{\cdot}5H_2O$.

safety goggles
7 large test tubes
glass-marking pencil
mortar and pestle
test-tube rack
2 100-mL beakers
50-mL graduated cylinder
gas burner
ring stand
ring support
wire gauze
spatula
thermometer
copper(II) sulfate pentahydrate, $CuSO_4{\cdot}5H_2O$ [T] [I]
weighing paper
distilled water
crushed ice
sodium chloride, NaCl
paper towels

SAFETY FIRST!

In this lab, observe all precautions, especially the ones listed below. If you see a safety icon beside a step in the Procedure, refer to the list below for its meaning.

Caution: Wear your safety goggles. (All steps.)

Caution: Do not touch hot equipment. (Step 8.)

Caution: $CuSO_4{\cdot}5H_2O$ is toxic and irritating. Avoid contact with this material. (Steps 1, 2.)

Caution: Exercise care when working with an open flame. Tie back hair and loose clothing. Do not use the burner near flammable materials. (Step 5.)

Wash your hands thoroughly with soap and water.

Name ______________________ Date ________________ Class ________________

Note: Return or dispose of all materials according to the instructions of your teacher. (Steps 4, 9.)

PROCEDURE

As you perform the experiment, record your observations in Data Tables 1 and 2.

Part A. Effects of Particle Size and Mixing

1. Label four large test tubes with the numbers 1–4. Use a spatula to put four pea-sized crystals of copper(II) sulfate pentahydrate, $CuSO_4{\bullet}5H_2O$, on a piece of weighing paper.
2. Put one crystal of $CuSO_4{\bullet}5H_2O$ into tube 1 and another crystal into tube 2. Crush a third crystal with the mortar and pestle and pour the powder into tube 3. Crush the fourth crystal and pour the powder into tube 4.

Step 3.
Students should use water from the same container for all four test tubes to be certain that each sample of water is at the same temperature.

3. Fill each of the four test tubes about one-third full of water. Place tubes 1 and 3 in the test-tube rack without shaking them. Flick tubes 2 and 4. Note how long it takes for the contents of each of the four tubes to dissolve. Record your observations in Data Table 1.

4. Follow your teacher's instructions for proper disposal of the materials. Be sure to wash your hands thoroughly after completing Part A.

Step 4.
Collect the copper sulfate solution. Use it for growing crystals or when specific concentrations are not needed.

Part B. Effect of Temperature

5. Add 50 mL of distilled water to a 100-mL beaker. Using a gas burner, heat the water until it is almost boiling. While the water is heating, proceed to Step 6.
6. Half-fill a 100-mL beaker with crushed ice and then add approximately 30 mL of distilled water to the beaker. While the water is chilling, proceed to Step 7.
7. Label three large test tubes with the numbers 1–3. Add 5 g of sodium chloride to each test tube. Place the tubes in a test-tube rack.

Step 8.
Students should use the same size of test tube for each sample and add the same amount of water.

8. Fill tube 1 one-third full with ice-cold water (see Step 6). Fill tube 2 one-third full with distilled water at room temperature. Fill tube 3 one-third full with hot water (see Step 5). **CAUTION:** *Pour the hot water from the beaker, using a paper towel "handle," as shown in Figure 30.1.* Gently flick the contents of the test tubes. Note how long it takes for the contents of each tube to dissolve. Record your observations in Data Table 2.

9. Dispose of the contents of the three test tubes by pouring them down the drain.

Use the following disposal method for chemical waste.
Disposal 2: $CuSO_4(aq)$ and $NaCl(aq)$.

Name ______________________ Date ______________ Class ______________

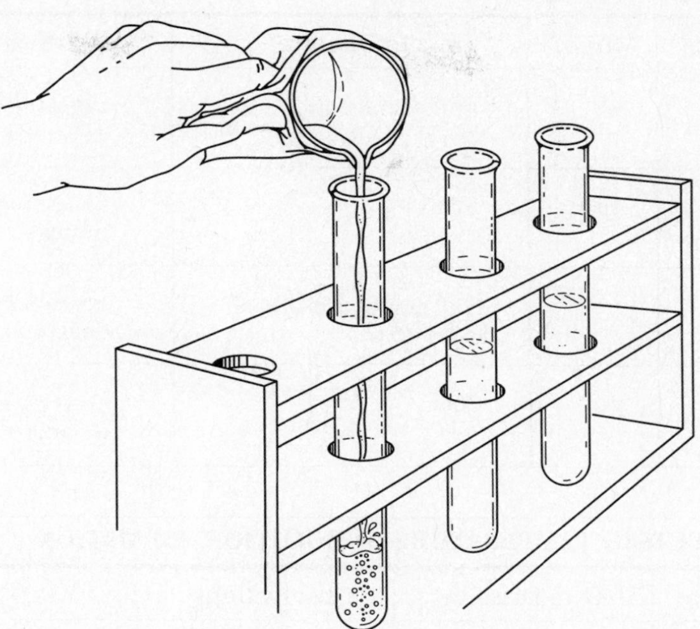

Figure 30.1

Name ______________________ Date ________________ Class ________________

OBSERVATIONS

DATA TABLE 1: EFFECTS OF PARTICLE SIZE AND MIXING ON SOLUTION FORMATION				
Tube	Particle Size	Mixed?	Time to Dissolve	Observations
1	large	no	undissolved after 60 m	deep-blue solution develops around crystal
2	large	yes	5 m	clear blue solution obtained
3	small	no	still some undissolved after 60 m	deep-blue solution develops around crystal
4	small	yes	30 s	clear blue solution obtained

DATA TABLE 2: EFFECTS OF TEMPERATURE ON SOLUTION FORMATION			
Tube	Temperature	Time to Dissolve	Observations
1	0°C	100 s	
2	23°C	22 s	
3	100°C	10 s	

ANALYSES AND CONCLUSIONS

1. What effects does particle size appear to have on the rate at which a solute dissolves? Why should particle size make a difference in the rate of dissolving?

   The process of dissolving is a surface phenomenon. A crystal of copper(II) sulfate pentahydrate, ground into powder, dissolves more readily than a whole crystal because a greater surface area of the substance is exposed to the colliding water molecules.

2. Does shaking the test tube affect the rate at which a solute dissolves? Explain your results.

   Shaking or agitating the system makes copper(II) sulfate pentahydrate dissolve more rapidly because it brings fresh solvent (water) into contact with the solute.

Name ______________ Date ______________ Class ______________

3. Using kinetic theory, explain the effect of temperature on the dissolution rate of a solute.

A crystal of copper(II) sulfate pentahydrate dissolves much more rapidly in hot water than in cold water because the water molecules at the higher temperature have a higher kinetic energy than the water molecules at the lower temperature, and their collisions with the crystal surface are more frequent and more forceful.

GOING FURTHER

Develop a Hypothesis

Based on the results of this lab, develop a hypothesis concerning the effect of temperature on the amount of solute that will dissolve in a given volume of solvent.

In general, the aqueous solubility of a compound depends on the temperature of the solvent. The solubility may increase or decrease depending on the chemical nature of the solute.

Design an Experiment

Propose an experiment to test your hypothesis. If resources are available and you have your teacher's permission, perform the experiment.

Many experimental designs are possible. One possibility is to determine the solubility of a compound at various temperatures by measuring the density. Begin with a saturated solution at high temperature. Include seed crystals in the bottom of the vessel. Measure the decrease in the density of the liquid layer as the solution is cooled.

Name ______________________ Date ______________ Class ______________

EXPERIMENT

31 SUPERSATURATION

Text Reference
Section 16.1

Time Required
20 minutes

Objectives
- Prepare a supersaturated solution of sodium sulfate.
- Observe the effect of seeding the supersaturated solution.

PURPOSE

To prepare a supersaturated solution of a salt and observe the effect of adding a small seed crystal to it.

BACKGROUND

Perhaps you've made rock candy by placing a string in a sugar solution and letting the sugar crystallize on the string. But did you know this candy-making method will work only with a particular kind of sugar solution? Under certain conditions, a solution may contain more solute than is normally contained in a saturated solution at the same temperature. This type of solution is unstable and is called *supersaturated.* The addition of a single crystal of solute often causes the excess solute to crystallize. You must use a supersaturated solution when making rock candy. The addition of a string disturbs the unstable solution and begins the crystallization.

The solubility of most substances decreases as temperature decreases. This fact sometimes leads to the formation of supersaturated solutions. As the solution cools, the excess solute may or may not crystallize out. If the excess solute remains in the solution, the solution becomes supersaturated.

In this experiment, you will make a supersaturated solution and observe the effect of adding a seed crystal to it.

MATERIALS (PER PAIR)

safety goggles
centigram balance
medium test tube
10-mL graduated cylinder
test-tube holder
gas burner
test-tube rack
100-mL beaker
sodium sulfate decahydrate, $Na_2SO_4 \cdot 10H_2O$
distilled water
ice

SAFETY FIRST!

In this lab, observe all precautions, especially the ones listed below. If you see a safety icon beside a step in the Procedure, refer to the list below for its meaning.

Caution: Wear your safety goggles. (All steps.)

Caution: Do not touch hot equipment. (Step 2.)

Name ______________________ Date ______________ Class ______________

Caution: Exercise care when working with an open flame. Tie back hair and loose clothing. Do not use burner near flammable materials. (Step 2.)

Caution: Never heat only the bottom of a test tube. Make sure to warm the bottom and sides of the tube evenly. (Step 2.)

Note: Return or dispose of all materials according to the instructions of your teacher. (Step 5.)

The heating and cooling cycle may need to be repeated several times. Crystallization will occur upon cooling if small crystals, which would serve as sites for new crystal growth, remain in the solution.

PROCEDURE

As you perform the experiment, record your observations in Data Table 1.

1. Place 5 g of $Na_2SO_4 \cdot 10H_2O$ in a clean medium-sized test tube. Add 10 mL of distilled water.
2. Hold the test tube in a test-tube holder and heat it in a burner flame, agitating the mixture gently until all of the solid has dissolved. **CAUTION:** *When heating a test tube, never point the mouth of the tube at yourself or anyone else.* Place the test tube in a test-tube rack. Add one more crystal of $Na_2SO_4 \cdot 10H_2O$ to the warmed solution and gently agitate it. Record your observations in Data Table 1.
3. Place the test tube and contents in a beaker of ice water to cool. Be careful not to disturb the test tube during the cooling process. If crystals begin to form as the tube is cooling, reheat the tube to redissolve the crystals and cool the tube again.
4. When the solution is cold, gently remove the tube from the ice water bath and put it in the test-tube rack. Add one small crystal of $Na_2SO_4 \cdot 10H_2O$. Describe what you see. Touch the bottom of the test tube to the palm of your hand. Record your observations in Data Table 1.

5. Follow your teacher's instructions for the proper disposal of the materials.

Step 3.
The solution may be allowed to air-cool for 20 minutes while the class engages in a discussion. Crystallization is less likely to occur before the seed crystal is added if the solution is cooled slowly.

Step 4.
If the solution has been cooled on ice, temperature changes will be difficult to feel.

Use the following disposal methods for chemical waste.

Disposal 1: $Na_2SO_4 \cdot 10H_2O(s)$.

Disposal 2: $Na_2SO_4(aq)$.

Name ____________________ Date ______________ Class ______________

OBSERVATIONS

DATA TABLE 1: OBSERVATIONS	
Step	Observations
2	The crystal dissolves.
4	The addition of the seed crystal caused the immediate formation of crystals. Within 20 seconds, the contents of the test tube had solidified. The crystals form in a starlike pattern.

ANALYSES AND CONCLUSIONS

1. Why is it necessary to heat the mixture in Step 2 of the Procedure?

It is necessary to heat the mixture in order to get the solute to dissolve.

2. Is the solution unsaturated, saturated, or supersaturated at the end of Step 2? Explain.

The solution is unsaturated because the added crystal dissolved.

3. Is the solution unsaturated, saturated, or supersaturated at the end of Step 3? Give evidence for your answer.

The solution is supersaturated because it contains more solute than it can theoretically hold at 0°C.

4. At the end of Step 4, when crystallization is complete, is the solution unsaturated, saturated, or supersaturated? Explain.

The solution is saturated. It contains the maximum amount of solute that can be dissolved at that temperature.

5. Describe a simple test to determine whether a solution is unsaturated, saturated, or supersaturated. Explain how to interpret the test.

Add a single small crystal and gently shake the solution. If the crystal dissolves, the solution was unsaturated. If the crystal retains its original size, the solution was saturated. If addition of the crystal causes the production of more crystals, the solution was supersaturated.

GOING FURTHER

Develop a Hypothesis

Based on the results of this lab, develop a hypothesis concerning the effect of the rate of cooling of a supersaturated solution on its stability.

Generally, a slower rate of cooling creates a more stable supersaturated solution.

Design an Experiment

Propose an experiment to test your hypothesis. If resources are available and you have your teacher's permission, perform the experiment.

Name ______________________ Date ________________ Class ________________

32 INTRODUCTION TO CHROMATOGRAPHY

Text Reference
Section 16.2

Time Required
30–40 minutes

Objective
- Observe the separation of a mixture of substances by paper chromatography.

Stress the importance of separation methods in obtaining pure substances for study. In the biological sciences, chromatography is used to effect the isolation and purification of proteins, fats, carbohydrates, and nucleic acids.

Other chromatographic techniques such as column liquid chromatography and thin-layer chromatography may be introduced if desired.

PURPOSE

To separate food coloring dyes by paper chromatography.

BACKGROUND

You've probably seen different colors mixed together to form a new color. The mixing of paint is a common example: Red and yellow paints are mixed to make orange paint. Have you ever thought of how you might separate the orange paint to get the original colors back? Separations similar to this are often performed in chemistry. Chemical separations might be performed to determine the ingredients in a pill or to measure the amount of cholesterol in a sample of fat. *Chromatography* is a commonly used method for separating substances in a mixture. The name of the method is derived from the fact that chromatography was first applied to separating colored substances. (In Greek, *chromos* means "color.") Although the effectiveness of the separation is most easily detected if the components of the mixture are colored, the method is commonly applied to separating many kinds of mixtures.

In this experiment, you will separate the various food coloring dyes by paper chromatography.

MATERIALS (PER PAIR)

safety goggles
3 capillary tubes
pencil
3 large test tubes
3 cork stoppers
3 wire paper clips
test-tube rack
10-cm ruler
plastic wash bottle
filter paper strips, 1 cm × 15 cm
yellow, blue, and green food coloring
distilled water

SAFETY FIRST!

In this lab, observe all precautions, especially the ones listed below. If you see a safety icon beside a step in the Procedure, refer to the list below for its meaning.

Caution: Wear your safety goggles. (All steps.)

Note: Return or dispose of all materials according to the instructions of your teacher. (Step 6.)

Name ______________________ Date ______________ Class ______________

PROCEDURE

As you perform the experiment, record your data in Data Table 1.

Step 1.
The dye spot should be small and uniformly circular to produce the best separation.

1. Your teacher will show you how to use a capillary tube to apply dye (food coloring) to the filter paper strips. Use a pencil to mark a small circle, the size of the printed letter *o*, about 2 cm from one end of each of three filter paper strips. The penciled circle is the point of origin. Use a capillary tube to put one drop of dye at the point of origin on one of the filter strips. Repeat this procedure for the other dyes.

Step 2.
The filter paper strip should not touch the sides of the test tube. If it does, capillary action will cause the solvent to migrate unevenly up the strip. The student may need to make attempts with several paper strips in order to acquire good technique in suspending the strips in the tube.

2. Fill each of three large test tubes with water to a depth of approximately 2 cm. Use a cork stopper to suspend each filter paper strip in a test tube, as shown in Figure 32.1. The end of the paper strip should be below the water level; the dye spot should be above the water level. Put each tube, as it is prepared, in the test-tube rack.
3. Permit the solvent in each tube to rise up the filter paper until it is about 2 cm from the top of the paper.
4. Remove the strips from the tubes. Using a pencil, mark on each strip the distance the water has traveled from the point of origin. Record these distances as D_f in the data table.

Step 5.
The values for D_f and D_s are at best inexact. Instruct students to measure these distances from the origin to the *center* of the migrating spot.

5. Measure on each paper strip the distance each dye spot has traveled. Record these distances as D_s. If the original dye spot has separated into several spots, measure and record the D_s for each spot.

6. Dispose of the water in the sink and the solids in the trash.

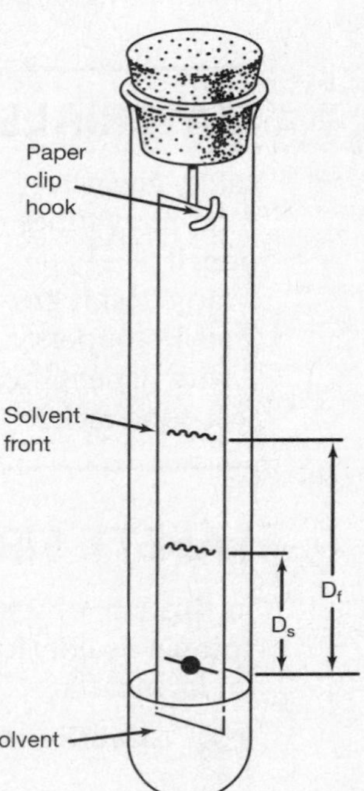

Figure 32.1

Name ______________________ Date ______________ Class ______________

OBSERVATIONS

DATA TABLE 1: PAPER CHROMATOGRAPHY OF FOOD DYES			
Dye	D_f Value (cm)	D_s Value (cm)	R_f Value (cm)
yellow	8.0	4.9	0.61
blue	9.2	7.2	0.78
green	9.0	5.5, 7.2	0.61, 0.80

ANALYSES AND CONCLUSIONS

1. Calculate the R_f value for each substance that produces a spot in your paper chromatograms. The formula for R_f follows.

$$R_f = D_s/D_f$$

D_s is the distance traveled by the solute and D_f is the distance traveled by the solvent. Record the R_f values in Data Table 1.

yellow dye: $R_f = \frac{4.9\text{ cm}}{8.0\text{ cm}} = 0.61$

blue dye: $R_f = \frac{7.2\text{ cm}}{9.2\text{ cm}} = 0.78$

green dye (two spots):

spot 1: $R_f = \frac{5.5\text{ cm}}{9.0\text{ cm}} = 0.61$

spot 2: $R_f = \frac{7.2\text{ cm}}{9.0\text{ cm}} = 0.80$

2. Do the yellow and blue dyes appear to be composed of a single colored compound? Explain your reasoning.

Each of these dyes produces only a single spot. Each dye appears to be composed of only one compound.

3. Does the green dye appear to be composed of a single colored compound? Explain.

The green dye produces yellow and blue spots. The green dye is a mixture of yellow and blue dyes. The R_f values for the yellow dye and for spot 1 from the green dye are the same (0.61). The R_f values for the blue dye and for spot 2 from the green dye are approximately the same (0.78 and 0.80).

4. Would it be a problem to use an ink pen or a marking pen instead of a pencil, as directed in Step 1 of the Procedure? Explain.

Yes. The ink from the pen would separate into its components and might produce confusing experimental results.

5. Consider the molecular interactions that might occur between the dye, the solvent, and the paper. Suggest an explanation for the different R_f values for different dyes.

The major factors contributing to different R_f values are the differences in solubility and absorption of the dye components. Components that are highly soluble in the solvent will travel farther. Components that are quickly absorbed by the paper (that is, strongly attracted to it) will not travel far.

6. Blue ink from two different pens appears to be the exact same color. Explain how to determine whether the inks are identical.

Perform chromatography on the two blue inks. If the two inks separate into the same components, then they can be considered identical.

GOING FURTHER

Develop a Hypothesis

Chromatography on paper can be done using solvents other than water. Develop a hypothesis concerning what types of mixtures would be better separated using a different solvent than water.

There are many paper chromatographic experiments that give reasonable results. For example, a 1:1 ethanoic acid–water mixture can be used to separate colored inks from several marking pens spotted at the origin. The ions in a 1:1 ethanoic acid–water mixture containing Pb^{2+}, Ag^{+}, and Hg^{2+}, may be separated by paper chromatography. The ions are made visible by first spraying the chromatogram with 0.3*M* K_2CrO_4 and then exposing it to NH_3 vapors.

Do Research

If resources are available, read articles and textbooks to collect information that may or may not support your hypothesis.

Name ______________________ Date ________________ Class ________________

33 FREEZING POINT

Text Reference
Section 16.4

Time Required
50 minutes

Objectives
- Measure the freezing point of pure benzoic acid and of a benzoic acid solution containing a solute.
- Observe the effect of a solute on the freezing point of benzoic acid.
- Describe the effect of solute concentration on the freezing point of benzoic acid.

For the materials, the molar mass, density, and melting point values are:

camphor: 152 g/mol, 0.990 g/cm^3, 176°C.

urea: 60.0 g/mol, 1.32 g/cm^3, 133°C.

potassium ethanoate: 98.1 g/mol, 1.57 g/cm^3, 292°C.

benzoic acid: 122 g/mol, 1.27 g/cm^3, 122°C.

PURPOSE

To examine the effect of a solute on the freezing behavior of a solution.

BACKGROUND

If you live in an area that has cold winters, you know that salt is often applied to the roads when it snows. The salt causes corrosion problems for the vehicles that use the salted roads, so what is the reason for its use? From Experiment 22 you know that a pure liquid freezes to a solid at a constant temperature unique to that substance. But what happens to the freezing point if a solute is dissolved in the pure liquid? Will the solution freeze at a higher or lower temperature than the pure liquid? Will the temperature remain constant throughout the freezing process?

In this experiment, you will investigate the effect of a solute on the freezing behavior of a solution. When you are done, you should understand why salt is used on roads in the winter.

MATERIALS (PER PAIR)

safety goggles
centigram balance
spatula
large test tube
ring stand and utility clamp
thermometer
copper wire stirrer
3-pronged jaw clamp
gas burner
timer with a second hand
benzoic acid, C_6H_5COOH [T] [I] [F]
one of the following solutes:
camphor, $C_{10}H_{16}O$ [F] [T] [I]
urea, $CO(NH_2)_2$ [I] [T] [C]
potassium ethanoate, CH_3COOK [I]

SAFETY FIRST!

In this lab, observe all precautions, especially the ones listed below. If you see a safety icon beside a step in the Procedure, refer to the list below for its meaning.

Caution: Wear your safety goggles. (All steps.)

Caution: Benzoic acid is an irritant and mildly toxic. (Steps 1–6.)

Caution: Avoid inhaling benzoic acid vapors. (Step 3.)

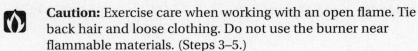

Name ______________________ Date ________________ Class ________________

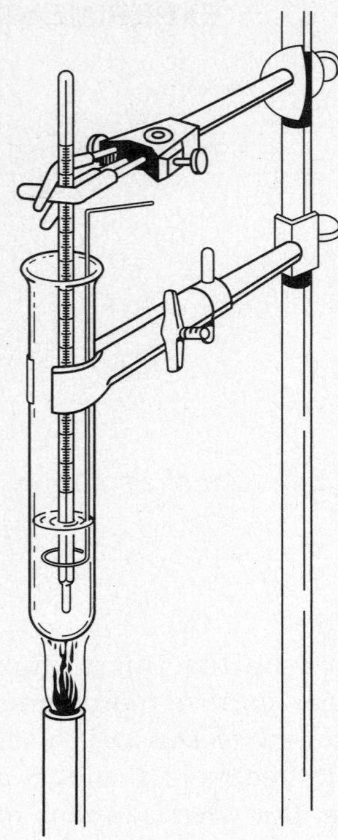

Figure 33.1

Caution: Exercise care when working with an open flame. Tie back hair and loose clothing. Do not use the burner near flammable materials. (Steps 3–5.)

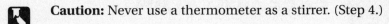

Caution: Never use a thermometer as a stirrer. (Step 4.)

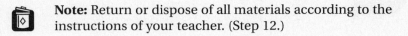

Note: Return or dispose of all materials according to the instructions of your teacher. (Step 12.)

PROCEDURE

As you perform the experiment, record your observations in Data Table 1.

Part A. The Freezing Point of Pure Benzoic Acid

1. Measure 10.0 grams of benzoic acid, to the nearest 0.1 g. Place the benzoic acid in a large, clean, dry test tube.
2. Secure the test tube in a utility clamp attached to a ring stand. Place the stirrer around the thermometer. With a three-pronged clamp, clamp the thermometer above the test tube so it rests on the solid benzoic acid.

3. **CAUTION:** *Do not heat the benzoic acid above 140°C. Above 140°C, benzoic acid gives off toxic fumes.* Gently heat the benzoic acid to melting, using the gas burner.

4. Lower the thermometer into the molten benzoic acid so that the bulb is immersed and the stirrer surrounds the thermometer, as shown in Figure 33.1. Secure the thermometer clamp.
5. Stir the molten benzoic acid. When the temperature of the benzoic acid reaches 140°C, discontinue heating and turn off the gas burner.
6. As the benzoic acid cools, take temperature readings every 30 seconds for the first 3 minutes and then every minute. Record all temperatures to the nearest 0.5°C. Stir for as long as possible, but do not force the stirrer. Collect data until the temperature drops to about 100°C.

Part B. The Freezing Point with 0.0050 Mole of Solute

The masses of 0.0050 mol of solutes:

camphor: 0.76 g

urea: 0.30 g

potassium ethanoate: 0.49 g

7. Calculate the mass of 0.0050 mole of the solute assigned to you by your teacher. Record its name in the data table. Measure out this calculated mass to the nearest 0.01 g and record the measurement.
8. Transfer the solute to the test tube of benzoic acid used in Part A. Carefully reheat the mixture, stirring constantly as it melts and the solute dissolves. Heat the mixture to about 140°C.

Name ______________________ Date ________________ Class ________________

9. Turn off the burner and repeat Step 6 for this mixture.

Part C. The Freezing Point with 0.010 Mole of Solute

10. Using the mixture from Part B, repeat Step 7 (add another 0.0050 mole of the same solute). The solution now contains 0.010 moles of solute.

Use the following disposal method for chemical waste.

Disposal 4b: C_6H_5COOH, $C_{10}H_{16}O$, $CO(NH_2)_2$, CH_3COOK

11. Remelt the mixture and heat it to 140°C. When all of the solute has dissolved, turn off the burner and repeat Step 6.

12. Follow your teacher's instructions for the proper disposal of the materials.

Name ______________________ Date ______________ Class ______________

OBSERVATIONS

DATA TABLE 1: COOLING OF BENZOIC ACID AND BENZOIC ACID PLUS SOLUTE					
		Temperature (°C) of Benzoic Acid Plus 0.0050 mol Solute		Temperature (°C) of Benzoic Acid Plus 0.010 mol Solute	
Time (m)	Temperature (°C) of Benzoic acid	0.30 g Urea	0.76 g Camphor	0.98 g Potassium Ethanoate	1.52 g Camphor
0	140.0	136.0	143.0	135.0	141.0
0.5	133.0	131.0	137.0	127.0	133.0
1	127.0	125.0	130.5	122.0	129.5
1.5	123.0	120.5	126.0	117.0	123.5
2	122.0	119.0	120.0	115.5	117.5
2.5	122.0	118.5	118.0	115.5	114.5
3	121.5	118.0	117.5	115.0	113.5
4	121.5	118.0	117.0	115.0	113.0
5	121.0	117.5	117.0	114.5	112.5
6	121.0	117.0	116.5	114.0	112.0
7	120.5	116.0	115.5	112.0	111.0
8	119.5	114.5	114.5	109.0	109.5
9	117.5	113.0	113.0	105.0	106.0
10	111.0	108.5	109.0	100.0	101.5
11	100.5	102.0	101.0	—	—

ANALYSES AND CONCLUSIONS

1. Plot a graph of temperature (°C) versus time (minutes) for all three freezing-point determinations. Plot and label all three curves on the same graph, connecting the points for each determination in a smooth curve. If your graph shows a dip similar to the one in Figure 33.2, it is likely that your solution supercooled. The true freezing point of the solution can be found by disregarding the dip and extrapolating from the highest point of the horizontal portion of the graph to the vertical axis.

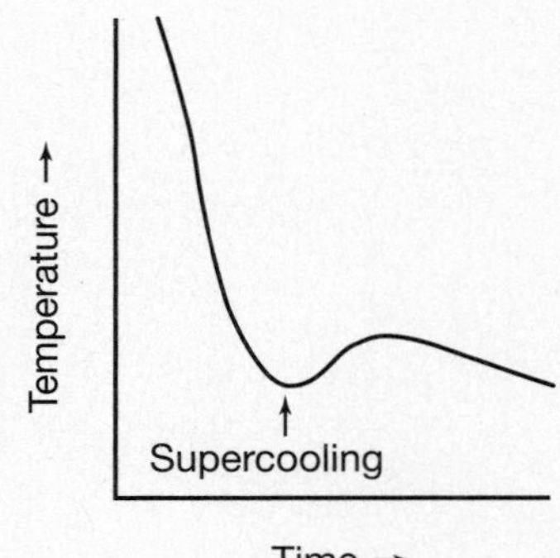

Figure 33.2

Name ______________________ Date ________________ Class ________________

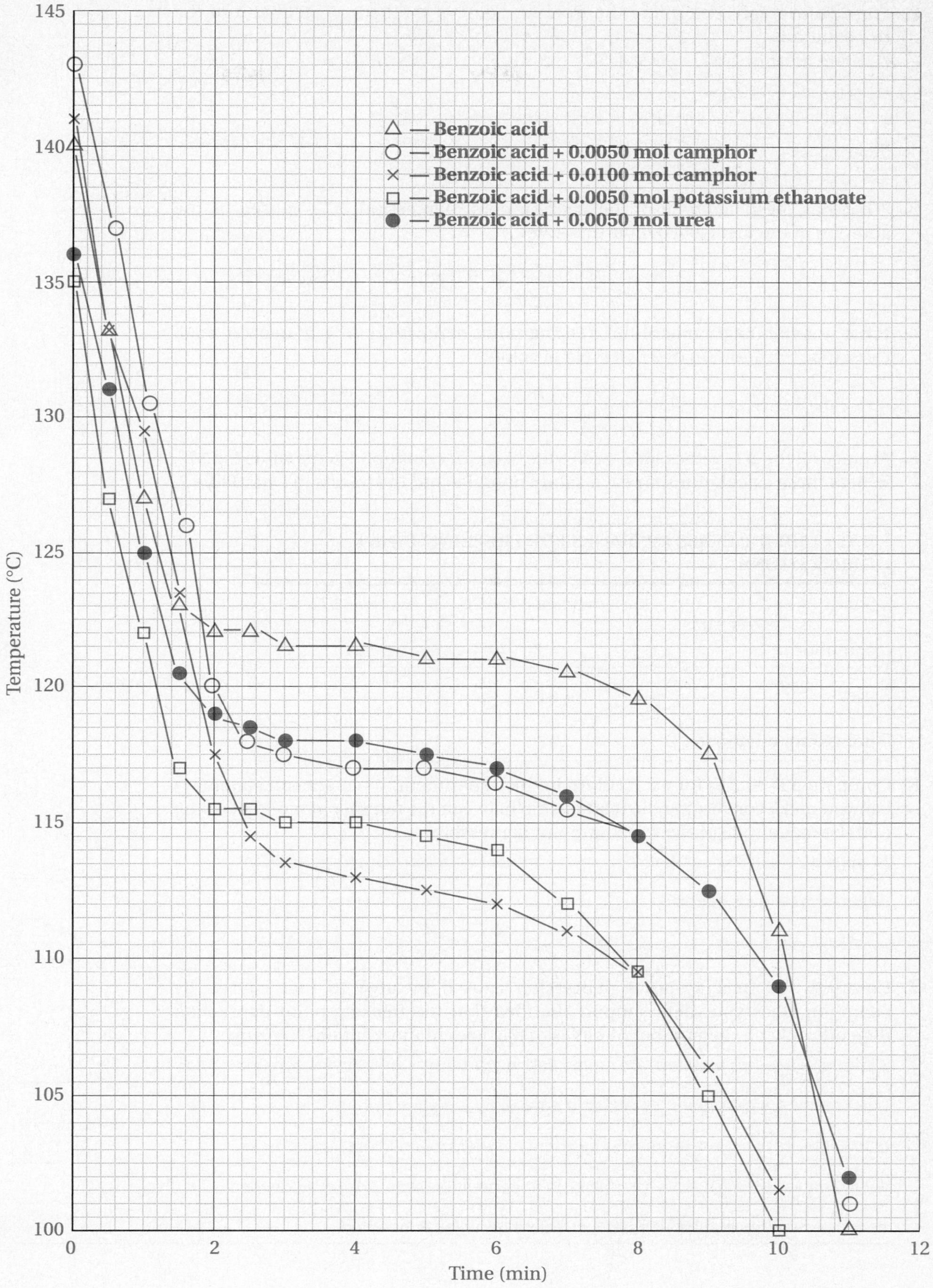

△ — Benzoic acid
○ — Benzoic acid + 0.0050 mol camphor
× — Benzoic acid + 0.0100 mol camphor
□ — Benzoic acid + 0.0050 mol potassium ethanoate
● — Benzoic acid + 0.0050 mol urea

Temperature (°C): 100, 105, 110, 115, 120, 125, 130, 135, 140, 145

Time (min): 0, 2, 4, 6, 8, 10, 12

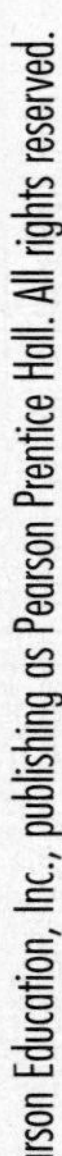

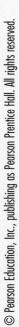

Name ________________ Date ________________ Class ________________

2. From your graph, determine the freezing point of the benzoic acid and of the two solutions.

Freezing point of pure benzoic acid 122.0°C

Freezing point of a solution containing
0.76 g (0.0050 mol) of camphor in 10.00 g benzoic acid 118.0°C

Freezing point of solution containing
1.52 g (0.010 mol) of camphor in 10.00 g benzoic acid 114.5°C

3. What was the magnitude of the freezing-point depression, ΔT_1, caused by the addition of the first 0.0050 mole of solute?

$$\Delta T_1 = \text{freezing point}_{\text{benzoic acid}} - \text{freezing point}_{\text{solution 1}}$$

$$122.0°\text{C} - 118.0°\text{C} = 4.0°\text{C}$$

4. What was the magnitude of the freezing-point depression, ΔT_2, of benzoic acid, caused by the addition of 0.010 mole of solute?

$$\Delta T_1 = \text{freezing point}_{\text{benzoic acid}} - \text{freezing point}_{\text{solution 2}}$$

$$122.0°\text{C} - 114.5°\text{C} = 7.5°\text{C}$$

5. Average all the ΔT_1 values obtained in the class for camphor. Do the same for ΔT_2. Repeat these calculations for each solute used. Record the results in Data Table 2.

DATA TABLE 2: CLASS AVERAGES FOR FREEZING-POINT DEPRESSIONS

Solute	Average ΔT_1(°C)	Average ΔT_2(°C)
camphor	4.0	8.5
urea	3.5	—
potassium ethanoate	6.5	—

6. Compare ΔT_1 to ΔT_2 for each solute in this experiment. What general statement can you make concerning the relationship between the number of moles of solute and the magnitude of the freezing-point depression?

In general, when the number of moles of solute is doubled, the freezing-point depression is also doubled.

7. Compare the freezing-point depression caused by urea to that caused by camphor. Does your data support the idea that the freezing-point depression depends only on the number of moles of particles in the solution? Explain.

Although camphor and urea are molecular compounds with very different molecular masses, the freezing-point depression caused by camphor and urea are very similar. 0.0050 mol of camphor produces the same number of particles in solution as 0.0050 mol of urea. Thus, the freezing-point depression would seem to depend upon the number, and not the type, of solute particles in solution.

8. The freezing-point depression of potassium ethanoate is greater than that of the other two solutes when an equal number of moles of each is used. Explain.

Potassium ethanoate is an ionic compound that dissolves to yield two ions, K^+ and CH_3COO^-, in solution. This means that 0.0050 mol of potassium ethanoate yields 0.010 mol of particles in solution. Thus, for a given number of moles, potassium ethanoate should produce twice the freezing-point depression as the same number of moles of either camphor or urea, which are both molecular solids. (The experimental results shown here indicate a 70% increase rather than the predicted 100% increase in freezing-point depression for potassium ethanoate relative to the other two solutes. This is due to the fact that, in benzoic acid, some of the potassium ethanoate remains "ion-paired" and behaves as single particles.)

9. The freezing point of benzoic acid remains relatively constant throughout the freezing process. Is the same true for the freezing point of a solution? Explain any difference.

The freezing point of a solution does not remain constant during the solidification process. (The graph verifies this.) As a solution freezes, its composition constantly changes. The solution as a whole does not freeze all at once; the component that is the least soluble at the lower temperature freezes first.

GOING FURTHER

Develop a Hypothesis

Based on the results of this lab, develop a hypothesis concerning how the *boiling* point of a solution compares to that of the pure solvent.

____

____

Design an Experiment

Propose an experiment to test your hypothesis. If resources are available and you have your teacher's permission, perform the experiment.

____

____

THE SPECIFIC HEAT OF A METAL

Text Reference
Sections 17.1 and 17.2

Time Required
40 minutes

Objectives
- Measure the specific heat of lead.
- Identify an unknown metal from its specific heat (optional).

PURPOSE

To determine the specific heat of a substance.

BACKGROUND

On a sunny day, the water in a swimming pool may warm up a degree or two while the concrete around the pool may become too hot to walk on in your bare feet. This may seem strange because both the concrete and the water are being heated by the same source—the sun. This evidence suggests it takes more heat to raise the temperature of some substances than others. This, in fact, is true: The amount of heat that is required to raise the temperature of 1 g of a substance by 1°C is the called the *specific heat capacity,* or simply the *specific heat,* of that substance. Water, for example, has a specific heat of 1.0 cal/(g°C). This value is high in comparison with the specific heats for other materials, such as concrete. In this experiment, you will use a simple calorimeter and your knowledge of the specific heat of water to determine the specific heat of lead.

Advance Preparation
Unknown metal samples
Use 1-cm diameter rods of aluminum, brass, copper, zinc, and stainless steel. Saw them into lengths between 2 cm and 5 cm.

Students may wish to cut some cardboard lids for their cups. There should be holes in the lids to accommodate the stirring rods and thermometers.

MATERIALS (PER PAIR)

safety goggles
400-mL beaker
ring stand
ring support
wire gauze
gas burner
50-mL beaker
centigram balance
large test tube
utility clamp
100-mL graduated cylinder
plastic-foam cup
250-mL beaker
thermometer
glass stirring rod
lead shot, Pb [T]
distilled water
unknown metal [T]

SAFETY FIRST!

In this lab, observe all precautions, especially the ones listed below. If you see a safety icon beside a step in the Procedure, refer to the list below for its meaning.

Caution: Wear your safety goggles. (All steps.)

Caution: Lead is a toxic metal. Wash your hands thoroughly after use. (Step 2.)

Caution: Do not touch hot equipment. (Steps 1, 3, 6.)

Caution: If you should break a thermometer, immediately report the incident to your teacher. Never use a thermometer as a stirrer. (Step 6.)

Note: Return or dispose of all materials according to the instructions of your teacher. (Step 7.)

PROCEDURE

As you perform the experiment, record your data in Data Table 1.

1. Heat 250 mL of water in a 400-mL beaker until it is boiling gently.

2. While the water is heating, determine and record the mass of a clean, dry 50-mL beaker to the nearest 0.01 g. Add between 80 g and 120 g of lead shot to the beaker. Measure the combined mass of the beaker and lead to the nearest 0.01 g and record the measurement.

3. Transfer the lead shot to a large, dry test tube. Use the utility clamp to suspend the test tube in the boiling water, as shown in Figure 34.1. The lead shot should be below the level of the water in the beaker. Leave the test tube in the boiling water bath for at least 10 minutes.

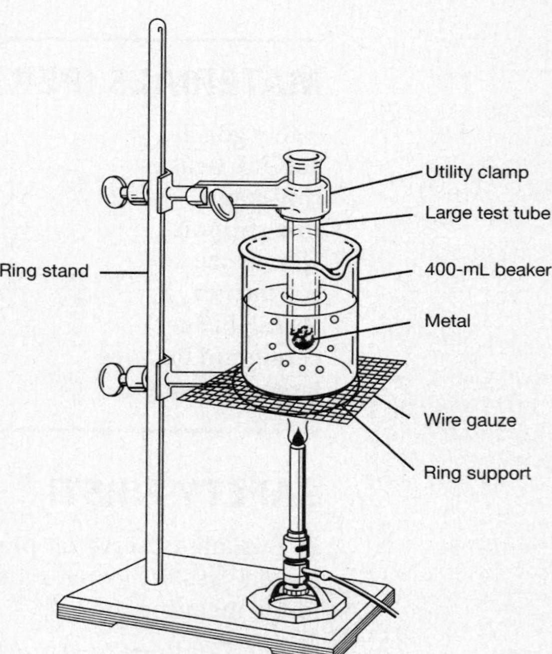

Figure 34.1

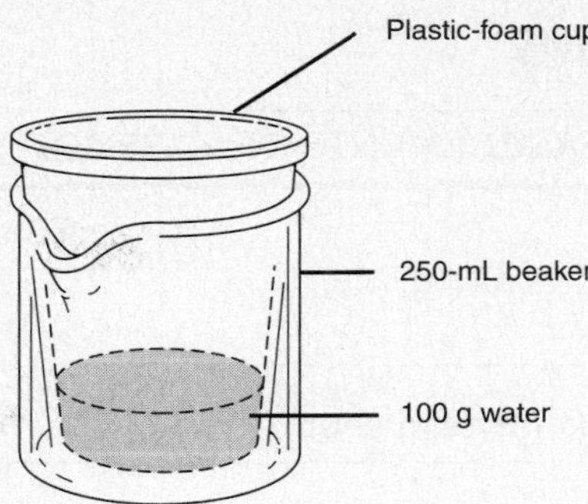

Figure 34.2

4. While the lead shot is heating, measure 100 mL of distilled water in a graduated cylinder. Pour the water into a plastic-foam cup and place the cup in a 250-mL beaker for support, as shown in Figure 34.2.

5. Measure and record the temperature of the water in the plastic-foam cup and of the water in the boiling bath.

6. Remove the test tube from the boiling water and quickly pour the lead shot into the water-filled, plastic-foam cup. Place a thermometer and a glass stirring rod into the cup. Use the stirring rod to gently stir the lead shot. *Do not stir the lead shot with the thermometer.* Note the temperature frequently and record the maximum temperature reached.

Step 7.
The lead shot can be towel-dried initially and then air-dried between classes.

7. Pour the water off and return the lead shot to your teacher.

8. (Optional) Follow the same procedure to determine the specific heat of an unknown metal.

Name ______________________ Date ______________ Class ______________

OBSERVATIONS

DATA TABLE 1: MEASUREMENTS OF MASS AND TEMPERATURE		
	Trial 1	Trial 2
mass of 50-mL beaker	32.14 g	32.16 g
mass of 50-mL beaker + lead shot	142.76 g	138.24 g
mass of lead shot	110.62 g	106.08 g
initial temperature of water in cup	23.00°C	23.20°C
initial temperature of lead shot (temperature of boiling water)	99.02°C	99.24°C
maximum temperature of lead + water	25.54°C	25.47°C
mass of water	100 g	100 g

ANALYSES AND CONCLUSIONS

1. Determine the changes in temperature of the water (ΔT_{water}) and of the lead shot (ΔT_{lead}) for each trial.

trial 1 $\Delta T_{water} = 25.54°C - 23.00°C = 2.54°C$

$\Delta T_{lead} = 25.54°C - 99.02°C = -73.48°C$

trial 2 $\Delta T_{water} = 25.47°C - 23.20°C = 2.27°C$

$\Delta T_{lead} = 25.47°C - 99.24°C = -73.77°C$

2. Calculate the heat gained by the water in each trial.

trial 1

$$q_{water} = m_{water} \times c_{water} \times \Delta T_{water} = 100\text{ g} \times 1.00\text{ cal/(g°C)} \times 2.54°C = 254\text{ cal}$$

trial 2

$$q_{water} = m_{water} \times c_{water} \times \Delta T_{water} = 100\text{ g} \times 1.00\text{ cal/(g°C)} \times 2.27°C = 227\text{ cal}$$

Name ______________________ Date ______________ Class ______________

3. Remembering that the heat gained by the water is equal to, but has the opposite sign of, the heat lost by the lead, calculate the specific heat of lead for each trial.

trial 1

$$q_{lead} = -q_{water} = m_{lead} \times c_{lead} \times \Delta T_{lead}$$

$$c_{lead} = \frac{-q_{water}}{m_{lead} \times \Delta T_{lead}} \times \frac{254 \text{ cal}}{110.62 \text{ g} \times (-73.48°\text{C})}$$

$$= 0.0312 \text{ cal/(g°C)}$$

trial 2

$$q_{lead} = -q_{water} = m_{lead} \times c_{lead} \times \Delta T_{lead}$$

$$c_{lead} = \frac{-q_{water}}{m_{lead} \times \Delta T_{lead}} \times \frac{227 \text{ cal}}{106.08 \text{ g} \times (-73.77°\text{C})}$$

$$= 0.0290 \text{ cal/(g°C)}$$

4. Calculate the average value for the specific heat of lead in your experiment.

$$\text{average} = \frac{\text{trial 1 value} + \text{trial 2 value}}{2}$$

$$= \frac{0.0312 + 0.0290}{2}$$

$$= 0.0301 \text{ cal/(g°C)}$$

5. If you tested an unknown, repeat these calculations to determine the specific heat of the unknown metal.

6. Calculate the percent error in the specific heat value that you determined experimentally. Use the accepted value given by your teacher.

$$\text{percent error} = \frac{|\text{experimental value} - \text{accepted value}|}{\text{accepted value}} \times 100\%$$

The accepted value for the specific heat of lead is 0.0306 cal/(g°C).

$$\text{percent error} = \frac{|0.0301 \text{ cal/(g°C)} - 0.0306 \text{ cal/(g°C)}|}{0.0306 \text{ cal/(g°C)}} \times 100\%$$

$$= \frac{0.0005 \text{ cal/(g°C)}}{0.0306 \text{ cal/(g°C)}} \times 100\%$$

$$= 1.63\%$$

$$= 2\% \text{ (one significant figure)}$$

Name ______________ Date ______________ Class ______________

7. You assumed that the initial temperature of the lead shot was the same as that of the boiling water. If the lead shot was actually at a lower temperature than the water, how would your value for the specific heat be affected?

The value calculated for the specific heat of lead would be low.

8. Identify other possible sources of error in this experiment.

Errors could be introduced in taking the temperatures and in measuring the mass of the lead shot.

9. Compare your value for the specific heat of lead to the values obtained by your classmates. Can specific heat be used to identify substances? Explain.

Yes. It is a value that is constant for the same substance under different conditions, and that varies for the different substances under identical conditions.

GOING FURTHER

Develop a Hypothesis

Based on the results of this lab, develop a hypothesis about how the measured specific heat of lead would differ if the hot lead was added to water in vessels made of different materials.

Design an Experiment

Propose an experiment to test your hypothesis. If resources are available and you have your teacher's permission, perform the experiment.

Name ______________________ Date ________________ Class ________________

35 HEATS OF REACTION

Text Reference
Sections 17.2 and 17.4

Time Required
50 minutes

Objectives
- Measure the heat changes for three different exothermic reactions carried out at constant pressure.
- Demonstrate that heats of reaction are additive.

Three related exothermic reactions will be carried out and the heats of reaction determined. Two of the reactions add up algebraically to give the third. Students will verify that the heats of reaction are likewise additive. This is an example of Hess's law.

(1) $\Delta H = 10.6$ kcal/mol
(2) $\Delta H = -23.9$ kcal/mol
(3) $\Delta H = -13.3$ kcal/mol

Advance Preparation

0.5M hydrochloric acid
Pour 84 mL of concentrated HCl into 1800 mL of distilled water and dilute to 2 L.

1.0M hydrochloric acid
Pour 84 mL of concentrated HCl into 900 mL of distilled water and dilute to 1 L.

1.0M sodium hydroxide
Dissolve 40.0 g of NaOH in 900 mL of distilled water and dilute to 1 L. Add the NaOH slowly while stirring.

Review the safety procedures and caution the students about the corrosive nature of the chemicals before they begin to work.

PURPOSE

To measure the heats of reaction for three related exothermic reactions and to verify Hess's law of heat summation.

BACKGROUND

Energy changes occur in all chemical reactions; energy is either absorbed or released. If energy is released in the form of heat, the reaction is called *exothermic*. If energy is absorbed, the reaction is called *endothermic*. In this experiment, you will measure the amounts of heat released in these three related exothermic reactions:

(1) $NaOH(s) \rightarrow Na^+(aq) + OH^-(aq) + x_1$ kcal

(2) $NaOH(s) + H^+(aq) + Cl^-(aq) \rightarrow H_2O + Na^+(aq) + Cl^-(aq) + x_2$ kcal

(3) $Na^+(aq) + OH^-(aq) + H^+(aq) + Cl^-(aq) \rightarrow H_2O + Na^+(aq) + Cl^-(aq) + x_3$ kcal

After determining the heats of reaction, you will analyze your data and verify the additive nature of heats of reaction.

MATERIALS (PER PAIR)

safety goggles and apron
plastic-foam cup
100-mL graduated cylinder
400-mL beaker
thermometer
50-mL beaker
centigram balance
spatula
wire stirrer
distilled water
sodium hydroxide pellets, NaOH [C] [T]
0.5M hydrochloric acid, HCl [T] [I]
1.0M hydrochloric acid, HCl [T] [I]
1.0M sodium hydroxide, NaOH [C] [T]

SAFETY FIRST!

In this lab, observe all precautions, especially the ones listed below. If you see a safety icon beside a step in the Procedure, refer to the list below for its meaning.

Caution: Wear your safety goggles. (All steps.)

Caution: 0.5M and 1.0M hydrochloric acid are eye and skin irritants. (Steps 4, 7.)

Name ______________________ Date ________________ Class ________________

NaOH readily absorbs moisture from the air. Such a substance is said to be hygroscopic. In fact, NaOH is so hygroscopic that it can absorb enough water from moist air to completely dissolve in the absorbed water. If this happens, the NaOH will look just like water on the laboratory bench. Such very hygroscopic substances are said to be *deliquescent*.

Caution: Sodium hydroxide is a very corrosive material that can cause severe skin burns and permanent eye damage. Under no circumstances, handle solid sodium hydroxide with your fingers. Sodium hydroxide pellets absorb water from the air and can eventually be mistaken for a puddle of water. Never leave the sodium hydroxide container uncovered; never leave pellets on the balance or on the laboratory bench. (Steps 2, 5, 7.)

Caution: If you should break a thermometer, immediately report the incident to your teacher. Never use a thermometer as a stirrer. (Steps 3, 8.)

Note: Return or dispose of all materials according to the instructions of your teacher. (Steps 3, 6, 9.)

PROCEDURE

As you perform the experiment, record your data in Data Table 1.

Procedure note: After each reaction, dispose of the solution as directed by your teacher and rinse the cup and thermometer with water.

Reaction 1

1. Measure 100 mL of distilled water into a plastic-foam cup. Place the cup inside a 400-mL beaker for support. This assembly, together with a thermometer, will serve as your calorimeter.

2. Measure and record the mass of a 50-mL beaker to the nearest 0.01 g. **CAUTION:** *NaOH is extremely corrosive.* Using a spatula, add as close to 2.00 g as possible of sodium hydroxide pellets to the beaker. Measure and record the combined mass of the beaker and sodium hydroxide to the nearest 0.01 g. (Do this operation as quickly as possible to avoid error due to absorption of water by the NaOH.)

3. Measure and record the temperature of the water in the foam cup to the nearest 0.5°C. Add the NaOH pellets to the water in the calorimeter. Stir the mixture gently with a wire stirrer until all the solid has dissolved. **CAUTION:** *Hold the thermometer with your hand at all times.* Record the highest temperature reached during the reaction.

Reaction 2

4. **CAUTION:** *Low-concentration hydrochloric acid can irritate your skin.* Measure 100 mL of 0.5*M* HCl into the plastic-foam cup and place the cup inside a 400-mL beaker.

5. Using a spatula, measure out 2.00 g of solid NaOH pellets. **CAUTION:** *NaOH is extremely corrosive.*

Name ____________ Date ____________ Class ____________

6. Measure and record the temperature of the HCl solution in the foam cup. Add the NaOH pellets to the acid solution and stir *gently* until the solid is dissolved. Measure and record the highest temperature reached by the solution during the reaction.

Reaction 3

7. Place the plastic-foam cup inside a 400-mL beaker. Measure 50 mL of 1.0*M* HCl into the cup. Rinse the graduated cylinder and fill with 50 mL of 1.0*M* NaOH.

8. Measure and record the temperature of the HCl solution (in the cup) and the NaOH solution (in the cylinder) to the nearest 0.5°C. Rinse the thermometer between measurements.

9. Pour the NaOH solution into the foam cup. Stirring the mixture gently, measure and record the highest temperature reached.

Step 9.
Advise students to make certain that the solutions are stirred sufficiently to ensure complete mixing. Warn them that it is easy to poke a hole in the cup with the thermometer, resulting in lost data and a chemical spill.

Use the following disposal method for chemical waste.
Disposal 3: All solutions in reactions 1, 2, and 3.

Name ______________________ Date ________________ Class ______________

OBSERVATIONS

DATA TABLE 1: EXPERIMENTAL DATA				
Parameter	Reaction 1	Reaction 2	Parameter	Reaction 3
mass (beaker)	0.41 g	0.44 g	initial temperature (HCl solution)	21.5°C
mass (beaker + NaOH)	2.41 g	2.44 g	initial temperature (NaOH solution)	22.5°C
mass (NaOH)	2.00 g	2.00 g	average initial temperature	22.0°C
initial temperature	22.0°C	22.5°C	final temperature	28.0°C
final temperature	27.0°C	34.5°C		

ANALYSES AND CONCLUSIONS

1. Determine the change in temperature, ΔT, for each reaction. Record your results in Data Table 2.

2. Calculate the mass of the reaction mixture in each reaction. (To do this, first determine the total volume of the solution. Then calculate the mass of the solution, based on the assumption that the density of the solution is the same as that of pure water, 1.0 g/mL.) Record your results in Data Table 2.

   reaction 1 100 g (H_2O) + 2.00 g (NaOH) = 102 g sol.
   reaction 2 100 g (HCl) + 2.00 g (NaOH) = 102 g sol.
   reaction 3 50 g (HCl) + 50 g (NaOH) = 100 g sol.

3. Calculate the total heat released in each reaction, assuming that the specific heat of the solution is the same as that of pure water, 1.0 cal/(g°C). Remember:

$$\text{heat of reaction} = \text{mass} \times \text{specific heat} \times \Delta T$$

   Record your results in Data Table 2.

   reaction 1 $\text{heat} = 102\text{ g} \times 1.0 \frac{\text{cal}}{(\text{g°C})} \times 5.0\text{°C} = 5.1 \times 10^2\text{ cal}$

   reaction 2 $\text{heat} = 102\text{ g} \times 1.0 \frac{\text{cal}}{(\text{g°C})} \times 12.0\text{°C} = 1.2 \times 10^3\text{ cal}$

   reaction 3 $\text{heat} = 100\text{ g} \times 1.0 \frac{\text{cal}}{(\text{g°C})} \times 6.0\text{°C} = 6.0 \times 10^2\text{ cal}$

Name ______________________ Date ______________ Class ______________

4. Calculate the number of moles of NaOH used in reactions 1 and 2, and record the results in Data Table 2.

$$\text{number of moles (NaOH)} = \frac{\text{mass (NaOH)}}{\text{molar mass (NaOH)}} = \frac{2.00\ \text{g}}{40.0\ \text{g/mol}} = 0.0500\ \text{mol}$$

5. In reaction 3, the number of moles of NaOH can be calculated from the concentration of the solution (1.0*M*, or 1.0 mole of NaOH per liter of solution) and the volume used. The calculation is shown below.

$$50.0\ \text{mL NaOH} \times \frac{1\ \text{mol NaOH}}{1000\ \text{mL NaOH}} = 0.050\ \text{mol NaOH}$$

Enter this result in Data Table 2.

6. Calculate the energy released per mole of NaOH for each reaction and enter your results in Data Table 2.

reaction 1 $\frac{5.1 \times 10^2\ \text{cal}}{0.0500\ \text{mol}} = 1.0 \times 10^4\ \text{cal/mol NaOH}$

$= 10\ \text{kcal/mol NaOH}$

reaction 2 $\frac{1.22 \times 10^3\ \text{cal}}{0.0500\ \text{mol}} = 2.4 \times 10^4\ \text{cal/mol NaOH}$

$= 24\ \text{kcal/mol NaOH}$

reaction 3 $\frac{6.0 \times 10^2\ \text{cal}}{0.0500\ \text{mol}} = 1.2 \times 10^4\ \text{cal/mol NaOH}$

$= 12\ \text{kcal/mol NaOH}$

DATA TABLE 2: RESULTS OF CALCULATIONS

Reaction Number	Mass of Reaction Mixture	ΔT	Total Heat Released	mol NaOH Consumed	Heat Released per mol NaOH
1	102 g	5.0°C	5.1×10^2 cal	0.0500 mol	1.0×10^4 cal or 10 kcal
2	102 g	12.0°C	1.2×10^3 cal	0.0500 mol	2.4×10^4 cal or 24 kcal
3	100 g	6.0°C	6.0×10^2 cal	0.0500 mol	1.2×10^4 cal or 12 kcal

7. Show that the equations for reactions 1 and 3, which are given in the Background section, add up to give the equation for reaction 2. Include the energy released per mole of NaOH in each equation.

$$NaOH(s) \rightarrow Na^+(aq) + OH^-(aq) \quad + 10\ \text{kcal}$$

$$Na^+(aq) + OH^-(aq) + H^+(aq) + Cl^-(aq) \rightarrow H_2O + Na^+(aq) + Cl^-(aq) + 12\ \text{kcal}$$

$$NaOH(s) + H^+(aq) + Cl^-(aq) \rightarrow H_2O + Na^+(aq) + Cl^-(aq) + 22\ \text{kcal}$$

8. Examine all the class data. Does the sum of the energy released per mole of NaOH for reactions 1 and 3 equal the energy released per mole of NaOH in reaction 2? What factors might account for any difference?

The experimental results are close.

Possible reasons for the discrepancy include the following:

1. loss of heat from the calorimeter

2. use of incorrect masses due to the assumptions made concerning the densities of the solutions

3. inability to obtain an accurate measurement of the mass of NaOH(s)

4. inaccuracy of volume measurements made with a graduated cylinder

5. the heat capacity of the solutions is not equal to 1.0 cal/(g°C)

9. Calculate the percent difference between the heat given off in reaction 2 and the sum of the heats given off in reactions 1 and 3. Assume that the heat given off in reaction 2 is correct.

$$\text{percent difference (in evolved heat)} = \frac{|(\text{heat}_1 + \text{heat}_3) - \text{heat}_2|}{\text{heat}_2} \times 100\%$$

$$\text{percent difference} = \frac{|(10\text{ kcal} + 12\text{ kcal}) - 24\text{ kcal}|}{24\text{ kcal}} \times 100\%$$

$$= \frac{|-2\text{ kcal}|}{24\text{ kcal}} \times 100\%$$

$$= \frac{2}{24} \times 100\%$$

$$= 0.08 \times 100\%$$

$$= 8\%$$

10. Would changing the amount of NaOH used in reaction 1 affect the value obtained for the energy given off per mole of NaOH? Explain.

An increase in the mass of NaOH dissolved in water would increase the amount of heat energy evolved. It would not change the amount of heat energy evolved per mole of NaOH.

11. State in your own words what is meant by the additive nature of heats of reaction.

If the equations for two chemical reactions can be algebraically added together to form the equation for a third chemical reaction, then the heat of reaction for the third reaction is the sum for the heats of reaction for the first two equations.

Name ______________ Date ______________ Class ______________

12. Taking into account your answer to problem 4, explain why you were asked to use exactly 2.00 g of NaOH in reactions 1 and 2, and an equivalent number of moles of NaOH in reaction 3.

For the heats of reactions to be additive, the same number of moles of reactant must be used in each reaction.

GOING FURTHER

Develop a Hypothesis

Suppose nitric acid (HNO_3) was substituted for HCl in reactions 2 and 3. Propose a hypothesis about how the heat change for reaction 2 would be affected.

Nitric acid and hydrochloric acid are both strong acids. Each is completely dissociated in solution. Because the anion of the acid is a spectator ion in this reaction, no change is expected.

Design an Experiment

Propose an experiment to test your hypothesis. If resources are available and you have your teacher's permission, perform the experiment.

Experimental design should be identical to the one used in this experiment.

Name ______________________ Date ________________ Class ________________

36 FACTORS AFFECTING REACTION RATES

Text reference
Section 18.1

Time required
50 minutes

Objectives

- Observe the effects of temperature, concentration, particle size, surface area, and catalysts on the rates of chemical reactions.
- Explain these effects in terms of collision theory.

Advance Preparation

0.1M calcium chloride
1.1 g $CaCl_2$/100 mL water

0.1M iron(III) chloride
2.7 g $FeCl_3 \cdot 6H_2O$/100 mL water

0.1M iron(III) nitrate
4.0 g $Fe(NO_3)_3 \cdot 9H_2O$/100 mL water

0.1M manganese(II) chloride
1.3 g $MnCl_2$/100 mL water

0.1M potassium nitrate
1.0 g KNO_3/100 mL water

0.1M sodium chloride
0.6 g NaCl/100 mL water

6M hydrochloric acid, HCl
Pour 500 mL conc. HCl slowly, stirring, into 400 mL distilled water; dilute to 1 L.

3M hydrochloric acid, HCl
Add 50 mL 6*M* HCl to 40 mL water; dilute to 100 mL.

1M hydrochloric acid, HCl
Add 17 mL of 6*M* HCl to 90 mL water; dilute to 100 mL.

0.1M hydrochloric acid, HCl
Add 1.7 mL 6*M* HCl to 90 mL water; dilute to 100 mL.

PURPOSE

To investigate the factors that can speed up or slow down chemical reactions.

BACKGROUND

You may have noticed that chemical reactions occur at different speeds. The explosion of fireworks is instantaneous; the rusting of an iron gate is relatively slow. In most situations, you would like to make the rusting of iron proceed as slowly as possible. On the other hand, a chemical company might want to speed up the reactions that produce the chemicals they sell. In order to understand how the rates of chemical reactions can be controlled, it is necessary to understand the factors that influence the rates of chemical reaction.

In this experiment, you will study the effect that temperature, reactant concentration, particle size, catalysts, and surface area have on chemical reaction rates.

MATERIALS (PER PAIR)

safety goggles
gloves (optional)
10-mL graduated cylinder
16 medium test tubes
2 250-mL beakers
ring stand
ring support
wire gauze
thermometer
gas burner
test-tube rack
watch or timer
aluminum foil
crucible tongs
100-mL graduated cylinder
250-mL plastic bottle
tape, for label
dropper pipet
metal cutter
centigram balance
paper towels
6*M* hydrochloric acid, HCl [C] [T]
ice
zinc strips, Zn, 0.25 mm × 0.50 cm × 2.00 cm
steel wool
wood splints
matches
distilled water
3% hydrogen peroxide, H_2O_2
0.1*M* iron(III) chloride, $FeCl_3$ [T] [I] [C]
0.1*M* sodium chloride, NaCl
0.1*M* iron(III) nitrate, $Fe(NO_3)_3$ [T]
0.1*M* calcium chloride, $CaCl_2$ [T]
0.1*M* potassium nitrate, KNO_3
0.1*M* manganese chloride, $MnCl_2$ [T]
0.1*M* hydrochloric acid, HCl [T] [I]
1*M* hydrochloric acid, HCl [T] [I]
3*M* hydrochloric acid, HCl [C] [T]
powdered zinc, Zn [F] [T]

Name ______________________ Date ______________ Class ______________

3% hydrogen peroxide
Use household peroxide or add 20 mL 30% H_2O_2 to 170 mL water and dilute to 200 mL. This solution should be prepared fresh, preferably from an unopened bottle. Try the experiment ahead of time. The degree to which the peroxide is diluted may need to be reduced in order to yield a reasonable rate of O_2 production in the reaction with $FeCl_3$.

zinc strips and powder
Cut a zinc sheet, 0.25 mm thick, into 0.50 cm × 2.00 cm strips. The strips can be cleaned with steel wool. Clean the powdered zinc by washing with 3M HCl, rinsing with distilled water, and drying. Otherwise, the powdered Zn may not react at all in Part D.

SAFETY FIRST!

In this lab, observe all precautions, especially the ones listed below. If you see a safety icon beside a step in the Procedure, refer to the list below for its meaning.

 **Caution:** Wear your safety goggles. (All steps.)

 **Caution:** Concentrated hydrochloric acid is highly corrosive and can cause severe burns. (Steps 1, 6, 7.)

 **Caution:** Powdered zinc is flammable; keep it away from open flames. (Step 10.)

 **Caution:** Iron(III) chloride is an irritant. (Step 6.)

 **Note:** Return or dispose of all materials according to the instructions of your teacher. (Step 12.)

PROCEDURE

As you perform the experiment, record your data and observations in Data Tables 1, 2, 3, and 4.

Part A. Effect of Temperature on Reaction Rate

The reaction of zinc metal with hydrochloric acid will be examined.

1. Pour 5.0 mL of 6*M* hydrochloric acid into each of three clean test tubes. Place one of the tubes in an ice water bath (ice-water mixture in 250-mL beaker). Place another in a hot water bath maintained at 50°C. (Heat the water in a 250-mL beaker over a gas burner.) Place the third tube in a test-tube rack at room temperature. Allow about 10 minutes for the tubes to reach the temperature of their surroundings.
2. Clean a zinc strip with steel wool. Cut three small pieces of zinc to the same size. Each piece should be approximately 0.5 cm × 2.0 cm. Save the remainder of the strip for Step 8.
3. Note the time in Data Table 1. Then drop one piece of zinc into each of the three test tubes containing hydrochloric acid. Cover each tube loosely with a piece of aluminum foil and wait for 2 minutes. Test for the identity of the gas produced by using tongs to hold a burning splint near the mouth of each of the tubes. Note the time at which each reaction ceases.

Step 3.
The Zn strip reacts with HCl more rapidly at higher temperatures.

Part B. Effect of a Catalyst on Reaction Rate

The decomposition of hydrogen peroxide will be studied.

4. Measure 90 mL of distilled water into a clean 250-mL plastic bottle and add 10 mL of 3% hydrogen peroxide solution. Label the mixture as 0.3% hydrogen peroxide. This will be your test solution.

Name ____________________ Date ______________ Class ______________

5. Rinse seven clean test tubes and a 10-mL graduated cylinder with the 0.3% hydrogen peroxide. Discard the rinses. Measure 5 mL of 0.3% hydrogen peroxide into each of the seven test tubes. Place the test tubes in a rack.

6. Add 5 drops of each of the following solutions to separate test tubes of the hydrogen peroxide: 6*M* hydrochloric acid, 0.1*M* iron(III) chloride, 0.1*M* sodium chloride, 0.1*M* iron(III) nitrate, 0.1*M* calcium chloride, 0.1*M* potassium nitrate, and 0.1*M* manganese chloride. Flick each tube to mix its contents. Observe each solution and report the rate of gas production from each. Use the terms *fast, slow, very slow,* or *none* to describe the rate of gas production. Describe the catalytic activity as *high, low,* or *none.* Record your observations in Data Table 2.

Part C. Effect of Concentration on Reaction Rate, at Constant Temperature

The reactions of zinc metal with hydrochloric acid solutions of varying concentrations will be examined.

7. Pour 5 mL of each of the following hydrochloric acid solutions into separate clean test tubes: 0.1*M*, 1*M*, 3*M*, and 6*M*.

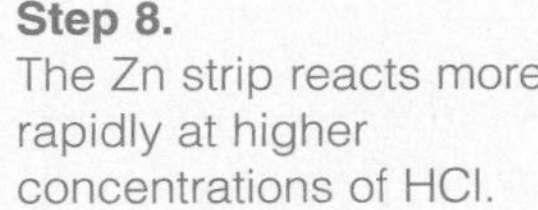

Step 8.
The Zn strip reacts more rapidly at higher concentrations of HCl.

8. Cut four small pieces (1 cm × 1 cm) from the zinc strip you cleaned in Part A. (Save the remainder of the zinc strip for use in Part D.) Drop one piece of zinc into each of the acid solutions. Record the start time and the end time of each reaction. Record your observations in Data Table 3.

Part D. Effect of Particle Size or Surface Area on Reaction Rate

The reaction of zinc metal with hydrochloric acid will be used to study the effect of particle size and surface area on the rate of reaction.

9. Cut a piece of zinc (0.5 cm × 2.0 cm) from a clean strip of the metal. Determine the mass of the piece of zinc to the nearest 0.01 g. Place the piece of zinc in a clean, dry test tube.

10. Measure an equal quantity of powdered zinc into a second clean, dry test tube.

11. Place both test tubes in a rack; then add 5 mL of 1*M* hydrochloric acid to each. Observe the reactions for several minutes and record your observations in Data Table 4.

12. Follow your teacher's instructions for proper disposal of the materials.

Use the following disposal methods for chemical waste.

Disposal 1: Zn(*s*) in Parts A, C, and D.

Disposal 2: All catalysts in Part B, except HCl(*aq*).

Disposal 3: The reaction solutions in Parts A, C, and D, and the HCl(*aq*) in Part B.

Name ______________________ Date ________________ Class ________________

OBSERVATIONS

DATA TABLE 1: EFFECT OF TEMPERATURE ON REACTION RATE

Reaction Condition	Time Reaction Started	Time Reaction Ended	Reaction Duration	Burning Splint Test Result
ice water 0°C			315 s	positive, H_2 (faint)
room temp.			28 s	positive, H_2
hot water 50°C			18 s	positive, H_2

DATA TABLE 2: EFFECT OF CATALYSTS ON REACTION RATE

Test	HCl 6*M*	$FeCl_3$ 0.1*M*	NaCl 0.1*M*	$Fe(NO_3)_3$ 0.1*M*	$CaCl_2$ 0.1*M*	KNO_3 0.1*M*	$MnCl_2$ 0.1*M*
oxygen production	none	fast	none	fast	none	none	none
catalytic activity	none	high	none	high	none	none	none

DATA TABLE 3: EFFECT OF CONCENTRATION ON REACTION RATE

Reaction Condition	Time Reaction Started	Time Reaction Ended	Reaction Duration	Observations
0.1*M* HCl			more than 50 min	scarcely reacted, a few bubbles of H_2
1*M* HCl			more than 30 min	reaction about half completed, steady production of H_2
3*M* HCl			95 s	fast reaction, zinc dissolves, fast production of H_2
6*M* HCl			25 s	very fast reaction, zinc dissolves rapidly, very fast production of H_2

DATA TABLE 4: EFFECT OF PARTICLE SIZE OR SURFACE AREA ON REACTION RATE

Substance Tested	Observations
sheet zinc	slow reaction, some production of H_2, not much heat
powdered zinc	very rapid reaction, zinc dissolves, production of H_2, solution becomes hot

Name ______________________ Date __________________ Class __________________

ANALYSES AND CONCLUSIONS

1. Write a balanced chemical equation for the reaction between hydrochloric acid and zinc metal.

$$Zn(s) + 2HCl(aq) \rightarrow ZnCl_2(aq) + H_2(g)$$

2. Write a balanced chemical equation for the decomposition of hydrogen peroxide.

$$2H_2O_2(aq) \rightarrow 2H_2O(l) + O_2(g)$$

3. Which ionic compounds used in Part B were effective catalysts?

$FeCl_3$ and $Fe(NO_3)_3$ are effective catalysts. The HCl solution contains Cl^- ions and the KNO_3 solution contains NO_3^- ions. Neither HCl nor KNO_3 are catalysts. Therefore, the catalyst is the Fe(III) ion. (You may wish to have students add a very small pinch of MgO_2 to a tube of diluted H_2O_2 (0.3%). MnO_2 is a powerful catalyst of the peroxide decomposition.)

4. Examine the data in Data Table 2 and identify the ion responsible for the catalytic activity.

Fe^{3+}

5. Many reaction rates approximately double for every 10°C increase in temperature. Are the results you obtained in Part A consistent with this general statement?

Certainly the reaction rate increases with temperature. The "10° rule" seems to hold.

6. How does the surface area of a substance change as it is broken into smaller pieces?

The surface area increases.

7. Describe in your own words the effect of temperature on the rate of a reaction. Explain this effect in terms of the collision theory of reactions.

Rates of chemical reactions increase as temperature increases. More colliding molecules have sufficient energy to overcome the activation energy barrier at high temperatures.

8. Describe in your own words the effect of concentration on the rate of a reaction. Explain this effect in terms of the collision theory of reactions.

Rates of chemical reactions increase as the concentrations of the reactants are increased. Any increase in the concentration of reacting particles makes more collisions possible.

Name ______________________ Date ______________ Class ______________

9. Describe in your own words the effect of particle size or surface area on the rate of a reaction. Explain this effect in terms of the collision theory of reactions.

The smaller the particle size of a substance, the more surface area is exposed to another reactant. The effect on rate is the same as increasing the concentration.

10. Describe in your own words the effect of a catalyst on the rate of a reaction. Explain this effect in terms of the collision theory of reactions.

A catalyst lowers the magnitude of the activation energy barrier. With a lower barrier, more collisions are energetic enough to create products. The reaction rate increases.

GOING FURTHER

Develop a Hypothesis

Based on the results of this lab, develop a hypothesis concerning the effect of changing the temperature on the rate of production of gas from an Alka-Seltzer tablet dropped in water.

Design an Experiment

Propose an experiment to test your hypothesis. If resources are available and you have your teacher's permission, perform the experiment.

Drop equal masses of Alka-Seltzer tablets into beakers of water at significantly different temperatures; use ice water, room-temperature water, and water that is almost boiling.

Name ______________________ Date ________________ Class ________________

37 THE CLOCK REACTION

Text Reference
Section 18.1

Time Required
50 minutes

Objectives

- Measure the time required to produce a specific amount of product in a chemical reaction.
- Explain how concentration of reactants affects the rate of the reaction.
- Make a graph of the results of these rate studies.

Advance Preparation

1% starch solution
Add a small amount of water to 1 g of soluble starch to form a thin paste. Add the paste, stirring, to 100 mL of boiling water.

0.20M potassium iodide
33.2 g KI/L water

0.0050M sodium thiosulfate
Dissolve 0.80 g anhydrous $Na_2S_2O_3$ or 1.24 g $Na_2S_2O_3 \cdot 5H_2O$ in 500 mL of water and dilute to 1 L.

0.10M ammonium peroxydisulfate
22.8 g $(NH_4)_2S_2O_8$/L water.

Caution: Solid ammonium peroxydisulfate remains stable for months when pure and dry. However, it decomposes in the presence of moisture with the production of O_2 and the production of NH_4HSO_4. Ammonium peroxydisulfate is a strong oxidizing agent and has been known to detonate from heat or friction. The following precautions should be taken when using ammonium peroxydisulfate:

PURPOSE

To determine how the concentration of reactants affects reaction rates.

BACKGROUND

Suppose you work in a chemical plant that produces a valuable compound. The compound is produced at specific conditions, but now your company has asked you to increase the speed of the reaction. Can you change the conditions to make the reaction faster? In order to speed up the reaction, you must know something about the factors that influence reaction rates. To test the influence of these factors on the rate of your reaction, you must be able to find out how long it takes to produce a certain amount of the product, or how long it takes to use up a certain amount of one of the reactants.

The time it takes for a reaction to go to completion is easy to measure if a color change signals when one of the reactants is used up. This kind of reaction is called a *clock reaction*. To tell how long a clock reaction takes, all you need to do is time the reaction from the moment the reactants are mixed to the moment that the color appears.

In this experiment, you will conduct a quantitative study of the effect of concentration on the rate of a clock reaction.

MATERIALS (PER PAIR)

safety goggles
3 35-mL graduated cylinders
safety labels
100-mL beaker
dropper pipet
stirring rod
stopwatch
thermometer
plastic wash bottle

solution A: 0.20*M* potassium iodide, KI [T]
solution B: 0.0050*M* sodium thiosulfate, $Na_2S_2O_3$
solution C: 0.10*M* ammonium peroxydisulfate, $(NH_4)_2S_2O_8$ [I]
soluble starch
distilled water

SAFETY FIRST!

In this lab, observe all precautions, especially the ones listed below. If you see a safety icon beside a step in the Procedure, refer to the list below for its meaning.

Caution: Wear your safety goggles. (All steps.)

(a) Order the minimum amount required for the experiment and discard all the remainder at the end of the experiment.

(b) Keep solid ammonium peroxydisulfate dry, in a cool place, and away from organic material. The risk associated with ammonium peroxydisulfate exists primarily when it is in its most concentrated form (the solid). The risk to students once the solution has been prepared is minimal.

(c) Open the ammonium peroxydisulfate container (should be a glass jar with a plastic lid) gently; it should not be necessary to apply any undue force to loosen the lid. If the lid should prove hard to remove, do not use the ammonium peroxydisulfate. Contact a local expert in hazardous chemical waste disposal.

(d) Before disposing of small amounts of the solid, chemically reduce it with a concentrated solution of sodium thiosulfate, $Na_2S_2O_3$.

Caution: If you should break a thermometer, immediately report the incident to your teacher. Never use a thermometer as a stirrer. (Step 2.)

Note: Return or dispose of all materials according to the instructions of your teacher. (Step 3.)

PROCEDURE

As you perform the experiment, record your data and observations in Data Table 2.

Procedure Note: Seven mixtures of solutions A, B, and C will be used in this experiment. The compositions of the mixtures are given in Data Table 1. Mixture 1 has the maximum concentration of each reactant. In mixtures 2, 3, and 4, solution A is diluted to vary the concentration of the iodide ion. In mixtures 5, 6, and 7, solution C is diluted to vary the concentration of the peroxydisulfate ion. All the solutions should be at room temperature.

1. Label three clean, dry graduated cylinders with the letters A, B, and C. Pour the solutions given for mixture 1 into these cylinders. Measure all volumes to the nearest 0.5 mL.

2. Pour the 10.0 mL of solution B into a clean 100-mL beaker. Add 5 drops of starch solution, using a dropper pipet. One person should be ready to signal the other person when to pour solutions A and C into the beaker. At the signal, the other person should pour the solutions into the beaker and stir the mixture occasionally until a blue color appears. Note the exact time that the solutions were poured together and the exact time that blue appears. Record in Data Table 2 the temperature of the solution and the time required, in seconds, for blue to appear.

DATA TABLE 1: PROPORTIONS FOR MIXTURES

Mixture	Solution A (I^-)	Solution B ($S_2O_3^{2-}$)	Solution C ($S_2O_8^{2-}$)
1	20.0 mL	10.0 mL	20.0 mL
2	15.0 mL + 5.0 mL water	10.0 mL	20.0 mL
3	10.0 mL + 10.0 mL water	10.0 mL	20.0 mL
4	5.0 mL + 15.0 mL water	10.0 mL	20.0 mL
5	20.0 mL	10.0 mL	15.0 mL + 5.0 mL water
6	20.0 mL	10.0 mL	10.0 mL + 10.0 mL water
7	20.0 mL	10.0 mL	5.0 mL + 15.0 mL water

Name ______________________ Date ________________ Class ________________

Step 1.
With most 10-mL and 25-mL graduated cylinders, volumes can only be measured, at best, to the nearest 0.5 mL. For greater accuracy, graduated pipets or burets could be used.

Step 2.
With each of the mixtures used in this experiment, the blue color appears when 2.5×10^{-5} moles of I_2 have been produced.

Step 3.
As a guide, the reaction times for duplicate determinations should agree within ±2%. For example, a reaction time of 300 s should produce results in the range of 294 s to 306 s.

Caution students to wash the beaker, stirring rod, and thermometer thoroughly with distilled water before preparing each new mixture.

Use the following disposal method for chemical waste.

Disposal 2: All solutions used in this experiment.

3. Discard the solution as directed by your teacher. Wash the beaker and rinse it well with distilled water. Shake it as dry as possible. Repeat the reaction with mixture 1 until you can obtain two approximately equal reaction times (trial 1, trial 2).
4. Repeat the experiment, using any mixture assigned by your teacher. Try to predict the outcome of each trial before you do it.

Name ______________ Date ______________ Class ______________

OBSERVATIONS

DATA TABLE 2: REACTION TIMES				
Mixture	Temperature (°C)	Time for Color to Appear (s) Trial 1	Trial 2	Average Time of Reaction (s)
1	24	400	390	395
2	24	515	525	520
3	24	715	695	705
4	24	1625	1565	1595
5	24	485	505	495
6	24	755	775	765
7	24	2410	2330	2370

ANALYSES AND CONCLUSIONS

Class Data on the Effect of Concentration

1. Use class data to complete Data Table 2. If more than one trial was done for a mixture, compute the average of the reaction times.
2. Calculate the number of moles of iodide ion and peroxydisulfate ion in each of the seven mixtures studied. Enter these results in Data Table 3.

DATA TABLE 3: CALCULATIONS				
Mixture	mol I^-	Initial Concentration I^- (mol/L)	Mol $S_2O_8^{2-}$	Initial Concentration $S_2O_8^{2-}$ (mol/L)
1	4.0×10^{-3}	8.0×10^{-2}	2.0×10^{-3}	4.0×10^{-2}
2	3.0×10^{-3}	6.0×10^{-2}	2.0×10^{-3}	4.0×10^{-2}
3	2.0×10^{-3}	4.0×10^{-2}	2.0×10^{-3}	4.0×10^{-2}
4	1.0×10^{-3}	2.0×10^{-2}	2.0×10^{-3}	4.0×10^{-2}
5	4.0×10^{-3}	8.0×10^{-2}	1.5×10^{-3}	3.0×10^{-2}
6	4.0×10^{-3}	8.0×10^{-2}	1.0×10^{-3}	2.0×10^{-2}
7	4.0×10^{-3}	8.0×10^{-2}	0.50×10^{-3}	1.0×10^{-2}

3. For each of the mixtures used, the total volume was 50.0 mL. Using this volume and the number of moles calculated in problem 2, determine the initial concentration of iodide and peroxydisulfate ions in each reaction mixture. Enter these initial concentrations in Data Table 3.

4. Plot a graph of iodide ion concentration versus reaction time. Use the data and calculated concentrations for mixtures 1, 2, 3, and 4. Connect the plotted points with a smooth curve.

5. On the same graph that you made for problem 4, plot a curve representing the concentration of peroxydisulfate versus time. Use the data and calculated concentration for mixtures 1, 5, 6, and 7.

6. Describe the relationship between reaction concentration and reaction rate.

   As the concentration of either the I^- or $S_2O_8^{2-}$ ion decreases, the time taken for the reaction to reach completion increases—that is, the reaction rate decreases.

GOING FURTHER

Develop a Hypothesis

Based on the results of this lab, develop a hypothesis about how the concentration of thiosulfate ions will affect the rate of this reaction.

When the concentration of $S_2O_3^{2-}$ is doubled, the time required for the blue color to appear is also doubled.

Design an Experiment

Propose an experiment to test your hypothesis. If resources are available and you have your teacher's permission, perform the experiment.

Name ______________________ Date ________________ Class ________________

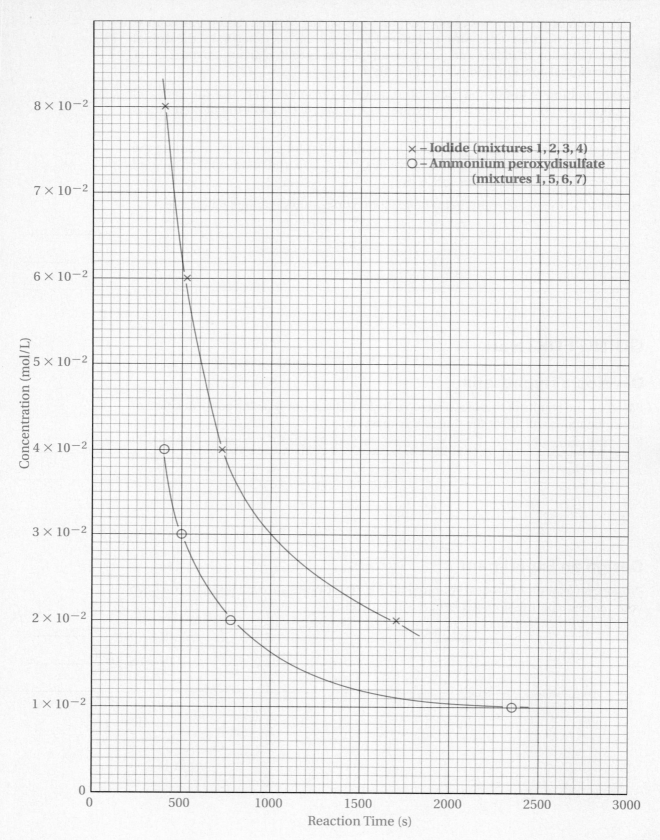

× – Iodide (mixtures 1, 2, 3, 4)
○ – Ammonium peroxydisulfate (mixtures 1, 5, 6, 7)

Concentration (mol/L)

8×10^{-2}
7×10^{-2}
6×10^{-2}
5×10^{-2}
4×10^{-2}
3×10^{-2}
2×10^{-2}
1×10^{-2}
0

0 500 1000 1500 2000 2500 3000

Reaction Time (s)

38 DISTURBING EQUILIBRIUM

Text Reference
Section 18.2

Time Required
30 minutes

Objectives
- Observe the effect of a change in conditions on a system at equilibrium.
- Explain the effects observed by applying Le Châtelier's principle.

Advance Preparation
0.1M iron(III) chloride
2.7 g $FeCl_3 \bullet 6H_2O$/100 mL water
Saturated potassium nitrate
The solubility of KNO_3 is 40 g per 100 mL water.
0.1M potassium thiocyanate
1.0 g KSCN/100 mL water

PURPOSE

To determine how equilibrium systems respond to stresses.

BACKGROUND

Imagine you are starting a terrarium. You add dirt, plants, and water, then seal the container. Some of the water in the terrarium will vaporize. Soon the air in the terrarium will hold as much water as possible. At this point, some of the vapor will begin to condense. Eventually, as much water is condensing as is vaporizing; the liquid water and its vapor are in *equilibrium*. What happens to the equilibrium if the conditions change? A change of conditions in the system is called a stress. For example, if the terrarium gets colder (undergoes a stress), some of the water vapor will condense. In response to the stress, a new equilibrium will be established. The new equilibrium will have less water vapor and more liquid water than the old equilibrium.

Are there any rules to help predict what happens when a stress is applied to physical and chemical systems in equilibrium? Yes, Le Châtelier's principle applies to systems in equilibrium. It states that, if a stress is placed on a system at equilibrium, the system will change in a way that relieves the stress.

In this experiment, you will impose stresses on physical and chemical systems at equilibrium to see how the systems change in response to the stresses.

MATERIALS (PER PAIR)

safety goggles
dropper pipet
5 medium test tubes
spatula
250-mL beaker
test-tube rack
50-mL graduated cylinder
50-mL graduated cylinder
100-mL beaker
glass-marking pencil
white card, 3 in. × 5 in.
saturated potassium nitrate solution, KNO_3 [T]
potassium chloride crystals, KCl
ice
distilled water
0.1*M* potassium thiocyanate, KSCN [T]
potassium nitrate crystals, KNO_3 [T]
0.1*M* iron(III) chloride, $FeCl_3$ [I] [T]

Name ______________________ Date ______________ Class ______________

Figure 38.1

SAFETY FIRST!

In this lab, observe all precautions, especially the ones listed below. If you see a safety icon beside a step in the Procedure, refer to the list below for its meaning.

 **Caution:** Wear your safety goggles. (All steps.)

 **Caution:** Aqueous iron(III) chloride is an irritant. Avoid skin contact with this chemical. (Steps 4, 6.)

 **Note:** Return or dispose of all materials according to the instructions of your teacher. (Step 7.)

PROCEDURE

As you perform the experiment, record your observations in Data Table 1.

Part A. Effect of Temperature on a Physical Equilibrium

1. Add 2–3 mL of saturated potassium nitrate solution to a clean test tube. Using a spatula, add one crystal of potassium nitrate to the solution to act as a seed crystal.
2. Cool the test tube in a 250-mL beaker of ice water for 10 minutes. Record the results.
3. Remove the tube from the ice water and place it in the test-tube rack. Record what happens as the solution warms to room temperature.

Step 2.
$KNO_3(aq) \rightarrow KNO_3(s)$ + heat

Part B. Common Ion Effect on a Chemical Equilibrium

4. Use a graduated cylinder to add 50 mL of distilled water to a 100-mL beaker. Add 1 mL of 0.1*M* iron(III) chloride and 1 mL of 0.1*M* potassium thiocyanate to the water; stir. The color that appears is due to the presence of ferrothiocyanate ions, $FeSCN^{2+}$. Your teacher will write on the board the reaction that is observed. Record your observations.
5. Label four identical clean, dry test tubes with the numbers 1–4. Pour 5 mL of the mixture from Step 4 into each. Hold the tubes over a white background and look down into them, as shown in Figure 38.1. The solutions should appear equally dark.

6. Tube 1 is the control in this experiment. To tube 2, add 20 drops of 0.1*M* iron(III) chloride. To tube 3, add 20 drops of 0.1*M* potassium thiocyanate. Flick each tube to mix the solutions. To tube 4, add 1 g of potassium chloride crystals. Flick the tube to dissolve the crystals. Compare the colors of the solutions in tubes 2, 3, and 4 with the color of the solution in the control tube (tube 1). Record your observations.

7. Discard the solutions as directed by your teacher.

Step 4.
$Fe^{3+}(aq)$ + $SCN^-(aq)$ → $FeSCN^{2+}(aq)$
pale yellow, colorless, red

Step 6.
tube 2 [adding $FeCl_3$]:
$SCN^- + Fe^{3+} \rightarrow FeSCN^{2+}$

tube 3 [adding KSCN]:
$Fe^{3+} + SCN^- \rightarrow FeSCN^{2+}$

tube 4 [adding KCl]:
No effect; the K^+ and Cl^- ions do not affect the equilibrium.

Use the following disposal methods for chemical waste.

Disposal 1: $KNO_3(s)$.

Disposal 2: All solutions in Part B.

Name ______________________ Date ________________ Class ________________

OBSERVATIONS

DATA TABLE 1: OBSERVATIONS	
System	Observations
KNO_3 (saturated) (cooled)	Before cooling, there is a single KNO_3 crystal at the bottom of a colorless solution. After cooling in an ice bath, many more crystals of KNO_3 are deposited.
KNO_3 (saturated) (warmed)	As the cooled solution slowly returns to room temperature, the crystals redissolve. (A crystal the size of the seed crystal should remain undissolved.)
Fe^{3+}/SCN^- reaction	When the pale yellow solution of $FeCl_3$ and the colorless solution of KSCN were mixed, the resulting solution was blood red. (Note: This was also the color in tube 1.)
Fe^{3+}/SCN^- mixture + additional Fe^{3+}	Tube 2: The addition of more Fe^{3+} to the Fe^{3+} and SCN^- mixture caused the color to change to a darker red.
Fe^{3+}/SCN^- mixture + additional SCN^-	Tube 3: The addition of more SCN^- to the Fe^{3+} and SCN^- mixture caused the color to change to a darker red.
Fe^{3+}/SCN^- mixture + $KCl(s)$	Tube 4: The addition of solid KCl produced no apparent effect. The color of the solution did not change.

ANALYSES AND CONCLUSIONS

1. Write a balanced equation for the equilibrium that exists before the saturated potassium nitrate was cooled.

$$KNO_3(s) \underset{}{\overset{H_2O}{\rightleftharpoons}} KNO_3(aq)$$

2. Did lowering the temperature (Step 2) affect the equilibrium? Explain your answer.

Yes. As the solution was cooled, crystals of KNO_3 were deposited. The equilibrium shifted to the left.

3. Did increasing the temperature (Step 3) disturb the equilibrium? What evidence do you have for your answer?

Yes. As the solution was warmed, KNO_3 crystals dissolved. The equilibrium shifted to the right.

Name ______________ Date ______________ Class ______________

4. Explain what happened in the potassium nitrate system in terms of Le Châtelier's principle.

When KNO_3 dissolves in water, heat is absorbed—the solution becomes colder. $KNO_3(s) + H_2O + heat \rightleftharpoons KNO_3(aq)$. If the solution is cooled (that is, heat is lost from the system), the reaction moves in the direction to produce heat. The equilibrium, therefore, is shifted to the left, and more KNO_3 comes out of solution.

5. Write a balanced equation for the equilibrium that existed after the ferric and thiocyanate ions were combined in the beaker.

$$\underset{\text{(pale yellow)}}{Fe^{3+}} + \underset{\text{(colorless)}}{SCN^-} \rightleftharpoons \underset{\text{(blood red)}}{FeSCN^{2+}}$$

6. What evidence was there that the equilibrium shifted when iron(III) chloride was added? In which direction did it shift?

The color of the solution changed from blood red to a deeper red, indicating an increase in the concentration of $FeSCN^{2+}$. The equilibrium shifted to the right.

7. What evidence was there that the equilibrium shifted when potassium thiocyanate was added? In which direction did it shift?

The color of the solution changed from blood red to a deeper red, indicating an increase in the concentration of $FeSCN^{2+}$. The equilibrium shifted to the right.

8. Explain the effect of adding potassium chloride to the system.

Neither K^+ nor Cl^- ions are involved in the equilibrium reaction. Therefore, KCl does not have any effect upon the equilibrium position—it does not cause a stress.

9. Explain the changes observed in the ferrothiocyanate ion system in terms of Le Châtelier's principle.

The equilibrium reaction is $Fe^{3+} + SCN^- \rightleftharpoons FeSCN^{2+}$. When more Fe^{3+} ions are added to this reaction at equilibrium, they produce a stress. The equilibrium is disturbed. The reaction goes in the direction to relieve the effect of the stress; it produces more $FeSCN^{2+}$. When more SCN^- ions are added, a similar situation exists. The additional SCN^- is a stress, and the equilibrium is disturbed. The stress is relieved as the reaction goes in the direction to produce more $FeSCN^{2+}$.

Name ______________________ Date ________________ Class ________________

GOING FURTHER

Develop a Hypothesis

Based on the results of this experiment, develop a hypothesis concerning the effect of a catalyst on the relative amounts of reactants and products of a chemical reaction at equilibrium.

Catalysts do not affect the position of an equilibrium, only the time it takes to reach equilibrium.

Design an Experiment

Propose an experiment to test your hypothesis. If resources are available and you have your teacher's permission, perform the experiment.

Name ______________________ Date ________________ Class ________________

39 A SOLUBILITY PRODUCT CONSTANT

Text Reference
Section 18.3

Time Required
30 minutes (plus overnight drying)

Objectives
- Measure the concentration of Pb^{2+} ions in a saturated solution of lead(II) chloride.
- Based on the data, and using principles of stoichiometry, compute the K_{sp} of lead(II) chloride.

Point out that precipitation of an ionic compound occurs when the solubility product exceeds the K_{sp}.

Advance Preparation
saturated lead(II) chloride
The saturated solution of $PbCl_2$ should be made up well ahead of the laboratory period to permit time for intermittent shaking, followed by settling. The final saturated solution should contain some undissolved solid.

The solubility of $PbCl_2$ is 0.99 g/100 mL H_2O at 20°C. Approximately 2 L of saturated solution should meet the needs of 15 student lab pairs.

0.5M potassium chromate
Dissolve 48.6 g of K_2CrO_4 in 400 mL of distilled water. Dilute to 500 mL.

PURPOSE

To determine the solubility product constant (K_{sp}) of lead(II) chloride.

BACKGROUND

From everyday experiences, you are familiar with several substances that are soluble in water. Table sugar (sucrose) and table salt (NaCl) are examples of soluble compounds. Many other substances, such as limestone ($CaCO_3$) and gasoline, are insoluble in water. *Solubility* and *insolubility* are relative terms, however. Almost all substances have at least a slight solubility in water. If you put a slightly soluble substance in water, a dynamic equilibrium is established between the dissolved substance and its solid form. In this equilibrium, the rate of dissolution of ions from the solid equals the rate of precipitation of the ions from the solution. How can you express in numerical terms the fraction of dissolved substance in the solution? One way is to use the K_{sp}, the solubility product constant.

In this experiment, you will find the K_{sp} of a slightly soluble salt, lead(II) chloride ($PbCl_2$). You will precipitate Pb^{2+} ions as lead(II) chromate ($PbCrO_4$) from a saturated solution of lead(II) chloride. The amount of lead chromate precipitated will tell you the concentration of Pb^{2+} ions in the saturated solution. When you know the concentration of lead ions, you can calculate the concentration of chloride ions and compute the K_{sp} for lead(II) chloride.

MATERIALS (PER PAIR)

- safety goggles
- 2 250-mL beakers
- centigram balance
- 100-mL graduated cylinder
- ring stand
- ring support
- wire gauze
- gas burner
- glass stirring rod
- filter funnel
- plastic wash bottle
- drying oven/heat lamp
- filter paper
- saturated lead(II) chloride solution, $PbCl_2(aq)$ T
- 0.5*M* potassium chromate, K_2CrO_4 T
- distilled water

SAFETY FIRST!

In this lab, observe all precautions, especially the ones listed below. If you see a safety icon beside a step in the Procedure, refer to the list below for its meaning.

Caution: Wear your safety goggles. (All steps.)

Caution: Lead compounds and chromate compounds are toxic. (Steps 2–9.)

Caution: Exercise extreme care when working with a hot water bath and an open flame. Before beginning, ensure that there is no danger that the beaker will be capsized. Remember that cold equipment looks the same as hot equipment. Do not touch the beaker with your bare hands. (Step 3.)

Note: Return or dispose of all materials according to the instructions of your teacher. (Step 9.)

Note: Wash your hands thoroughly after completing the experiment. (Step 9.)

PROCEDURE

As you perform the experiment, record your data in Data Table 1.

1. Place a filter paper in a clean, dry 250-mL beaker. Determine the combined mass to the nearest 0.01 g and record the measurement in Data Table 1. Remove the filter paper from the beaker.

Step 2.
Any accidental transfer of $PbCl_2$ crystals will result in a high value for K_{sp}.

2. Slowly, to avoid disturbing the crystals, decant 100 mL of clear supernatant from the saturated $PbCl_2$ solution into the beaker. Add 20 mL of 0.5*M* K_2CrO_4 to the solution in the beaker.

3. Using a gas burner, heat the mixture in the beaker to the boiling point while occasionally stirring. Allow the mixture to cool, undisturbed, for 5 minutes.

Step 5.
Demonstrate the proper techniques for washing and decanting.

4. Using the filter paper from Step 1, assemble a filtration setup (refer to Figure 2.2 on p. 27).
5. Decant the liquid from the beaker into the filter funnel. Avoid transferring the precipitate to the filter paper. Wash the precipitate in the beaker by adding 30 mL of distilled water and swirling the mixture gently. Again decant the liquid into the filter funnel. Repeat the washing procedure once more.

Step 7.
For best results, the beaker and its contents must be thoroughly dried in a drying oven at 80°C. A wet or damp sample will give a K_{sp} value that is much too high.

6. Place the filter paper and any solid material retained on it in the beaker that contains the washed precipitate.
7. The contents of the beaker will now be dried according to your teacher's instructions.
8. Determine the combined mass of the beaker and its dry contents to the nearest 0.01 g and record the measurement.

Use the following disposal method for chemical waste.

Disposal 6: The reaction solution and filter paper.

9. Dispose of the filtrate and precipitate as instructed by your teacher. Be sure to wash your hands thoroughly after completing this experiment.

Name ______________________ Date ______________ Class ______________

OBSERVATIONS

DATA TABLE 1: DETERMINATION OF THE MASS OF LEAD(II) CHROMATE	
mass of beaker + filter paper	97.50 g
mass of beaker + filter paper + precipitate	98.25 g
mass of precipitate ($PbCrO_4$)	0.75 g
volume of saturated $PbCl_2$ solution used	100 mL
molar mass $PbCrO_4$	323.2 g
molar mass $PbCl_2$	278.1 g

ANALYSES AND CONCLUSIONS

1. In a saturated aqueous solution of lead(II) chloride, an equilibrium is established between the solid lead(II) chloride and its ions. Write the balanced chemical equation that describes this equilibrium.

$$PbCl_2(s) \rightleftharpoons Pb^{2+}(aq) + 2Cl^-(aq)$$

2. Write a balanced equation for the reaction of Pb^{2+} ions and CrO_4^{2-} ions.

$$Pb^{2+}(aq) + CrO_4^{2-}(aq) \rightarrow PbCrO_4(s)$$

3. Calculate the number of moles of $PbCrO_4$ you obtained in the experiment.

$$0.75\text{ g } PbCrO_4 \times \frac{1\text{ mol}}{323.2\text{ g}} = 2.3 \times 10^{-3}\text{ mol } PbCrO_4$$

4. Determine the concentration (mol/L) of Pb^{2+} ions in the saturated $PbCl_2$ solution.

$$[Pb^{2+}] = 2.3 \times 10^{-3} \frac{\text{mol } Pb^{2+}}{100\text{ mL}} \times \frac{100\text{ mL}}{0.10\text{ L}}$$

$$= 2.3 \times 10^{-2}\text{ mol/L}$$

5. Find the Cl^- concentration (mol/L) in the saturated solution.

$$[Cl^-] = \frac{2\text{ mol } Cl^-}{1\text{ mol } Pb^{2+}} \times \frac{2.3 \times 10^{-2}\text{ mol } Pb^{2+}}{1\text{ L}}$$

$$= 4.6 \times 10^{-2}\text{ mol/L}$$

6. Set up the solubility product expression and calculate the K_{sp} for $PbCl_2$.

$$K_{sp} = [Pb^{2+}][Cl^-]^2$$

$$= (2.3 \times 10^{-2})(4.6 \times 10^{-2})^2$$

$$= 4.9 \times 10^{-5}$$

Name ______________________ Date __________________ Class ________________

7. Calculate the percent error in your results. Use a chemistry handbook to look up the accepted K_{sp} values for $PbCl_2$ and $PbCrO_4$.

The reported K_{sp} for $PbCrO_4$ is 1.77×10^{-14} at 18°C. The K_{sp} of $PbCl_2$ is reported as 1.6×10^{-5}, 1.4×10^{-4}, and 2.4×10^{-4} in various sources. One of these values may be used as the accepted value from which the percent error can be calculated.

$$\text{percent error} = \frac{|\text{accepted value} - \text{experimental value}|}{\text{accepted value}} \times 100\%$$

8. Suggest likely sources of error in this experiment.

The most likely sources of error are the incomplete transfer of $PbCl_2$ to the beaker, incomplete drying of the precipitate, and inaccurate determinations of the mass of $PbCrO_4$.

9. Barium ions are extremely toxic. Yet patients in hospitals are required to drink a suspension of barium sulfate in order to have their stomachs and intestinal tracts X-rayed. Find the K_{sp} value for barium sulfate and explain why patients are not at risk with this treatment.

The K_{sp} of barium sulfate is on the order of 2×10^{-10} at body temperature. Only a small amount of Ba^{2+} is present.

GOING FURTHER

Develop a Hypothesis

Based on the results of this lab, develop a hypothesis about how other factors such as temperature, pH, and the presence of other dissolved ions and gases would affect the solubility constants of various salts, including lead(II) chloride.

Design an Experiment

Propose an experiment to test your hypothesis. If resources are available and you have your teacher's permission, perform the experiment.

Name ____________________ Date ____________________ Class ____________________

40 ESTIMATION OF pH

Text Reference
Section 19.2

Time Required
30–45 minutes

Objectives

- Observe the characteristic color changes of several acid–base indicators.
- Estimate the pH of solutions, using acid–base indicators.

Advance Preparation

0.1M ethanoic acid solution
Add 1.5 mL of 6*M* CH_3COOH to 95 mL of water and dilute to 100 mL.

0.1M ammonia solution
Add 1.5 mL of 6*M* $NH_3(aq)$ to 95 mL of water and dilute to 100 mL.

Aspirin solution
Crush 2 tablets and add them to 50 mL of water.

Sodium hydrogen carbonate (baking soda) solution
Add 5 g of $NaHCO_3$ to 90 mL of water and dilute to 100 mL.

Bromthymol blue indicator
0.1 g bromthymol blue/L water

Shampoo solution
Dilute 5 mL shampoo to 50 mL with water.

0.1M hydrochloric acid
Add 1.5 mL of 6*M* HCl to 90 mL of water and dilute to 100 mL.

Litmus indicator
Dissolve 1 g of litmus powder in 100 mL of water; filter.

PURPOSE

To estimate the pH of solutions by using acid–base indicators.

BACKGROUND

If you are interested in gardening, you may know that plants such as azaleas and rhododendrons prefer acidic soils. A part of soil testing consists of the measurement of the pH of the soil. pH is important for many other applications in the home and in industry. For example, maintenance of the proper pH of water is important in caring for swimming pools. There are several ways to test pH. One of the most important ways is by means of acid–base indicators such as phenolphthalein. In neutral and acidic solutions, phenolphthalein is colorless. In alkaline solutions, it is pink. By adding a few drops of a weak solution of the indicator to a solution to be tested, you can tell immediately whether the test solution is alkaline. Other acid–base indicators change colors at different pH values. By systematically testing a solution with a series of indicators, you can often arrive at a good estimate of the pH of a solution.

In this experiment, you will estimate the pH of several solutions by using acid–base indicators. You will then use the same indicators to test the pH of several common household chemicals.

MATERIALS (PER PAIR)

safety goggles
dropper pipet
5 small test tubes
test-tube rack
10-mL graduated cylinder
stirring rod
plastic wash bottle
pH meter (optional)
0.1*M* hydrochloric acid, HCl [I]
0.1*M* ethanoic acid, CH_3COOH
0.1*M* ammonia, NH_3 [T]
0.1*M* sodium hydroxide, NaOH [I]
distilled water
methyl red solution
litmus solution (or litmus paper)
bromthymol blue solution
phenolphthalein solution

household chemicals such as:

lemon juice
vinegar
bleach
baking soda
carbonated beverage
shampoo
cold tea
aspirin
milk
liquid antacid

Name ______________________ Date ______________ Class ______________

SAFETY FIRST!

In this lab, observe all precautions, especially the ones listed below. If you see a safety icon beside a step in the Procedure, refer to the list below for its meaning.

Caution: Wear your safety goggles. (All steps.)

Caution: Hydrochloric acid and sodium hydroxide are irritants at the concentrations used in this experiment. (Step 1.)

Caution: Ammonia is an irritant. Do not inhale ammonia fumes. (Step 1.)

Caution: Return or dispose of all materials according to the instructions of your teacher. (Step 6.)

PROCEDURE

As you perform the experiment, record your observations in Data Tables 2 and 3.

1. Add 1–2 mL of the following to five separate, clean test tubes: 0.1*M* hydrochloric acid, 0.1*M* ethanoic acid, 0.1*M* ammonia, 0.1*M* sodium hydroxide, and distilled water.

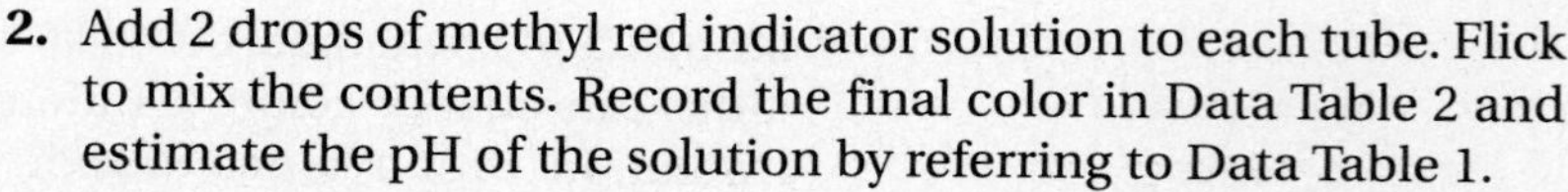

2. Add 2 drops of methyl red indicator solution to each tube. Flick to mix the contents. Record the final color in Data Table 2 and estimate the pH of the solution by referring to Data Table 1.
3. Using fresh samples of the solutions, repeat the procedure for each of the other indicators named in Data Table 1. If you are using paper indicator strips, use a glass rod to transfer a drop of the solution to the indicator strip. Record the results of all the tests in Data Table 2.
4. Test the common household chemicals that are available to you. Test liquids directly. Solids should be dissolved or suspended in water before testing. Record your results in Data Table 3.
5. If a pH meter is available, use it to determine the pH of the household chemicals.

6. Follow your teacher's instructions for proper disposal of the materials.

Methyl red indicator

Dissolve 1 g of methyl red in 1 mL of water.

Phenolphthalein indicator

Dissolve 0.5 g of phenolphthalein in 100 mL of 95% ethanol.

0.1M sodium hydroxide solution

Add 1.5 mL of 6*M* NaOH to 95.0 mL of water and dilute to 100 mL.

Distilled water may have a pH as low as 4. This water must be boiled to remove dissolved CO_2 to obtain a pH estimate near 7. Boiling in an Erlenmeyer flask for about 15 minutes (with boiling chips) is usually sufficient to bring the distilled water from pH 4 to pH 7. Cover the flask with a watch glass and allow the water to cool to room temperature before use.

Step 4.
The brown color of tea could seem to be an interference, but you will find that the color changes of the indicators are quite apparent.

Step 5.
Instruct students in the use of the pH meter if this part of the experiment is to be completed. If a pH standard is needed, a solution of pH 6.86 may be prepared by dissolving 0.001 mol KH_2HPO_4 and 0.001 mol Na_2HPO_4 in 1 L of distilled water.

Use the following disposal methods for chemical waste.

Disposal 2: $H_2O(l)$ + indicator.

Disposal 3: Contents of the test tubes from Steps 2 and 3, except for the tube containing $H_2O(l)$.

Name ______________________ Date ________________ Class ________________

OBSERVATIONS

DATA TABLE 1: COMMON ACID–BASE INDICATORS

Indicator	Color in Acid (HIn form)	Color in Base (In^- form)	pH Range
litmus	red	blue	5.2–7.5
bromthymol blue	yellow	blue	6.0–7.6
phenolphthalein	colorless	pink	8.2–10.0

DATA TABLE 2: INDICATOR REACTIONS WITH STANDARD SOLUTIONS

Solution	Methyl Red	Litmus	Bromthymol Blue	Phenolphthalein	Estimated pH
0.1*M* HCl	red	red	yellow	colorless	1
0.1*M* ethanoic acid	red	red	yellow	colorless	6
distilled water	red	red	green	colorless	7
0.1*M* ammonia	yellow	blue	blue	pink	8
0.1*M* NaOH	yellow	blue	blue	pink	13

DATA TABLE 3: INDICATOR REACTIONS WITH HOUSEHOLD CHEMICALS

Substance	Methyl Red	Litmus	Bromthymol Blue	Phenolphthalein	Estimated pH	Measured pH
aspirin	red	red	yellow	colorless	below 4.8	3.9
tea	yellow	red	green	colorless	about 7.0	7.4
baking soda	yellow	blue	blue	pink	above 8.2	9.2
cola (diet)	red	red	yellow	colorless	below 5.2	5.2
vinegar	red	red	yellow	colorless	below 4.8	3.9

Name ______________ Date ______________ Class ______________

ANALYSES AND CONCLUSIONS

1. Compare the pH of 0.1*M* ethanoic acid with that of 0.1*M* hydrochloric acid. Compare the pH of 0.1*M* ammonia with that of 0.1*M* sodium hydroxide. Explain any differences.

   The 0.1*M* HCl solution is more acidic (has lower pH) than the 0.1*M* ethanoic acid solution. This is because HCl completely dissociates in aqueous solution. Thus, the hydrogen ion concentration is 0.1*M*. The pH = 1. $HCl \rightarrow H^+ + Cl^-$.
   Only about 1% of ethanoic acid ionizes in solution. Ethanoic acid is a week acid; the hydrogen ion concentration is only about 1×10^{-3} *M*. The pH = 3. Similarly, in water, NaOH completely dissociates into sodium ions and hydroxide ions.
   The concentration of OH^- is 0.1*M* (pH = 13). The pH of aqueous ammonia is less (pH = 11). The reaction of 0.1*M* ammonia with water produces some hydroxide ions because NH_3 is a weak base. $NH_3 + H_2O \rightleftharpoons NH_4^+ + OH^-$

2. Which of the indicators used in this experiment could most accurately identify a neutral solution? Explain.

   Bromthymol blue gives the best indication of a neutral solution. At pH 7, the indicator is about half in the basic blue form and half in the acidic yellow form. The color of a neutral solution containing bromthymol blue is, therefore, green.

3. Are the household chemicals you tested acidic, basic, or neutral?

   Answers will vary depending upon the household chemicals tested.

GOING FURTHER

Develop a Hypothesis

Based on the results of this lab, develop a hypothesis about how acid–base indicators change colors at different pH's.

Most acid–base indicators are weak acids that exhibit one color in the non-ionized state and another color in the ionized state. The color that predominates in solution depends on the pH of the solution.

Do Research

If resources are available, read articles or books to collect information about the chemical structures of acid–base indicators under different conditions of pH that may or may not support your hypothesis.

Name ______________________ Date ________________ Class ________________

41 REACTIONS OF ACIDS

Text Reference
Section 19.4

Time Required
20 minutes

Objectives
- Observe several common reactions involving acids.
- Identify the gas produced by the reaction of metals with acid.
- Identify the gas produced by the reaction of carbonate and bicarbonate salts with acid.
- Write chemical equations for the reactions observed.

Advance Preparation
6M hydrochloric acid
Dilute concentrated HCl 1:1 with distilled water.
Other materials
Cut a sufficient number of 2-cm-long pieces of copper wire, iron wire (small nails may also be used), and magnesium ribbon. Zinc sheet, 0.25 mm thick, should be cut into 0.50-cm × 2.00-cm strips.

PURPOSE

To investigate common reactions of acids.

BACKGROUND

Because of its usefulness in many industrial processes, sulfuric acid is one of the most important bulk chemicals produced. The uses of acids are not limited to industry, however. Artists pull beautiful prints from metal lithographic plates that have been etched with hydrochloric acid. Hydrofluoric acid is used to etch designs on glass. You encounter natural acids when you pour vinegar (which contains ethanoic acid) on a salad or eat a tart apple (which contains malic acid). Acids can also cause problems. Acid precipitation can corrode metal; dissolve marble and limestone statues; and even damage buildings.

In this experiment, you will investigate some common reactions of acids. These characteristic reactions are often used to test for certain ions or metals.

MATERIALS (PER PAIR)

safety goggles
glass-marking pencil
6 small test tubes
test-tube rack
dropper pipet
forceps
2 spatulas
test-tube holder
gas burner
6*M* hydrochloric acid, HCl [C] [T]
paper
iron wire or small nails, Fe
copper wire, Cu
magnesium ribbon, Mg [F]
zinc strips, Zn, 0.25 mm × 0.5 cm × 2.00 cm
sodium hydrogen carbonate, $NaHCO_3$
calcium carbonate, $CaCO_3$
wood splints
matches

SAFETY FIRST!

In this lab, observe all precautions, especially the ones listed below. If you see a safety icon beside a step in the Procedure, refer to the list below for its meaning.

Caution: Wear your safety goggles. (All steps.)

Caution: Concentrated hydrochloric acid is highly corrosive and can cause severe burns. (All steps.)

Caution: Magnesium is flammable. Keep it away from open flames. (Step 2.)

Name _______________ Date _______________ Class _______________

Review the safety procedures and caution students about the corrosive nature of 6*M* HCl before they begin to work.

Note: Return or dispose of all materials according to the instructions of your teacher. (Step 4.)

PROCEDURE

Students should observe that Mg, Zn, and Fe, but not Cu, will displace hydrogen from the acid, and that acids react with hydrogen carbonate and carbonate ions to produce carbon dioxide and water.

As you perform the experiment, record your observations in Data Table 1.

1. Label six small test tubes with the numbers 1–6. Place the tubes in a test-tube rack. **CAUTION:** *Hydrochloric acid is corrosive, especially at the 6M concentration.* Add 2 mL of 6*M* hydrochloric acid to each tube.
2. Obtain the items indicated below and place them on labeled pieces of paper. Using forceps, carefully transfer the materials to the numbered test tubes, as the following list indicates.

tube 1	2-cm length of clean iron wire or a small nail
tube 2	2-cm length of copper wire
tube 3	2-cm length of magnesium ribbon
tube 4	small strip of zinc

Using a spatula, transfer the following materials to the numbered test tubes as indicated.

tube 5	pea-sized quantity of sodium hydrogen carbonate
tube 6	pea-sized piece of calcium carbonate

Step 3.
Hydrogen will produce a small explosive pop when a burning splint is introduced.

$$2H_2 + O_2 \rightarrow 2H_2O$$

Carbon dioxide does not support combustion. It will extinguish a glowing splint.

3. Observe the tubes for several minutes to determine if a gas is produced. Attempt to identify any gas produced by holding a burning wood splint at the mouth of the test tube. If it appears no gas is being produced, place the test tube in a holder and warm the tube gently, *without boiling*, in a burner flame. **CAUTION:** *Do not point the mouth of the tube toward yourself or anyone else.* Remove the tube from the flame and test for the presence of gas production. Record your observations.

Use the following disposal methods for chemical waste.

Disposal 1: Fe(*s*), Mg(*s*), Cu(*s*), and Zn(*s*).

Disposal 3: All the reaction solutions used in this experiment.

4. Follow your teacher's instructions for proper disposal of the materials.

Name ______________________ Date ______________ Class ______________

OBSERVATIONS

DATA TABLE 1: REACTIONS WITH HYDROCHLORIC ACID	
Substance	Observations
iron	Little reaction in the cold; reaction more vigorous when mixture was gently warmed. Gas was produced and gave a sharp pop when tested with a lighted splint (hydrogen present). The solution became yellow; not all the iron reacted.
copper	No reaction even when mixture was warmed gently.
magnesium	Rapid production of gas; gas gave a sharp pop when tested with a lighted wood splint (hydrogen present). All the magnesium metal reacted with the acid, and the resulting solution was colorless.
zinc	Rapid production of gas; less vigorous than magnesium reaction. The gas produced gave a sharp pop when tested with a lighted splint (hydrogen present). All the zinc eventually reacted with the acid, resulting in a colorless solution.
sodium hydrogen carbonate	Rapid production of gas; gas extinguished a lighted wood splint (carbon dioxide present). After the reaction ceased, no solid was left.
calcium carbonate	Rapid production of gas; gas extinguished a lighted wood splint (carbon dioxide present). After the reaction ceased, no solid was left.

ANALYSES AND CONCLUSIONS

1. List the four metals tested in order of increasing reactivity with hydrochloric acid. List any nonreactive metals first, then the least reactive, and so on, up to the most reactive.

   Cu Fe Zn Mg
   nonreactive least most
   reactive reactive

2. Was the same gas produced when all the metals reacted with hydrochloric acid? What was the gas? How did you identify the gas?

   Yes. The gas produced was hydrogen. When hydrogen is tested with a lighted wood splint in the presence of oxygen (air), a sharp pop results.

Name ________________ Date ________________ Class ________________

3. Write a balanced equation for the reaction of the two metals that reacted most vigorously with hydrochloric acid.

$Mg(s) + 2HCl(aq) \rightarrow MgCl_2(aq) + H_2(g)$

$Zn(s) + 2HCl(aq) \rightarrow ZnCl_2(aq) + H_2(g)$

4. Was the same gas produced when sodium hydrogen carbonate and calcium carbonate reacted with hydrochloric acid? What was the gas? How did you identify this gas?

Yes. Carbon dioxide. This gas extinguishes a lighted wood splint.

5. Write balanced equations for the reactions of sodium hydrogen carbonate and calcium carbonate with hydrochloric acid.

$NaHCO_3(s) + HCl(aq) \rightarrow NaCl(aq) + H_2O(l) + CO_2(g)$

$CaCO_3(s) + 2HCl(aq) \rightarrow CaCl_2(aq) + H_2O(l) + CO_2(g)$

GOING FURTHER

Develop a Hypothesis

Based on the results of this lab, develop a hypothesis about how the relative strength of the acid used would affect the rate of the reaction with metals and carbonates.

Design an Experiment

Propose an experiment to test your hypothesis. If resources are available and you have your teacher's permission, perform the experiment.

Name ______________________ Date __________________ Class __________________

42 NEUTRALIZATION REACTIONS

Text Reference
Section 19.4

Time Required
40 minutes

Objectives
- Perform a neutralization reaction between HCl and NaOH.
- Isolate and identify the salt produced by the neutralization reaction.

Advance Preparation
1M hydrochloric acid
Add 80 mL concentrated HCl to 900 mL of distilled water and dilute to 1 L.
phenolphthalein indicator
Dissolve 2 g of phenolphthalein in 200 mL of 95% ethanol.
1M sodium hydroxide
Dissolve 40 g of NaOH pellets in 900 mL of chilled distilled water and dilute to 1 L.

PURPOSE

To produce and isolate a salt by neutralizing a base with an acid.

BACKGROUND

Early chemists discovered that sour acids and bitter bases combine to form relatively bland-tasting (neutral) salts. (**CAUTION:** *Never taste any chemical in the laboratory*.) For example, equivalent amounts of hydrochloric acid and sodium hydroxide combine to form neutral water and neutral sodium chloride, common table salt.

$$HCl(aq) + NaOH(aq) \rightarrow NaCl(aq) + H_2O(l)$$

In this reaction, the H^+ and OH^- ions—which are responsible for the properties of the acid and base, respectively—combine to produce water. The products of the reaction do not have the properties of an acid or a base. The reaction is, therefore, called a *neutralization reaction*.

In this experiment, you will use a neutralization reaction between a strong acid and a strong base to make a salt.

MATERIALS (PER PAIR)

- safety goggles
- 250-mL beaker
- ring stand
- ring clamp
- wire gauze
- gas burner
- 10-mL graduated cylinder
- 50-mL beaker
- glass stirring rod
- dropper pipet
- evaporating dish
- crucible tongs
- 1*M* sodium hydroxide, NaOH [C] [T]
- phenolphthalein solution
- 1*M* hydrochloric acid, HCl [T] [I]

SAFETY FIRST!

In this lab, observe all precautions, especially the ones listed below. If you see a safety icon beside a step in the Procedure, refer to the list below for its meaning.

Review the safety procedures and caution the students about the corrosive nature of acids and bases before they begin to work.

Caution: Wear your safety goggles. (All steps.)

Caution: Hydrochloric acid is an irritant at the concentration used in this experiment. Sodium hydroxide is corrosive and can cause severe burns. (Steps 2, 3.)

Caution: Do not touch or taste any of the chemicals. (Step 5.)

Phenolphthalein is a powerful laxative.

Name ______________________ Date ________________ Class ________________

Caution: Exercise care when working with hot water baths. The steam can cause severe burns. Use tongs to handle the evaporating dish. (Steps 4, 5.)

Caution: Exercise care when working with an open flame. Tie back hair and loose clothing. Do not use the burner near flammable materials. (Step 1.)

Note: Return or dispose of all materials according to the instructions of your teacher. (Step 6.)

PROCEDURE

As you perform the experiment, record your observations in Data Table 1.

1. Fill a 250-mL beaker three-fourths full with water and set up a boiling water bath. While the water is heating, proceed to the next step.

2. Pour 5.0 mL of $1M$ sodium hydroxide solution into a 50-mL beaker. Add 1 or 2 drops of phenolphthalein indicator solution to the sodium hydroxide.

3. Add, drop by drop, $1M$ hydrochloric acid to the beaker, using a dropper pipet. Stir constantly while adding the acid. Continue adding acid until the color of the solution just disappears.

Step 3. Exactly 50 mL of $1M$ HCl is required to neutralize 5.0 mL of $1M$ NaOH. If burets and pipets are available, the volume of HCl required to neutralize exactly 5.00 mL of NaOH may be precisely determined.

4. Transfer about 5 mL of the neutralized solution to a clean evaporating dish. Place the evaporating dish over the boiling water bath, as shown in Figure 42.1. Evaporate the solution to dryness. **CAUTION:** *Be careful not to be burned by the steam coming from the water bath.*

5. Turn off the gas burner and remove the evaporating dish from the beaker, using tongs. Examine the residue in the evaporating dish. **CAUTION:** *Do not touch or taste the residue.*

6. Follow your teacher's instructions for proper disposal of the materials.

Use the following disposal methods for chemical waste.

Disposal 2: NaCl(*s*)

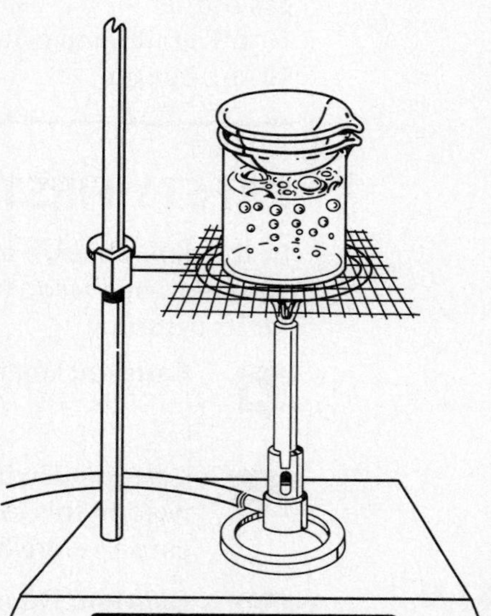

Figure 42.1

Name ______________________ Date ________________ Class ________________

OBSERVATIONS

DATA TABLE 1: OBSERVATIONS	
Step	Observation
2	When phenolphthalein is added to NaOH solution, the solution turns pink.
3	The pink basic solution turns colorless when neutralized with 1 *M* HCl. Approximately 5 mL of 1 *M* HCl is required to neutralize 5 mL of 1 *M* NaOH.
5	A residue of colorless crystal NaCl formed when the neutralized solution evaporated.

ANALYSES AND CONCLUSIONS

1. Write a balanced equation for the neutralization reaction that took place in this experiment.

   $NaOH(aq) + HCl(aq) \rightarrow NaCl(aq) + H_2O(l)$

2. How does the product that was prepared in this experiment compare with the same product as it is prepared commercially?

   The chemical structure of the NaCl prepared in the laboratory and the chemical structure of the commercial product are identical. The commercial product is somewhat purer, however, because it does not contain traces of phenolphthalein or unreacted NaOH.

3. Why should you not taste the residue from this reaction, even though you known the salt produced is commonly used in food?

   The purity of the product is not known. It is contaminated with phenolphthalein (a laxative), and possibly contains NaOH or traces of toxic salts.

4. How could you determine whether the phenolphthalein remains in the residue of the reaction?

   Add a drop of NaOH solution to the solid residue. The residue will turn pink if phenolphthalein is present.

5. Design an experiment in which you produce and examine the products of several other neutralization reactions. Include in your procedure a step in which you determine whether the product is truly free of all traces of acid or base.

A salt is the neutralization product of the reaction of an acid with a base. A general scheme would be:

acid(aq) + base(aq)   salt(aq)   salt(s)

An acid–base indicator must be added to identify the equivalence point. The presence of residual traces of acid or base could be detected by redissolving the dry salt in water and testing the pH of the solution with acid–base indicators. This procedure will work with any salt of a strong acid and strong base. The pure salts produce neutral solutions. The procedure will not work with salts of weak acids and strong bases or salts of strong acids and weak bases because these salts undergo hydrolysis and produce acidic or basic solutions.

(See Experiment 44, Salt Hydrolysis.)

GOING FURTHER

Develop a Hypothesis

Research the most common antacids to determine the active ingredients used to neutralize stomach acid. Based on the results of this lab, develop a hypothesis about the effectiveness of various antacid products in neutralizing acid.

Design an Experiment

Propose an experiment to test your hypothesis. If resources are available and you have your teacher's permission, perform the experiment.

Start with a given quantity of an acid of known concentration. Add a piece of antacid product of known mass. After the neutralization reaction has ceased, titrate the sample with a base of known concentration to determine the amount of acid remaining in the sample. Repeat the procedure with other antacid products. Either use samples of the same size or adjust for different samples in the calculations.

Name ______________________ Date ________________ Class ________________

43 ACID–BASE TITRATIONS

Text Reference
Section 19.4

Time Required
two 50-minute periods
(Parts A and B may be done in one session; Part C may be done in a second session.)

Objectives
- Prepare a standard solution of NaOH by titration with a standard solution of $KHSO_4$.
- Measure the normality of ethanoic acid in vinegar with the NaOH standard.

Advance Preparation
phenolphthalein solution
Dissolve 0.5 g of phenolphthalein in 100 mL of 95% ethanol. Place the solution in a dropper bottle.
6M sodium hydroxide
Caution: Add 240 g of NaOH pellets gradually to 700 mL of chilled distilled water, stirring. Dilute to 1 L.
Other materials
Any commercial brand of vinegar may be used (200 mL/15 student lab pairs). If you are using more than one brand of vinegar, check that the concentration of ethanoic acid is the same in each bottle.

PURPOSE

To measure the normality of ethanoic acid in vinegar, using a standardized solution of sodium hydroxide.

BACKGROUND

Every day, scientists in many fields conduct experiments designed to answer one question: How much acid or base does this solution contain? The chemical reactions used to answer this question are, for the main part, neutralization reactions, and *titration* is the method generally used.

You can neutralize an acid with a base very precisely by using the technique of titration. During a titration, a solution of known acidity (a standard solution) is gradually added to a solution of unknown basicity. At the point of neutralization, the number of equivalents of acid must be equal to the number of equivalents of base. Thus, titration tells you the equivalents of base in your unknown solution. The neutralization, or equivalence point, of the reaction is estimated by the color change of an acid–base indicator or by a neutral reading (pH 7.0) on a pH meter. You can also reverse the titration procedure so a standard base solution is used to titrate an unknown acidic solution.

In this experiment, you will prepare a standard solution of an acidic compound, potassium hydrogen sulfate ($KHSO_4$). You will then use this solution to make a standard solution of sodium hydroxide by titration. Finally, you will use your standardized sodium hydroxide solution to titrate vinegar, a dilute solution of ethanoic acid, CH_3COOH.

MATERIALS (PER PAIR)

safety goggles
centigram balance
weighing bottle
filter funnel
spatula
100-mL graduated cylinder
250-mL volumetric flask
2 rubber stoppers, for volumetric flasks
3 250-mL plastic bottles
labels
10-mL graduated cylinder
2 50-mL burets
double buret clamp
ring stand
2 sheets white paper, 25 cm × 25 cm
100-mL beaker
2 250-mL Erlenmeyer flasks
10-mL pipet
25-mL pipet
pipet suction bulb
100-mL volumetric flask
plastic wash bottle
potassium hydrogen sulfate, $KHSO_4$ [T]
distilled water
6*M* sodium hydroxide, NaOH [C] [T]
phenolphthalein solution
vinegar, dilute ethanoic acid, CH_3COOH

Name ______________________ Date ________________ Class ________________

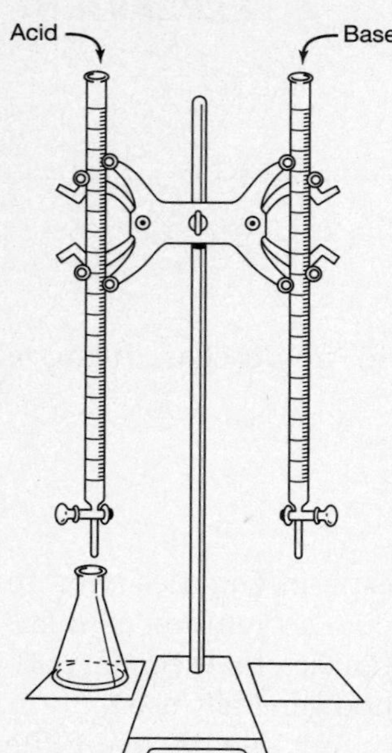

Figure 43.1

SAFETY FIRST!

In this lab, observe all precautions, especially the ones listed below. If you see a safety icon beside a step in the Procedure, refer to the list below for its meaning.

 **Caution:** Wear your safety goggles. (All steps.)

 **Caution:** Sodium hydroxide is corrosive and can cause severe burns. (Steps 4–16.)

 **Caution:** Potassium hydrogen sulfate is a toxic substance. (Steps 1–13.)

 **Note:** Return or dispose of all materials according to the instructions of your teacher. (Steps 6, 12, 16.)

PROCEDURE

As you perform the experiment, record your data and observations in Data Tables 1, 2, and 3.

Part A. Preparation of a Standard Solution of Potassium Hydrogen Sulfate

Before students begin, stress the toxic and corrosive properties of the reactants and explain the disposal procedures.

1. Determine the mass of a sample of potassium hydrogen sulfate (the *acid*) in a weighing bottle, using the most accurate balance available to you. Using a funnel and a spatula, transfer 3–4 g of the acid to a clean 250-mL volumetric flask. Remeasure the mass of the weighing bottle and remaining sample. The difference between the two mass values is the mass of the acid in the flask.

Step 2. Use a wash bottle filled with distilled water for this addition.

2. Add about 100 mL of distilled water to the flask, washing into the flask any acid crystals clinging to the funnel. Remove the funnel and gently swirl the flask to dissolve the acid. When the acid is completely dissolved, fill the flask to the 250-mL mark with distilled water.
3. Stopper and mix the contents thoroughly by inverting the flask and swirling the mixture. Transfer the solution to a clean, dry 250-mL plastic bottle labeled "approximately 0.1*N* $KHSO_4$" and mark the label with your initials.

Part B. Standardization of a Solution of Sodium Hydroxide

Step 4.
6*M* NaOH = 6*N* NaOH

$$N_2 = \frac{N_1V_1}{V_2} = \frac{(6N)(5\text{ mL})}{250\text{ mL}} = \frac{30}{250} = 0.12N$$

4. **CAUTION:** *Sodium hydroxide is corrosive.* Using a 10-mL graduated cylinder, measure out 5 mL of 6*M* sodium hydroxide. Transfer this solution to a clean, dry 250-mL plastic bottle labeled "approximately 0.1*N* NaOH" and mark the label with your initials. Add 250 mL of distilled water to the bottle, cap it, and shake it to mix the contents.
5. Clean and mount two 50-mL burets, as shown in Figure 43.1. Place a white sheet of paper or a white plastic base beneath each buret. Label the left buret "acid" and the right buret "base."

Name ______________________ Date ______________ Class ______________

Step 6.
Rinsing with three small aliquots of a solution removes the distilled water from the buret, eliminating the need to dry the buret.

Step 8.
Using distilled water to rinse the tip of the buret does not change the number of equivalents of acid (or base) in the flask and, therefore, will not affect the end point of the titration.

Step 9.
The pH range of color change for phenolphthalein is 8.3–10.0. Its color in acid is colorless; its color in base is red.

6. Rinse the "acid" buret with three 5-mL portions of the standard solution of potassium hydrogen sulfate. Let each portion drain out of the buret before adding the next rinse. Discard these rinses. Fill the buret with the potassium hydrogen sulfate solution. Before beginning the titration, remove any bubbles trapped in the tip of the buret and the stopcock.
7. Using the sodium hydroxide solution, rinse and fill the "base" buret. Use a wash bottle of distilled water to rinse off the tip of each buret; catch the runoff in a 100-mL beaker. Record the initial volume in each buret to the nearest 0.01 mL.
8. Add 10–12 mL of the acid solution to a clean 250-mL Erlenmeyer flask. Use the wash bottle to rinse the last drop of acid from the tip of the buret into the flask. Add 50 mL of distilled water and 1–2 drops of phenolphthalein to the flask.
9. Now, slowly add sodium hydroxide solution from the "base" buret to the flask. As you add the base, gently swirl the solution in the flask. A pink color will appear and quickly disappear as the solutions are mixed. As more and more base is added, the pink color will persist for a longer time before disappearing. This is a sign that you are nearing the equivalence point, also called the end point. Wash down the sides of the flask and the tip of the buret with distilled water from the wash bottle. Continue to add sodium hydroxide more slowly, until a single drop of base turns the solution a pale pink color that persists for 15–30 seconds.
10. If you overshoot the end point—that is, if you add too much base so the solution turns bright pink—simply add a few drops of acid from the acid buret to turn the solution colorless again. Approach the end point again, adding base drop by drop, until one drop causes the color change to pale pink.
11. When you are sure that you have achieved the end point, record the final volume reading of each buret. **Note:** Do not allow the level of the solution in either buret to go below the 50-mL mark. If you do, you will have to discard your sample and begin again.

12. Discard the solution in the Erlenmeyer flask as directed by your teacher, and rinse the flask well with distilled water. Refill both burets if necessary. Read the initial volume in each buret and do another titration, as described in Steps 8–11.
13. Before proceeding, calculate the normality of the sodium hydroxide solution for each titration, as described in Analyses and Conclusions, problems 1–6. If the normalities obtained from the two titrations do not agree within 1%, perform a third titration.

Name ____________________ Date ________________ Class ________________

Part C. Determination of the Normality of Ethanoic Acid in Vinegar

Step 14.
The 10% vinegar solution is a dilution of an already dilute solution of ethanoic acid.

14. Using a clean, dry 10-mL pipet and suction bulb, transfer 10 mL of commercial vinegar into a clean 100-mL volumetric flask. Fill the flask to the 100-mL mark with distilled water. Stopper the flask and mix the solution by inverting the flask 20–30 times. Transfer this solution to a clean, dry 250-mL plastic bottle. Label the bottle "10% vinegar" and mark the label with your initials.

Step 15.
Caution students not to overshoot this end point because they will not have time to start over again.

15. Using a clean, dry 25-mL pipet, transfer a 20-mL sample of the diluted vinegar to a clean 250-mL Erlenmeyer flask. Add 50 mL of distilled water and 1–2 drops of phenolphthalein to the flask. Titrate the vinegar with the sodium hydroxide solution that you standardized in Part B. **Note:** If you overshoot the end point in these titrations, you will have to discard the sample and begin again. Do at least two titrations that agree to within 1%.

Use the following disposal method for chemical waste.

Disposal 3: All solutions used in this experiment. (Steps 6, 12, 16.)

16. Follow your teacher's instructions for proper disposal of the materials.

Name ______________ Date ______________ Class ______________

OBSERVATIONS

DATA TABLE 1: NORMALITY OF POTASSIUM HYDROGEN SULFATE	
initial mass of weighing bottle and $KHSO_4$	36.27 g
final mass of weighing bottle and $KHSO_4$	32.29 g
mass of $KHSO_4$ used	3.98 g
gram equivalent mass of $KHSO_4$	136.2 g
equivalents of $KHSO_4$ used in 250 mL	0.0292
normality of $KHSO_4$	0.117*N*

DATA TABLE 2: NORMALITY OF SODIUM HYDROXIDE

	Trial 1		Trial 2		Trial 3	
	Acid	Base	Acid	Base	Acid	Base
final volume	13.04	17.17	23.75	27.53		
initial volume	1.42	5.73	13.04	17.17		
volume used	11.62	11.44	10.71	10.36		
normality of NaOH	0.119*N*		0.121*N*			
average normality of NaOH	0.120*N*					

DATA TABLE 3: NORMALITY OF VINEGAR

	Trial 1		Trial 2		Trial 3	
	Vinegar	Base	Vinegar	Base	Vinegar	Base
final volume	—	19.09	—	36.31	—	20.14
initial volume	—	1.74	—	19.09	—	2.73
volume used	25.00	17.35	25.00	17.22	25.00	17.41
normality of vinegar	0.0833*N*		0.0827*N*		0.0836*N*	
average normality of 10% vinegar	0.0832*N*					

Name ______________________ Date ________________ Class ________________

ANALYSES AND CONCLUSIONS

As you do the following calculations, enter the results in Data Tables 1, 2, or 3.

1. Determine the mass of potassium hydrogen sulfate used.
2. Find the gram equivalent mass of potassium hydrogen sulfate.

$$\text{gram equivalent mass} = \frac{\text{molar mass}}{\text{number of equivalents per mole}}$$

$$\text{gram equivalent mass} = \frac{\text{molar mass}}{\text{ionizable hydrogens}}$$

$$= \frac{136.2\text{ g}}{1} = 136.2\text{ g/equiv}$$

3. Calculate the number of equivalents of potassium hydrogen sulfate used.

$$\text{number of equivalents} = \frac{\text{mass}}{\text{gram equivalent mass}}$$

$$\text{equiv} = \frac{\text{mass}}{\text{gem}} = \frac{3.98\text{ g}}{136.2\text{ g/equiv}} = 0.0292\text{ equiv}$$

4. Determine the normality of your standard solution of potassium hydrogen sulfate. Be sure to use units properly in your calculation.

$$\text{normality} = \frac{\text{number of equivalents}}{\text{volume}}$$

$$\text{normality} = \frac{\text{equiv}}{\text{L}} = \frac{0.0292\text{ equiv}}{0.250\text{ L}} = 0.117N$$

5. Determine the volumes of acid and base used in each titration performed in Part B.

See Data Table 2 for sample data.

6. The normality of the sodium hydroxide solution is calculated with this equation:

$$\text{normality}_{\text{base}} = \text{normality}_{\text{acid}} \times \frac{\text{volume}_{\text{acid}}}{\text{volume}_{\text{base}}}$$

Calculate the normality of your sodium hydroxide solution for each titration. Record the value obtained for each trial, as well as the average value for all trials.

trial 1: $N_B = \frac{N_A \times V_A}{V_B} = \frac{(0.117N)(11.62\text{ mL})}{(11.44\text{ mL})} = 0.119N$

trial 2: $N_B = \frac{(0.117N)(10.71\text{ mL})}{(10.36\text{ mL})} = 0.121N$

Avg $N = \frac{(0.119N) + (0.121N)}{2} = 0.120N$

7. Determine the volume of 10% vinegar and sodium hydroxide solutions used in each titration.

See Data Table 3 for sample data.

Name ______________________ Date ________________ Class ________________

8. Using the average normality of sodium hydroxide that was calculated in problem 6, determine the normality of your 10% vinegar solution (ethanoic acid).

$$\text{normality}_{\text{acid}} = \text{normality}_{\text{base}} \times \frac{\text{volume}_{\text{base}}}{\text{volume}_{\text{acid}}}$$

Record the value for each trial and the average value.

$$N_A = N_B \times V_B$$

trial 1: $N_A = \frac{(0.120N)(17.35\text{ mL})}{(25.00\text{ mL})} = 0.0833N$

trial 2: $N_A = \frac{(0.120N)(17.22\text{ mL})}{(25.00\text{ mL})} = 0.0827N$

trial 3: $N_A = \frac{(0.120N)(17.41\text{ mL})}{(25.00\text{ mL})} = 0.0836N$

$$\text{Avg } N = \frac{(0.0833N) + (0.0827N) + (0.0836N)}{3} = 0.0832N$$

9. Examine the class results for the normality of vinegar. Account for any difference among these values.

Differences could be due to:

1. Students' different perceptions of the true end point of the titration.
2. Errors in determining mass and transferring the potassium hydrogen sulfate.
3. Incorrect reading of burets.
4. If different bottles of vinegar were used (especially different brands), it's highly probable that the concentrations of ethanoic acid vary from bottle to bottle.

10. Explain why the plastic bottles into which you transferred your potassium hydrogen sulfate and vinegar solutions had to be dry, but you could add distilled water to the titration flask at any time and not affect your results.

The potassium hydrogen sulfate and vinegar solutions must be added to dry containers to avoid changing the concentrations of the solutions (mass/volume). During the titration, it is the actual number of equivalents of acid (or base) that is important, not the concentration. Adding water dilutes the solution (changes the concentration), but it does not change the number of equivalents of acid or base.

Name ______________________ Date ________________ Class ______________

11. Why are the burets rinsed with the acid and base solutions before filling?

Rinsing the buret with small portions of a solution removes the distilled water from the buret and eliminates the need to dry the buret.

12. Use your data from this experiment to calculate the percent by mass of ethanoic acid present in commercial, undiluted vinegar.

The 10% dilution is 0.0832*N*.

$$0.0832N = \frac{0.0832 \text{ equiv.}}{\text{L}} \times \frac{60.0 \text{ g}}{1 \text{ equiv.}} = 4.99 \text{ g/L}$$

$$4.99 \text{ g/L} = 0.499 \text{ g/100 mL} = 0.499\% \text{ m/v}$$

The undiluted vinegar is 10 times as concentrated, or 4.99% (m/v) ethanoic acid.

13. Explain why you cannot prepare a standard sodium hydroxide solution by determining the mass of the solid and dissolving it in a measured amount of water, as you did with the potassium hydrogen sulfate.

It is impossible to accurately determine the mass of NaOH because it is deliquescent—it rapidly picks up water from the air.

GOING FURTHER

Develop a Hypothesis

Based on the results of this lab, develop a hypothesis about how the pH of the 10% solution of vinegar changes during the titration with NaOH. In what ways would the pH curves for the titration of ethanoic acid (vinegar), ascorbic acid (vitamin C), and citric acid (lemon juice) be the same? Different?

Design an Experiment

Propose an experiment to test your hypothesis. If resources are available and you have your teacher's permission, perform the experiment.

SALT HYDROLYSIS

Text Reference
Section 19.5

Time Required
30 minutes

Objectives
- Measure the pH of aqueous solutions of several salts.
- Interpret the measurements data to decide which salts are hydrolyzing salts.
- Explain the formation of nonneutral salt solutions by writing chemical equations for salt hydrolysis.

Advance Preparation
Sufficient distilled water for the experiment should be boiled before the lab period so that students can proceed directly to the pH measurements. Boiling for 15 minutes in an Erlenmeyer flask (add boiling chips) removes dissolved carbon dioxide and raises the pH to 6–7. The flask should be covered with a watch glass during cooling.

Indicator solutions and pH test papers are equally effective. The pH test papers are easier to use.

PURPOSE

To investigate the formation of nonneutral salt solutions.

BACKGROUND

Solutions of many salts are neutral, but some are acidic and others are basic. Neutralization of strong acids by strong bases produces neutral salts, such as NaBr and KNO_3. However, salts formed when weak acids neutralize strong bases or when strong acids neutralize weak bases are not neutral; these reactions produce hydrolyzing salts. The name *hydrolyzing salts* is given to those salts that are able to react with water to form hydronium ions or hydroxide ions, a process called *hydrolysis*.

In this experiment, you will measure the pH of solutions of various salts. You will analyze your results to determine if one of the ions produced in solution can react with water to produce hydronium ions or hydroxide ions.

MATERIALS (PER PAIR)

safety goggles
7 small or medium test tubes
test-tube rack
spatula
10-mL graduated cylinder
dropper pipet
freshly boiled distilled water
sodium chloride, NaCl
sodium ethanoate, CH_3COONa [I]
ammonium chloride, NH_4Cl [T] [I] [C]
sodium carbonate, Na_2CO_3
sodium hydrogen carbonate, $NaHCO_3$
sodium phosphate, Na_3PO_4 [I]
wide-range indicator solution or wide-range pH test paper (pH 1–14)

SAFETY FIRST!

In this lab, observe all precautions, especially the ones listed below. If you see a safety icon beside a step in the Procedure, refer to the list below for its meaning.

Caution: Wear your safety goggles. (All steps.)

Caution: Avoid skin contact with these chemicals. Some of them are toxic. (All steps.)

Note: Return or dispose of all materials according to the instructions of your teacher. (Step 6.)

Name ____________________ Date ______________ Class ______________

PROCEDURE

As you perform the experiment, record the results of your pH measurements in Data Table 1.

1. Place small quantities (less than pea size) of sodium chloride, sodium ethanoate, ammonium chloride, sodium carbonate, sodium hydrogen carbonate, and sodium phosphate into separate labeled test tubes. Place the tubes in a test-tube rack.
2. Add about 5 mL of cool, previously boiled distilled water to each tube. Flick each tube gently to dissolve the sample.
3. Add 2 drops of wide-range indicator solution to each tube, or dip a small piece of wide-range pH test paper into each tube.
4. Determine the pH of the solution in each tube by comparing the color of the solutions or test papers to a standard chart of indicator reactions.
5. Determine the pH of the boiled distilled water.
6. Dispose of the liquid wastes down the drain.

Use the following disposal method for chemical waste.

Disposal 2: All solutions used in this experiment.

Name ______________________ Date ______________ Class ______________

OBSERVATIONS

DATA TABLE 1: MEASUREMENT OF pH OF SALT SOLUTIONS		
Aqueous Solution	Chemical Formula	Approximate pH
sodium chloride	$NaCl$	6–7
sodium ethanoate	CH_3COONa	8–9
ammonium chloride	NH_4Cl	4–5
sodium carbonate	Na_2CO_3	10–11
sodium hydrogen carbonate	$NaHCO_3$	7–8
sodium phosphate	Na_3PO_4	10–11
boiled distilled water (control)	H_2O	6–7

ANALYSES AND CONCLUSIONS

1. Which salts produce neutral aqueous solutions?

sodium chloride, $NaCl$

2. Which salts produce acidic aqueous solutions?

ammonium chloride, NH_4Cl

3. Which salts produce basic aqueous solutions?

sodium ethanoate, CH_3COONa; sodium hydrogen carbonate, $NaHCO_3$

sodium carbonate, Na_2CO_3; sodium phosphate, Na_3PO_4

4. Why is it important to know the pH of the boiled distilled water?

The boiled distilled water serves as a reference, or control, so that any *changes* in pH caused by the addition of salt can be noted.

5. For each salt, write a balanced equation to show how it ionizes in solution.

$NaCl \longrightarrow Na^+ + Cl^-$

$NaC_2H_3O_2 \longrightarrow Na^+ + C_2H_3O_3{}^-$

$NH_4Cl \longrightarrow NH_4{}^+ + Cl_3{}^-$

$Na_2CO_3 \longrightarrow 2Na^+ + CO_3{}^{2-}$

$NaHCO_3 \longrightarrow Na^+ + HCO_3{}^-$

$Na_3PO_4 \longrightarrow 3Na^+ + PO_4{}^{3-}$

Name ______________ Date ______________ Class ______________

6. For each salt whose solution is acidic, write an additional equation to show which ion in solution reacts with water to produce the hydronium ion.

$NH_4^+ + H_2O \rightarrow NH_3 + H_3O^+$

7. For each salt whose solution is basic, write an additional equation to show which ion in solution reacts with water to produce the hydroxide ion.

$C_2H_3O_2^- + H_2O \rightarrow C_2H_3O_2H + OH^-$

$CO_3^{2-} + H_2O \rightarrow HCO_3^- + OH^-$

$HCO_3^- + H_2O \rightarrow H_2CO_3 + OH^-$

$PO_4^{3-} + H_2O \rightarrow HPO_4^{2-} + OH^-$

8. What do all the acids of the anions identified in problem 7 have in common?

They are all weak acids.

9. Would you expect a sodium salt to produce an acidic solution? Explain.

No. Sodium hydroxide is a strong base.

GOING FURTHER

Develop a Hypothesis

Based on the results of this lab, develop a hypothesis about whether solutions of other salts, such as sodium nitrate, sodium sulfate, ammonium sulfate, potassium sulfate, and $FeCl_3$, would be acidic or basic.

Sodium nitrate, sodium sulfate, and potassium sulfate are salts formed from the neutralization of a strong acid with a strong base and are expected to be neutral. Ammonium sulfate is a salt formed from the neutralization of a weak acid with a strong acid and is expected to produce an acidic solution.

Design an Experiment

Propose an experiment to test your hypothesis. If resources are available and you have your teacher's permission, perform the experiment.

Students should use a pH meter to test their predictions for solutions of the salts named above.

45 BUFFERS

Text Reference
Section 19.5

Time Required
30 minutes

Objective
- Measure the pH changes that occur when acid and bases are added to buffered and unbuffered solutions.

Advance Preparation

1M hydrochloric acid
Add 8.3 mL of concentrated HCl to 90 mL of distilled water and dilute to 100 mL. About 25 mL will meet the needs of 15 student pairs.

1M sodium hydroxide
Dissolve 4.0 g of NaOH in 80 mL of distilled water and dilute to 100 mL.

0.1M sodium carbonate
Dissolve 1.1 g of Na_2CO_3 in 90 mL of distilled water and dilute to 100 mL.

0.1M sodium hydrogen carbonate
Dissolve 0.84 g of $NaHCO_3$ in 90 mL of distilled water and dilute to 100 mL.

0.1M disodium hydrogen phosphate
Dissolve 3.6 g $Na_2HPO_4 \bullet 12H_2O$ in 80 mL of distilled water; dilute to 100 mL.

0.1M sodium dihydrogen phosphate
Dissolve 2.8 g $NaH_2PO_4 \bullet H_2O$ in 180 mL of distilled water; dilute to 200 mL.

PURPOSE

To investigate the capacity of buffered solutions to withstand addition of acid and base without undergoing a significant change in pH.

BACKGROUND

Your blood must be maintained at pH 7.35–7.45 for you to stay healthy. However, chemical reactions taking place in your body are continuously pumping a stream of hydrogen ions into your blood. Your body maintains the proper blood pH, in spite of the hydrogen ions, due to blood buffers. *Buffered solutions* maintain a relatively constant pH when limited amounts of acid or base are added to them.

What are buffers? They usually consist of solutions of a weak acid and its salt or of a weak base and its salt. For example, a solution containing ethanoic acid (CH_3COOH) and its salt, sodium ethanoate (CH_3COONa), is a buffer. A solution containing ammonia (NH_3) and its salt, ammonium chloride (NH_4Cl), is also a buffer. Sodium ethanoate is formed by the neutralization of ethanoic acid by sodium hydroxide. Ammonium chloride is formed by the neutralization of ammonia by hydrochloric acid. In other words, a buffer can be created by the partial neutralization of a weak acid by a strong base or by partial neutralization of a weak base by a strong acid.

In this experiment, you will examine the effectiveness of different buffering systems in resisting changes in pH.

MATERIALS (PER PAIR)

- safety goggles and apron
- glass-marking pencil
- 7 medium test tubes
- test-tube rack
- 10-mL graduated cylinder
- 2 50-mL beakers
- 2 dropper pipets
- 0.1*M* sodium carbonate, Na_2CO_3
- 0.1*M* sodium hydrogen carbonate, $NaHCO_3$
- 0.1*M* disodium hydrogen phosphate, Na_2HPO_4 [I]
- 0.1*M* sodium dihydrogen phosphate, NaH_2PO_4 [I]
- *boiled* distilled water
- wide-range indicator solution (pH 1–14) or wide-range pH paper (pH 1–14)
- 1*M* hydrochloric acid, HCl [I] [T] [C]
- 1*M* sodium hydroxide, NaOH [I] [C] [T]

Name ______________________ Date ______________ Class ______________

Other materials
Unboiled distilled water may produce a pH reading as low as 4. Boiling the water for 15 minutes in an Erlenmeyer flask (add boiling chips) removes dissolved CO_2 and raises the pH to 6–7. The flask should by covered with a watch glass or parafilm during cooling.

SAFETY FIRST!

In this lab, observe all precautions, especially the ones listed below. If you see a safety icon beside a step in the Procedure, refer to the list below for its meaning.

Caution: Wear your safety goggles. (All steps.)

Caution: Aqueous sodium hydroxide is an irritant at the concentration used in this experiment. It is corrosive and can cause severe burns. (Step 7.)

Caution: Never pick up a dropper bottle by its cap. Always hold a dropper with the lip lower than the rubber bulb so that the liquid does not run into the bulb. (Steps 5–8.)

Note: Return or dispose of all materials according to the instructions of your teacher. (Step 9.)

PROCEDURE

As you perform the experiment, record your results in Data Table 1.

1. Label seven medium test tubes with the numbers 1–7.
2. Mix 5 mL of 0.1*M* Na_2CO_3 and 5 mL of 0.1*M* $NaHCO_3$ in a 50-mL beaker. This is a carbonate/hydrogen carbonate (CO_3^{2-}/HCO_3^-) buffer. Divide this buffer solution equally between test tubes 1 and 2.
3. In another 50-mL beaker, mix 5 mL of 0.1*M* Na_2HPO_4 and 5 mL of 0.1*M* NaH_2PO_4. This is a monohydrogen phosphate/dihydrogen phosphate ($HPO_4^{2-}/H_2PO_4^-$) buffer. Divide this buffer solution equally between test tubes 3 and 4.
4. Put 5 mL of 0.1*M* $NaHCO_3$ in test tube 5, 5 mL of 0.1*M* Na_2HPO_4 in test tube 6, and 5 mL of cool, previously boiled distilled water in test tube 7.
5. Use a dropper to add 3 drops of wide-range indicator to each test tube. Estimate the pH of each solution by comparing your results with those in the color chart supplied with the indicator. Record the results in Data Table 1.
6. Use a dropper to add 1 drop of 1*M* HCl to tubes 1, 3, 5, 6, and 7. Flick the test tubes to mix, note the color changes, and record the results.

7. Use a dropper to add 2 drops of 1*M* NaOH to tubes 1, 3, 5, 6, and 7—the tubes that received the HCl solution. Flick the test tubes to mix and note the color changes. Estimate and record the pH.
8. (Optional) Add hydrochloric acid, drop by drop, to tubes 2 and 4. Flick the test tubes to mix until the pH drops to about 2. Record the number of drops required for this to occur.

9. Follow your teacher's instructions for proper disposal of the materials.

Step 3.
Show students that an ion such as $H_2PO_4^-$ is the conjugate acid (proton donor) of the $HPO_4^{2-}/H_2PO_4^-$ buffer pair. The HPO_4^{2-} ion is the conjugate base (proton acceptor).

$$H_2PO_4^- + OH^- \rightarrow HPO_4^{2-} + H_2O$$
$$HPO_4^{2-} + H^+ \rightarrow H_2PO_4^-$$

Use the following disposal method for chemical waste.

Disposal 3: All solutions used in this experiment.

Name ____________________ Date ____________ Class ____________

OBSERVATIONS

DATA TABLE 1: EFFECTS OF ACID AND BASE ON BUFFERED AND UNBUFFERED SOLUTIONS

Tube	Contents of Tube	Initial pH	pH After Adding 1 Drop HCl	pH After Adding 2 Drops NaOH	Number of Drops HCl Added (Optional)
1	CO_3^{2-}/HCO_3^-	9.5	9.5	9.5	—
2	CO_3^{2-}/HCO_3^-	9.5	—	—	20
3	$HPO_4^{2-}/H_2PO_4^-$	6.5	6.5	6.5	—
4	$HPO_4^{2-}/H_2PO_4^-$	6.5	—	—	22
5	0.1*M* $NaHCO_3$	8.0	8.0	9.5	—
6	0.1*M* NaH_2PO_4	5.0	5.0	6.0	—
7	Boiled distilled water	7.0	5.0	9.5	—

ANALYSES AND CONCLUSIONS

1. Based upon your experimental evidence, how effective are the CO_3^{2-}/HCO_3^- and $HPO_4^{2-}/H_2PO_4^-$ buffer systems? Explain your answer.

Both are good buffer systems because their pHs do not change perceptibly when small amounts of HCl or NaOH are added. Addition of the same amount of HCl to distilled water would cause its pH to decrease by 2 units. Addition of the same amount of base to distilled water would cause its pH to increase by 2 units.

2. Do 0.1*M* $NaHCO_3$ and 0.1*M* NaH_2PO_4 solutions buffer as effectively as the CO_3^{2-}/HCO_3^- and $HPO_4^{2-}/H_2PO_4^-$ systems? Explain your answer.

No. According to the experimental results, 0.1*M* $NaHCO_3$ buffers somewhat against addition of acids and bases. The solution, by itself, does not contain a buffer pair. However, a buffer pair is created when acid or base is added.

$$HCO_3^- + H_3O^+ \rightarrow 2H_2O + CO_2$$

$$HCO_3^- + OH^- \rightarrow CO_3^{2-} + H_2O$$

A similar situation holds for 0.1*M* NaH_2PO_4.

Name ______________________ Date ______________ Class ______________

3. Write equations for the reaction of the $HPO_4^{2-}/H_2PO_4^-$ buffer system with an acid and a base.

addition of acid: $HPO_4^{2-} + H_3O^+ \rightarrow H_2PO_4^- + H_2O$

addition of base: $H_2PO_4^- + OH^- \rightarrow HPO_4^{2-} + H_2O$

4. Write equations for the reaction of the CO_3^{2-}/HCO_3^- buffer system with an acid and a base.

addition of acid: $CO_3^{2-} + H_3O^+ \rightarrow HCO_3^- + H_2O$

addition of base: $HCO_3^- + OH^- \rightarrow CO_3^{2-} + H_2O$

5. Do all buffers maintain the pH in the same range? In a chemistry handbook, look up the pH range of buffers in the list that follows. Prepare and measure the pH of each buffer solution. How do your experimental results compare to the published values? Which of these buffer systems would be effective at pH 5.0?

Buffer System	pH Range
monohydrogen phosphate/dihydrogen phosphate	6.1–7.4
ethanoate/ethanoic acid	3.7–5.6
carbonate/hydrogen carbonate	9.2–11.0
phosphate/monohydrogen phosphate	11.0–12.0

The ethanoate/ethanoic acid buffer system would be effective at pH 5.0.

GOING FURTHER

Develop a Hypothesis

The carbonate buffer system plays an important role in maintaining proper blood pH. However, under certain conditions, the buffering capacity of blood may be overwhelmed. For example, pH can be affected by irregular breathing patterns that alter the balance of gases, such as CO_2, in the blood. Inhaled air contains 0.04% CO_2; exhaled air contains 4% CO_2. Based on the results of this lab, develop a hypothesis about how the concentration of dissolved CO_2 in an aqueous solution affects the pH of the solution.

Design an Experiment

Propose an experiment to test your hypothesis. If resources are available and you have your teacher's permission, perform the experiment.

Name ______________ Date ______________ Class ______________

46 OXIDATION–REDUCTION REACTIONS

Text Reference
Section 20.1

Time Required
30 minutes

Objectives
- Observe oxidation–reduction reactions involving metals and metallic ions.
- Based on the data, rank the metals in terms of ease of oxidation.

Advance Preparation

0.1M copper(II) nitrate
Dissolve 4.8 g of $Cu(NO_3)_2 \cdot 3H_2O$ in 170 mL of distilled water and dilute to 200 mL.

0.1M lead(II) nitrate
Dissolve 6.6 g of $Pb(NO_3)_2$ in 150 mL of distilled water and dilute to 200 mL.

0.1M zinc nitrate
Dissolve 6.0 g of $Zn(NO_3)_2 \cdot 6H_2O$ in 150 mL of distilled water and dilute to 200 mL.

Other materials
The metal strips must be polished to remove any oxide layer. It may be worthwhile to clean the strips before class in order to save time. If students polish the strips, they should hold the steel wool in a piece of paper or wear gloves to protect against steel slivers.

PURPOSE

To investigate and compare the relative reduction potentials of copper, lead, and zinc.

BACKGROUND

The rusting of iron and the combustion of gasoline are common examples of oxidation–reduction reactions. Oxidation reactions are also thought to be partly responsible for the aging of the human body. Every oxidation reaction involves a transfer of electrons from the substance oxidized to the substance reduced. A substance undergoing oxidation gives up, or loses, electrons; a substance undergoing reduction gains electrons. The ease with which a substance oxidizes depends on the substance. For example, iron oxidizes more easily than either silver or gold.

In this experiment, you will study some oxidation–reduction reactions that occur between metals and metal ions. On the basis of your experiments, you will organize these substances into a series according to their relative ease of oxidation.

MATERIALS (PER PAIR)

safety goggles
glass-marking pencil
9 small test tubes
10-mL graduated cylinder
test-tube rack
plastic wash bottle
3 strips of copper, Cu, each 0.25 mm × 0.50 cm × 2.00 cm
3 strips of lead, Pb, each 0.25 mm × 0.50 cm × 2.00 cm
3 strips of zinc, Zn, each 0.25 mm × 0.50 cm × 2.00 cm
steel wool
0.1*M* copper(II) nitrate, $Cu(NO_3)_2$ [T]
0.1*M* lead(II) nitrate, $Pb(NO_3)_2$ [T]
0.1*M* zinc nitrate, $Zn(NO_3)_2$ [I]
distilled water

SAFETY FIRST!

In this lab, observe all precautions, especially the ones listed below. If you see a safety icon beside a step in the Procedure, refer to the list below for its meaning.

Caution: Wear your safety goggles. (All steps.)

Caution: Use a piece of paper or gloves to hold the steel wool to avoid getting metal slivers in your hand. (Steps 1, 2.)

Name ____________________ Date ______________ Class ______________

Caution: Copper and lead compounds are toxic. (Steps 2, 3.)

Note: Return or dispose of all materials according to the instructions of your teacher. (Step 6.)

PROCEDURE

As you perform the experiment, record your observations in Data Table 1.

1. Polish the small metal strips of copper, lead, and zinc with steel wool.

2. Label three test tubes "$0.1M$ $Cu(NO_3)_2$." Add 3 mL of $0.1M$ copper(II) nitrate to each test tube. In one tube, place a strip of copper. In another, place a strip of lead. In the third, place a strip of zinc. Put the tubes in a test-tube rack.

3. Repeat Step 2, labeling the tubes "$0.1M$ $Pb(NO_3)_2$" and using $0.1M$ lead(II) nitrate in place of copper(II) nitrate.
4. Repeat Step 2, labeling the tubes "$0.1M$ $Zn(NO_3)_2$" and using $0.1M$ zinc nitrate in place of copper(II) nitrate.
5. Allow the test tubes to stand undisturbed for 5–10 minutes. Record your observations in Data Table 1, briefly describing evidence of any reaction.
6. Return the metal strips for reuse and dispose of the solutions as instructed by your teacher.

Use the following disposal methods for chemical waste.

Disposal 1: All metal strips: $Zn(s)$, $Cu(s)$, and $Pb(s)$.

Disposal 2: All reaction solutions except those that contain $Pb(NO_3)_2$.

Disposal 7: All reaction solutions that contain $Pb(NO_3)_2$.

Name ______________________ Date ________________ Class ________________

OBSERVATIONS

DATA TABLE 1: REACTIONS OF METALS AND METAL IONS			
	Cu^{2+}	Pb^{2+}	Zn^{2+}
Cu(*s*)	no reaction	no reaction	no reaction
Pb(*s*)	precipitate of copper	no reaction	no reaction
Zn(*s*)	precipitate of copper	precipitate of lead	no reaction

ANALYSES AND CONCLUSIONS

1. Write balanced equations for any reactions that you observed between solid metals and metal ions.

$Cu^{2+} + Pb(s) \rightarrow Pb^{2+} + Cu(s)$

$Cu^{2+} + Zn(s) \rightarrow Zn^{2+} + Cu(s)$

$Pb^{2+} + Zn(s) \rightarrow Zn^{2+} + Pb(s)$

2. Which metal was oxidized by both of the other two metals?

Zn

3. Which metal was oxidized by only one of the other two metals?

Pb

4. Which metal was oxidized by neither of the other metals?

Cu

5. Write balanced *half-reactions* for the *reduction* of each of the three metal ions used in this experiment. Write the equations so that the metal ions are shown as reactants and the solid metals are shown as products. List these half-reactions so that the most easily oxidized metal is given last.

$Cu^{2+} + 2e^{-} \rightarrow Cu(s)$

$Pb^{2+} + 2e^{-} \rightarrow Pb(s)$

$Zn^{2+} + 2e^{-} \rightarrow Zn(s)$

6. The relative ease of oxidation of the halogens is in this order: chlorine, bromine, iodine, with iodine the most easily oxidized. Design an experiment that would allow you to determine if the halogens are less easily or more easily oxidized than the metals used in this experiment.

The reduction half-reactions for the halogens are: $Cl_2 + 2e^- \rightarrow 2Cl^-$

$Br_2 + 2e^- \rightarrow 2Br^-$

$I_2 + 2e^- \rightarrow 2I^-$

The halogens are listed in order of decreasing ease of reduction. In problem 5, the metal ions are listed in order of decreasing ease of reduction. The question is, where do the halogens and metals fit on the same scale? The question can be answered by mixing a solution containing I^- ions with a solution containing Cu^{2+} ions. I^- is the most easily oxidized halide ion, and Cu^{2+} is the most easily reduced metal ion. If I_2 is more easily reduced than Cu^{2+}, the transfer of electrons from I^- to Cu^{2+} will occur.

$$Cu^{2+}(aq) + 2I^-(aq) \rightarrow Cu(s) + I_2(aq)$$

The reaction does not occur as written; therefore, I_2 is more easily reduced than Cu^{2+}.

GOING FURTHER

Develop a Hypothesis

Many metals, including the ones examined in this lab, are oxidized by aqueous solutions of acids to produce hydrogen gas and metal ions. Based on the results of this lab, propose a hypothesis about the relative ease with which lead, copper, and zinc would be oxidized by an acid. Extend your hypothesis to include other metals such as iron, tin, and aluminum and discuss any periodic trends in oxidation by acids that would exist for the various metals.

Design an Experiment

Propose an experiment to test your hypothesis. If resources are available and you have your teacher's permission, perform the experiment.

Name ______________ Date ______________ Class ______________

CORROSION

Text Reference
Sections 21.1 and 21.2

Time Required
Two 40-minute periods

Objectives
- Observe how different chemical environments affect the corrosion of iron.
- Investigate whether structural stress influences corrosion.
- Draw conclusions and make predictions based on data.

Advance Preparation
0.1M iron(II) sulfate
Dissolve 1.5 g of $FeSO_4$ in 90 mL of distilled water and dilute to 100 mL.

phenolphthalein indicator
Dissolve 1 g of phenolphthalein in 200 mL of 95% ethanol.

0.1M potassium ferricyanide
Dissolve 3.3 g of $K_3Fe(CN)_6$ in 80 mL of distilled water and dilute to 100 mL.

Use distilled water to prepare each of the solutions.

Solution Set 1
0.1M hydrochloric acid
Dilute 50 mL of 1*M* HCl to 500 mL.

0.1M sodium chloride
2.9 g NaCl/500 mL

0.1M sodium dichromate
13.1 g $Na_2Cr_2O_7 \cdot 2H_2O$/500 mL)

0.1M sodium hydroxide
2.0 g NaOH pellets/500 mL

PURPOSE

To investigate various physical and chemical conditions that may affect the corrosion of iron.

BACKGROUND

Each year, the corrosion of metals does untold damage to cars, homes, and factories. *Corrosion* is a complex reduction–oxidation (redox) reaction in which metals are changed to their oxides or other compounds. In a corrosion reaction, electrons flow from the anode to the cathode. The anode and the cathode may be two different parts of the metal being corroded, or the cathode may be a different object that is in electrical contact with the metal being corroded.

In this experiment, you will study a variety of factors involved in the corrosion of iron.

MATERIALS (PER PAIR)

safety goggles
gloves (optional)
6 small test tubes
test-tube rack
250-mL beaker
ring stand
ring support
wire gauze
gas burner
glass stirring rod
dropper pipet
pliers
2 petri dishes, with lids
9 uncoated iron nails, Fe
steel wool
litmus paper or Hydrion paper
agar, powdered
0.1*M* potassium ferricyanide, $K_3Fe(CN)_6$ [T]
phenolphthalein solution
thin zinc strip, Zn (0.25 mm thick, 0.2 cm × 5.0 cm)
copper wire, Cu (1.5 mm diameter, 10 cm long)
0.1*M* iron(II) sulfate, $FeSO_4$ [T]
distilled water

Solution Set 1

0.1*M* sodium hydroxide, NaOH [I]
0.1*M* sodium dichromate, $Na_2Cr_2O_7$ [T] [I]
0.1*M* sodium chloride, NaCl
0.1*M* hydrochloric acid, HCl [I]

Solution Set 2

0.1*M* potassium hydroxide, KOH [C] [T]
0.1*M* sodium carbonate, Na_2CO_3
0.1*M* potassium nitrate, KNO_3 [I]
0.1*M* nitric acid, HNO_3 [C] [T]

Name ______________________ Date ________________ Class ________________

Solution Set 2

0.1M nitric acid
Dilute 50 mL of 1*M* HNO_3 to 500 mL

0.1M potassium nitrate
5.1 g KNO_3/500 mL

0.1M sodium carbonate
5.3 g Na_2CO_3/500 mL

0.1M potassium hydroxide
2.8 g KOH/500 mL

Solution Set 3

0.1M sodium oxalate
6.7 g $Na_2C_2O_4$/500 mL

0.1M sodium phosphate
19.0 g $Na_3PO_4 \cdot 12H_2O$/500 mL

0.1M sodium thiocyanate
4.0 g NaSCN/500 mL

0.1M sulfuric acid
6 mL 18*M* H_2SO_4/L

Other materials
To save time, the agar suspension (sometimes called agar-agar) can be prepared in advance. Gelatin can be used in place of agar. Agar and gelatin are proteins. They do not dissolve in water to form true solutions; instead they produce colloidal dispersions, or gels. Do not forget to add the $K_3Fe(CN)_6$ and phenolphthalein to the agar gel before it sets.

Review safety procedures and caution students about the corrosive nature of acids and bases before they begin to work.

Step 1.
Cleaning and polishing of nails and strips may be done ahead of time to save time and obviate the use of gloves by students.

Solution Set 3

0.1*M* sodium phosphate, $NaPO_4$ [I]
0.1*M* sodium oxalate, $Na_2C_2O_4$ [T]
0.1*M* sodium thiocyanate, NaSCN [T]
0.1*M* sulfuric acid, H_2SO_4 [C]

SAFETY FIRST!

In this lab, observe all precautions, especially the ones listed below. If you see a safety icon beside a step in the Procedure, refer to the list below for its meaning.

Caution: Wear your safety goggles. (All steps.)

Caution: Nitric, hydrochloric, and sulfuric acids are irritating and corrosive. (Step 2.)

Caution: Sodium oxalate and sodium dichromate are toxic. Avoid contact with these chemicals. (Step 2.)

Caution: Never pick up a dropper bottle by its cap. (All steps.)

Caution: Potassium ferricyanide can react with acids and chromates to produce toxic fumes. (Steps 6, 11, 12.)

Caution: Read all labels carefully and mix chemicals only according to directions. (All steps.)

Caution: Exercise care when working with hot agar. It can cause severe burns to the skin. (Step 5.)

Note: Return or dispose of all materials according to the instructions of your teacher. (Step 14.)

PROCEDURE

As you perform the experiment, record your observations in Data Table 1.

Part A. Reaction of Iron with Aqueous Solutions (Day 1)

1. Clean five iron nails with steel wool. Place each nail in a separate small test tube.

2. Your teacher will assign you one of the three sets of chemicals listed in the Materials section. Fill each of four test tubes with a different solution from the set until each nail is just covered. Fill the fifth tube with distilled water. Put the tubes in a test-tube rack.
3. Use litmus or Hydrion paper to determine whether each solution is acidic, basic, or neutral. Record the results in Data Table 1.
4. Allow the test tubes to stand overnight. You will study them tomorrow, when you begin with Step 10.

Name ______________________ Date ________________ Class ________________

Part B. Effects of Stress, and Protection by Other Metals (Day 1)

5. Heat 100 mL of distilled water to boiling in a 250-mL beaker. Remove the gas burner. **CAUTION:** *Hot agar causes severe burns to the skin.* Add, while stirring, 1 g of powdered agar. Replace the burner; heat and stir the mixture until the agar forms a suspension. Be careful not to burn the agar. Stop heating and turn off the gas burner.

6. Add 5 drops of 0.1*M* potassium ferricyanide and 3 drops of phenolphthalein to the agar suspension. Stir to mix thoroughly. Allow the agar to cool, but not set, while you proceed to the next step.

Step 7.
Demonstrate how to clean the copper and zinc strips and how to wrap Cu and Zn around the nails.

7. Clean four irons nails with steel wool. Place one nail in a petri dish. Use pliers to bend a second nail into a right angle. Place the bent nail beside, but not touching, the straight nail (see Figure 47.1). Tightly wrap a 10-cm piece of copper wire around a third nail. Wrap the fourth nail tightly with a thin strip of zinc metal. Place these two metal-wrapped nails in a second petri dish. Be sure that the nails do not touch (see Figure 47.1).

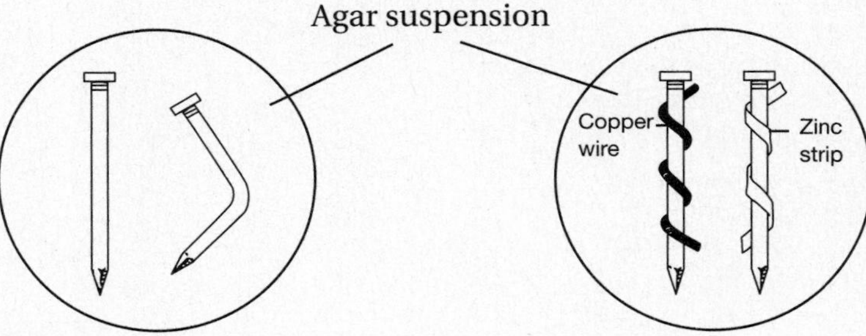

Figure 47.1

Step 8.
It is important to ensure that the nails are completely covered by agar. Uncovered portions will corrode in contact with air. The lids should be placed on the petri dishes to prevent agar from drying and cracking.

8. Pour the warm agar suspension into the petri dishes. The nails and attached pieces of metal should be covered by agar to a depth of at least 2 mm.
9. View the dishes against a white background and make observations at the end of the class period. Cover the dishes and keep them undisturbed overnight. You will observe them again tomorrow.

Name ______________________ Date ______________ Class ______________

Part C (Day 2)

10. Observe, against a white background, the test tubes that have stood overnight. In Data Table 1, record any evidence of reaction.

11. Test for the presence of ferrous ions, Fe^{2+}. In a separate small test tube, add one drop of 0.1*M* potassium ferricyanide to 1 mL of 0.1*M* iron(II) sulfate. Record your observations.

12. Now, test each of the five test tubes containing the nails for the presence of ferrous ions by adding 1 or 2 drops of 0.1*M* potassium ferricyanide. Record your observations. The presence of ferrous ions in the test tubes is evidence that corrosion has occurred.

13. Observe the dishes against a white background. Record your observations by sketching the dishes in Figure 47.2 on page 284. Show the location and color of any reaction products.

14. Follow your teacher's instructions for proper disposal of the materials.

Step 12.
To give a positive test with $Fe(CN)_6^{3-}$, a solution must contain Fe^{2+} ions. If the solution being tested has a pH > 5, the test will not work because the cations are present, not as ions in solution, but in an insoluble hydroxide. The K_{sp} value for the hydroxide is:

K_{sp} of $Fe(OH)_2 = 8 \times 10^{-16}$

This explains why solutions in which there was obvious corrosion of the nails did not all produce the blue color when tested with $Fe(CN)_6^{3-}$.

Step 13.
Nails may vary considerably in their manufacture and design. The color patterns obtained will be determined by the characteristics of the nails used.

Use the following disposal methods for chemical waste.

Disposal 1: Fe(*s*), Cu(*s*), and Zn(*s*).

Disposal 2: All other chemical wastes.

Name ______________________ Date ________________ Class ________________

OBSERVATIONS

DATA TABLE 1: OBSERVATIONS

Test Solution	pH	Initial Observations	Observations after 24 hours	*Test with $Fe(CN)_6^{3-}$
Set 1 $NaOH$	basic	clear colorless solution	no change in appearance of solution or nail	negative
$Na_2Cr_2O_7$	neutral	clear yellow solution	solution remained the same; rust appeared on nail	negative
$NaCl$	neutral	clear colorless solution	thick yellow gelatinous ppt. around nail; nail rusty	negative
HCl	acidic	clear colorless solution	clear colorless solution; gas produced; nail smaller in size but no evidence of rust	positive
Set 2 KOH	basic	clear colorless solution	thick yellow gelatinous ppt. around nail; nail rusty	negative
Na_2CO_3	basic	clear colorless solution	no change in appearance of ppt. around nail; nail rusty	negative
KNO_3	neutral	clear colorless solution	thick yellow gelatinous ppt. around nail; nail rusty	negative
HNO_3	acidic	clear colorless solution	solution changed to clear yellow; nail darkened in color	positive
Set 3 Na_3PO_4	basic	clear colorless solution	no change in appearance of solution; nail rusty	negative
$Na_2C_2O_4$	basic	clear colorless solution	no change in appearance of solution; nail rusty	negative
$NaSCN$	neutral	clear colorless solution	thick yellow gelatinous ppt. around nail; nail rusty	negative
H_2SO_4	acidic	clear colorless solution	clear colorless solution, gas produced, nail smaller in size but no evidence of rust	positive
Controls H_2O	neutral	clear colorless solution	no change in appearance of solution, nail rusty	negative
$FeSO_4$	reference test for presence of Fe^{2+} ions			positive

*Positive: production of blue color indicates the presence of Fe^{2+} ions in solution. Negative: no blue color

Name ____________________ Date ______________ Class ______________

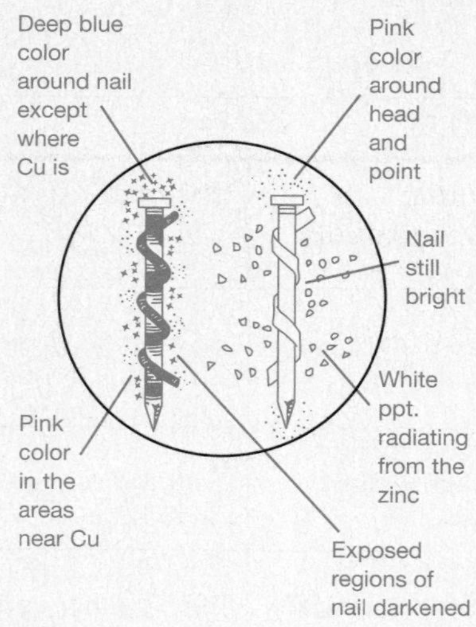

Figure 47.2

ANALYSES AND CONCLUSIONS

1. Obtain class data for the two sets of chemicals that you did not use in Part A. Enter this data in Data Table 1.

2. List the chemicals used in Part A for which there was no evidence of corrosion.

   Set 1, NaOH: The solution remained clear and colorless; the nail was not rusty.

3. List the chemicals used in Part A for which there was evidence of corrosion.

   Set 1: In the $Na_2Cr_2O_7$ and NaCl solutions, the nails were rusty. A thick yellow gelatinous ppt. of $Fe(OH)_2$ appeared around the nail in the $Na_2Cr_2O_7$ solution. The $Fe(CN)_6^{3-}$ test did not produce a blue color because there were no Fe^{2+} ions in solution. In HCl, the nail was free from rust, but it had decreased in size due to reaction with HCl. $Fe(CN)_6^{3-}$ produced a blue color, indicating the presence of Fe^{2+} ions in solution.

   Set 2: In the KOH, Na_2CO_3, and KNO_3 solutions, the nails were rusty. A thick yellow gelatinous ppt. of $Fe(OH)_2$ appeared around each nail in the KOH and KNO_3 solutions. None of these solutions contained Fe^{2+} in solution; they did not produce blue color with $Fe(CN)_6^{3-}$. In HNO_3, the nail was darker in color and the colorless HNO_3 turned yellow; the nail was reduced in size and the solution tested positive for Fe^{2+}.

   Set 3: In the Na_3PO_4, $Na_2C_2O_4$, and NaSCN solutions, the nails were rusty. A thick yellow gelatinous ppt. of $Fe(OH)_2$ appeared around the nail in

Name ______________________ Date ______________ Class ______________

the NaSCN solution. None of the solutions contained Fe^{2+} in solution; they did not produce a blue color with $Fe(CN)_6^{3-}$. In H_2SO_4, the nail was free from rust but much smaller in size due to reaction. The solution produced a blue color when tested with $Fe(CN)_6^{3-}$, indicating the presence of Fe^{2+} in solution.

Distilled water: The nail became rusty and was surrounded by a thin yellow gelatinous ppt. of $Fe(OH)_2$. It did not produce a blue with $Fe(CN)_6^{3-}$ because no Fe^{2+} ions were in solution.

4. Did either copper or zinc appear to protect the iron nail against corrosion? Explain.

The zinc protected the iron nail from corrosion. The nail stayed bright and free from rust.

5. Explain how the colors that developed in the petri dishes identify the anode and cathode for each reaction.

A pink color appeared around the cathode regions of the nails. At the cathode, reduction of O_2 takes place: $O_2 + 2H_2O + 4e^- \rightarrow 4OH^-$. The production of OH^- ions turns the phenolphthalein (in the agar gel) pink. The locations where the iron nails corrode are the anode regions. The agar turns a deep blue color as the Fe^{2+} ions in these locations react with $Fe(CN)_6^{3-}$. $K^+ + Fe^{2+} + Fe(CN)_6^{3-} \rightarrow KFe(Fe(CN)_6)$.

6. What were the usual sites where corrosion took place for the nails embedded in the agar?

Corrosion took place around the central region of both unwrapped nails. There was no evidence of corrosion at either head or point. The heads of the nails were acting as the cathodes—the agar in these regions was colored pink.

7. Examine the data for Part A. Are there any ions that seem to inhibit corrosion or to promote it? Try to explain these effects.

Corrosion of the iron nails did not take place in the NaOH solution. In the other solutions that tested basic or neutral, the nails rusted and a thick yellow gelatinous ppt. of $Fe(OH)_2$ was produced. In the strongly acidic solutions, the nails slowly dissolved and Fe^{2+} ions were produced in solution.

8. Explain the results obtained in distilled water.

The distilled water was saturated with air. The presence of oxygen initiated oxidation (corrosion) of the iron nail.

Name ______________________ Date ________________ Class ________________

9. Consider your answer to problem 6. What effect does bending seem to have on the tendency of iron to corrode?

With the nails used, there was no evidence that bending the nails accelerated corrosion at those locations.

10. Explain the effects caused by wrapping the nails with zinc or copper. Discuss the relative ease of oxidation of iron, zinc, and copper in your answer.

The nail wrapped with copper wire corroded (the agar gel became blue in color) along its length. The nail wrapped with zinc showed no evidence of corrosion. Instead, there was evidence that the zinc corroded: a white ppt. of $Zn(OH)_2$ formed around the zinc. With the copper-wrapped nail:

anode: $Fe \rightarrow Fe^{2+} + 2e^-$ cathode: $O_2 + 2H_2O + 4e^- \rightarrow 4OH^-$

With zinc-wrapped nail:

anode: $Zn \rightarrow Zn^{2+} + 2e^-$ cathode: $O_2 + 2H_2O + 4e^- \rightarrow 4OH^-$

Ease of oxidation: Cu < Fe < Zn

11. Is it correct to say that corrosion did not take place in the nail wrapped with zinc? Explain.

No. Although the nail itself showed no evidence of corrosion, the zinc did show evidence of corrosion.

GOING FURTHER

Develop a Hypothesis

Based on the results of this lab, propose a hypothesis about other ways of preventing or retarding the corrosion of iron-based materials.

The nails could be painted (oil paint, latex paint), coated with plastic, or electroplated (with Ni or Cr). Before pouring agar on the nails, adjust its pH to produce pHs of 5 and 9, as well as neutral. Use magnesium ribbon and aluminum foil to wrap the nails. Obtain some copper nails and wrap them with various metals. Oxygen could be excluded from the system.

Design an Experiment

Propose an experiment to test your idea(s). If resources are available and you have your teacher's permission, perform the experiment.

Name ______________________ Date ________________ Class ________________

48 ELECTROCHEMISTRY

Text Reference
Section 21.3

Time Required
40 minutes

Objectives
- Construct an electrolytic cell.
- Examine the use of an electrolytic cell to electroplate a metal.
- Learn how the direction of current through an electrolytic cell can be manipulated to reverse the electroplating process.

Impure metallic copper is purified using a cell similar to the one in Figure 48.1. A thin sheet of very pure copper is made into the cathode; a chunk of impure copper connected to the positive terminal functions as the anode. The electrodes are immersed in a copper(II) sulfate and sulfuric acid solution. When the circuit is closed, copper from the impure anode is oxidized and goes into solution. Cu^{2+} ions are reduced and plate out on the pure copper cathode. The impurities, called anode mud, collect beneath the anode. This mud contains valuable metals such as gold, platinum, and silver.

Advance Preparation
1M copper(II) sulfate
Add 250.0 g of $CuSO_4 \cdot 5H_2O$ to 700 mL of distilled water and dilute to 1 L. Approximately 2 L will be required to meet the needs of 15 student lab pairs.

PURPOSE

To investigate the use of electrolytic cells to cause chemical changes.

BACKGROUND

It is common for manufactured products to be coated with a very thin layer of metal. For example, maybe you've eaten with silver-plated tableware. Your watchband, belt buckle, or jewelry may be gold-plated. All these plated items were produced using the electroplating process. *Electroplating* consists of depositing a thin layer of metal on another metal, either to protect the surface from corrosion or for a decorative effect. An electrolytic cell set up to electroplate a fork with a silver coating is shown in Figure 48.1. When the fork is being silver-plated, the anode metal is silver, the electrolytic solution is aqueous silver nitrate, and the cathode is the fork. The fork becomes silver-plated as a result of the reduction of Ag^+ ions, from the solution, at the cathode.

$$Ag^+(aq) + e^- \rightarrow Ag(s) \quad \text{reduction}$$

At the same time, the silver ions are replenished by oxidation of silver atoms at the anode.

$$Ag^+(s) \rightarrow Ag^+(aq) + e^- \quad \text{oxidation}$$

In this experiment, you will electroplate a metal object using a typical electrolytic cell. You will then remove the plating by reversing the direction of flow of electrons in the electrolytic cell.

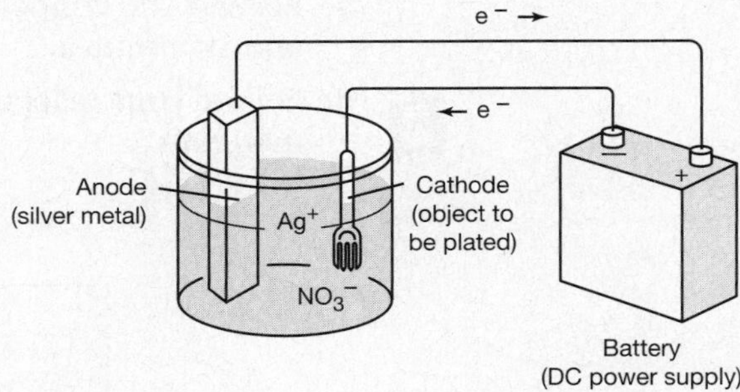

Figure 48.1

MATERIALS (PER PAIR)

safety goggles
gloves (optional)
4 alligator clips
250-mL beaker
100-mL graduated cylinder
6-volt battery
silver coin
steel wool
2 copper wire lengths
copper strip, Cu, 0.25 mm thick, 1 cm × 5 cm
1*M* copper(II) sulfate, $CuSO_4$ [T]
paper towels

Name ____________ Date ____________ Class ____________

SAFETY FIRST!

In this lab, observe all precautions, especially the ones listed below. If you see a safety icon beside a step in the Procedure, refer to the list below for its meaning.

Caution: Wear your safety goggles. (All steps.)

Caution: Use a piece of paper or gloves to hold the steel wool to avoid getting metal slivers in your hand. (Steps 1, 2.)

Note: Return or dispose of all materials according to the instructions of your teacher. (Step 6.)

PROCEDURE

As you perform the experiment, record your observations in Data Table 1.

1. Thoroughly clean a small silver object, such as a coin, with steel wool. Securely attach, with an alligator clip, a 25-cm length of copper wire to the object.
2. Polish a 1-cm × 5-cm strip of copper with steel wool. Use an alligator clip to attach a 25-cm length of copper wire to the strip.
3. Add 100 mL of 1*M* $CuSO_4$ to a 250-mL beaker and set up a system similar to that shown in Figure 48.2.
4. Use an alligator clip to connect the wire attached to the object to the negative terminal of a 6-volt battery. Use another alligator clip to connect the wire attached to the copper strip to the positive terminal. The object and the copper strip should not touch. Record your observations after 5 minutes have elapsed.
5. Reverse the connections and record your observations after 5 and 10 minutes.
6. Follow your teacher's instructions for proper disposal of the materials.

Step 4.
Explain to students why a direct current (DC) and not an alternating current (AC) must be used in electroplating.

No disposal required. All solutions may be reused. Reuse the beakers of copper(II) sulfate throughout the school day. Then save the solutions for use next year. If the solution becomes cloudy, add a few drops of 1*M* sulfuric acid until the solution clears.

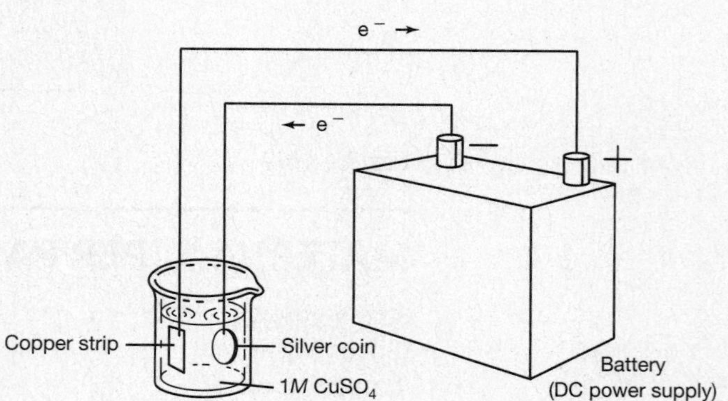

Figure 48.2

Name ______________________ Date ________________ Class ______________

OBSERVATIONS

DATA TABLE 1: OBSERVATIONS OF ELECTROPLATING	
Time of Observation	Condition of Coin
after 5 minutes of current flow	Coin becomes copper-plated.
5 minutes after reversal of current flow	Copper plate leaves coin.
10 minutes after reversal of current flow	Copper plate on coin disappears.

ANALYSES AND CONCLUSIONS

1. Write equations for the reactions that occur at the anode and at the cathode during electroplating.

   anode: $Cu(s) \rightarrow Cu^{2+}(aq) + 2e^-$

   cathode: $Cu^{2+} + 2e^- \rightarrow Cu(s)$

2. What is oxidized in this experiment? At which electrode does oxidation occur?

   Copper metal is oxidized at the anode because it loses electrons, producing Cu^{2+} ions.

3. What is reduced in this experiment? At which electrode does reduction take place?

   Copper ions are reduced at the cathode because they gain electrons, producing copper metal.

4. To which battery terminal must an object be attached for it to become electroplated?

   The object to be electroplated must be attached to the negative terminal.

5. Sketch your electrochemical cell. Show the direction of ion movement and electron flow.

Name ______________________ Date ________________ Class ______________

6. The dry cell or battery used in this experiment is an example of a voltaic cell. Explain the construction of a voltaic cell. Explain how a voltaic cell produces an electric current. What conditions can result in a "dead" battery? How does a car battery differ from the battery used in a flashlight?

A voltaic cell consists of two electrodes, an external pathway to allow for the transfer of electrons, and a medium that allows charge transfer. As oxidation occurs at the anode, electrons travel through the external circuit to the cathode, where reduction occurs. The electrons in the external circuit produce the electric current.

A dead battery can be caused by a short circuit that renders the cell useless or by the consumption of the anode and cathode materials over time.

A typical 12-volt lead storage (car) battery consists of six cells. The cathode of each cell is composed of lead(IV) oxide; the anode of each cell is composed of lead. Both electrodes are immersed in sulfuric acid.

There are a number of varieties of dry cells (flashlight batteries). One type consists of a zinc-can anode in contact with a paste of NH_4Cl, MnO_2, and carbon. The cathode is a graphite rod inserted in the paste.

GOING FURTHER

Develop a Hypothesis

In this lab, you used a dry cell, or voltaic cell, to bring about a chemical reaction. Develop a hypothesis about how a photovoltaic cell could be used to drive a chemical process. For example, how can solar energy be used to drive a chemical process? How might solar energy be converted into a form of chemical energy that could be stored and used later?

____

____

Design an Experiment

Propose an experiment to test your idea(s). If resources are available and you have your teacher's permission, perform the experiment.

____

____

Name ______________________ Date ________________ Class ________________

49 HYDROCARBONS: A STRUCTURAL STUDY

Text Reference
Section 22.4

Time Required
50 minutes

Objectives
- Make three-dimensional models of hydrocarbon molecules.
- Compare the three-dimensional models with the structural formulas of organic compounds.
- Use models as visual aids to learn about structural and geometric isomers.

Advance Preparation
Have enough ball-and-stick molecular model sets so that students may work in groups of four or fewer.

Space-filling models can be substituted if available. Demonstrate the difference between space-filling and ball-and-stick models of a molecule such as methane. (The size of an atom in space-filling models is in proportion to its van der Waals radius.)

Students need to know how to apply VSEPR theory to predict shapes of molecules.

PURPOSE

To investigate the three-dimensional shapes of hydrocarbon molecules by building molecular models.

BACKGROUND

The physical, chemical, and biological properties of molecules are determined, to a large extent, by their three-dimensional shapes. Often, a molecular compound in which the molecules are packed closely together forms large, dramatic crystals. When the molecules are not packed closely together, a molecular compound may remain a liquid, even at low temperatures. An understanding of molecular shapes is particularly important in organic chemistry and biochemistry. For example, many prescription and over-the-counter drugs are effective because their shapes resemble those of molecules produced by cells in the body.

Most people find it easier to think in three dimensions when they use three-dimensional models. By working with molecular models, you can learn to visualize and understand molecular shapes. In this experiment, you will use ball-and-stick models to study the shapes of hydrocarbon molecules.

MATERIALS (PER GROUP)

safety goggles
ball-and-stick molecular model kit

SAFETY FIRST!

In this lab, observe the precaution listed below.

Caution: Wear your safety goggles. (All steps.)

Name ______________________ Date ________________ Class ________________

PROCEDURE

Refer to Data Table 1 for the color code of the atoms. As you construct each model, complete Data Tables 2A and 2B.

Modify Data Table 1, if necessary, to match the colors in your molecular model sets.

DATA TABLE 1: COLOR CODE FOR MODELS	
Color	**Atom Represented**
black	carbon
yellow	hydrogen
red	oxygen
blue	nitrogen
green	chlorine
purple	iodine
orange	bromine

Part A. Continuous-Chain and Branched-Chain Alkanes

1. Make a model of methane, CH_4. Are all the angles formed by any two C—H bonds the same?

   Yes. Each is 109.5°.

2. Make a model of ethane, C_2H_6. What happens when you hold one carbon and its attached hydrogens in a fixed position and rotate the other carbon and its attached hydrogens?

   There is free rotation about the C—C bond.

3. Make a model of propane, C_3H_8. Can this model be rearranged to form a different molecule? Explain.

   No. There is only one structural formula possible.

4. Make a model of butane, C_4H_{10}. Can this model be rearranged to form a molecule that has the same molecular formula but a different structural formula? If so, name the structures. Molecules that have the same molecular formula, but different structural formulas, are called *structural isomers*.

   Yes. The structures are butane and 2-methyl propane.

Name ______________ Date ______________ Class ______________

5. Make a model of pentane, C_5H_{12}. Construct as many structural isomers of pentane as you can. For each structural isomer, list the name of the compound here and draw a sketch in Data Table 2A.

pentane; 2-methylbutane; 2, 2-dimethylpropane

Part B. Cycloalkanes

6. Construct a model of hexane, C_6H_{14}. Remove two hydrogen atoms from the model so that the carbon atoms of the end of the chain can join together to form a ring. This ring structure is cyclohexane C_6H_{12}.

Manipulate your cyclohexane molecule so that two carbons directly across the ring from each other are above the plane of the other four carbons. This is called the *boat conformation.* Now manipulate the molecule so that one of these carbons is above, and the other below, the plane of the remaining four carbons. This is called the *chair conformation.* In Data Table 2A, draw these two conformations.

Is there free rotation about a C—C bond in cyclohexane?

no

Part C. Alkenes and Geometric Isomers

7. Make a model of ethene, C_2H_4. What happens when you try to rotate the carbons about the double bond?

They do not rotate freely.

8. Remove one hydrogen from each carbon in ethene and replace it with a chlorine. The name of the resulting compound is 1,2-dichloroethene, $C_2H_2Cl_2$. There are two structures possible for this compound. They are called *geometric isomers,* and are distinguished by the prefix *cis-* or the prefix *trans-*. In the *cis* configuration, the chlorines are on the same side of the double bond. In the *trans* configuration, the chlorines are on opposite sides of the double bond. Construct models of both geometric isomers.

9. Make a model of butene, C_4H_8. This compound has two structural isomers. Name these isomers and, in Data Table 2B, give their molecular and structural formulas. Are there also geometric (*cis* and *trans*) isomers for butene?

yes if 2-butene; no if 1-butene.

Name ______________________ Date __________________ Class __________________

Park D. Alkynes

10. Make a model of ethyne, C_2H_2. In the space provided in Data Table 2B, describe the shape of the molecule. Can you rotate the molecule about the triple bond?

no

Part E. Arenes

11. Make a model of benzene, C_6H_6, using alternating single and double bonds to approximate the aromatic bonds. Do all the atoms in this molecule lie in the same plane?

yes

Can benzene exist in the boat and chair conformations?

no

Name ______________________ Date ______________ Class ______________

OBSERVATIONS

DATA TABLE 2A: INFORMATION ON MOLECULAR MODELS

Methane molecular formula CH_4

Structural Formula: Sketch:

```
    H
    |
H — C — H
    |
    H
```

H—C—H angle? All 109.5°

Ethane molecular formula C_2H_6

Structural Formula: Sketch:

```
    H   H
    |   |
H — C — C — H
    |   |
    H   H
```

Rotation around C—C bond? yes

Propane molecular formula C_3H_8

Structural Formula: Sketch:

```
    H   H   H
    |   |   |
H — C — C — C — H
    |   |   |
    H   H   H
```

Isomers? no

Butane molecular formula C_4H_{10}

Structural Formula: Sketch:

butane

```
    H   H   H   H
    |   |   |   |
H — C — C — C — C — H
    |   |   |   |
    H   H   H   H
```

Pentane molecular formula C_5H_{12}

Structural Formula: Sketch:

pentane

```
    H   H   H   H   H
    |   |   |   |   |
H — C — C — C — C — C — H
    |   |   |   |   |
    H   H   H   H   H
```

2-methylbutane

```
        H   H
        |   |
H3C  —  C — C — CH3
        |   |
       CH3  H
```

2, 2-dimethylpropane

```
        CH3
        |
H3C  —  C — CH3
        |
        CH3
```

Cyclohexane molecular formula C_6H_{14}

Structural Formula: Sketch:

```
      CH2
  H2C     CH2
   |       |
  H2C     CH2
      CH2
```

Conformations

Chair: Boat:

Rotation around C—C bond? no

Name ______________________ Date ______________ Class ______________

DATA TABLE 2B: INFORMATION ON MOLECULAR MODELS

Ethene molecular formula C_2H_4

Structural Formula: Sketch:

$CH_2 = CH_2$

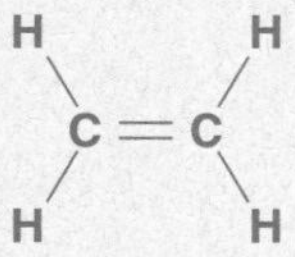

```
H       H
 \     /
  C = C
 /     \
H       H
```

Rotation around C=C bond? no

1,2-dichloroethene molecular formula $H_2C_2Cl_2$

Structural Formula: Sketch:

ClHC = CHCl

cis-

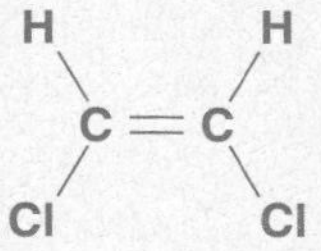

```
H       H
 \     /
  C = C
 /     \
Cl      Cl
```

trans-

```
H       Cl
 \     /
  C = C
 /     \
Cl      H
```

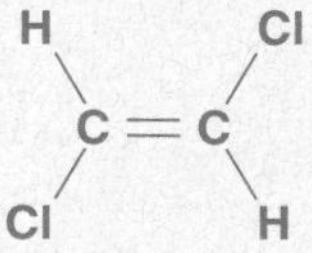

Butene molecular formula C_4H_8

Structural Formulas: Structural Isomers Sketch:

1-butene

$CH_2 = CH - CH_2 - CH_3$

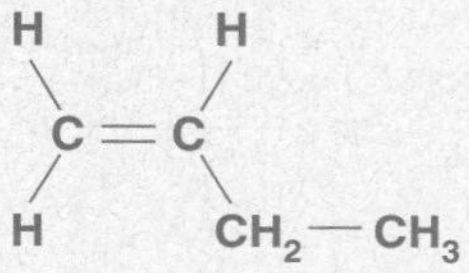

```
H       H
 \     /
  C = C
 /     \
H       CH2 — CH3
```

2-butene

$CH_3 - CH = CH - CH_3$

Geometric Isomers Sketch:

cis-2-butene

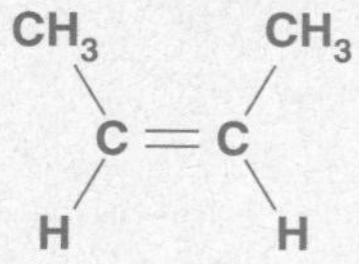

```
CH3     CH3
   \   /
   C = C
   /   \
H       H
```

trans-2-butene

```
CH3     H
   \   /
   C = C
   /   \
H       CH3
```

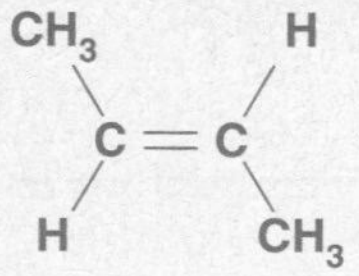

Ethyne molecular formula C_2H_2

Structural Formula: Sketch

HC ≡ CH

Shape? linear

Rotation around C≡C bond? no

Benzene molecular formula C_6H_6

Structural Formula: Sketch:

```
      CH
    //  \
  HC     CH
  |      ||
  HC     CH
    \\  /
      CH
```

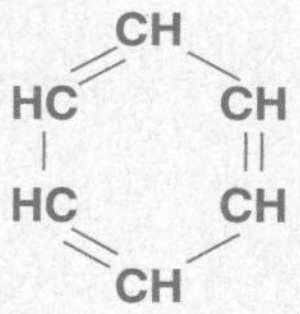

Is the molecule planar? yes

Chair and boat conformations? no

Name ______________________ Date ________________ Class ________________

GOING FURTHER

Do Research

The pigment in your eyes that responds to visible light is a compound known as 11-*cis*-retinal. This compound is a *polyene,* a hydrocarbon derivative that consists of a network of alternating single and double bonds. 11-*cis*-retinal interacts with visible light in a process known as *photoisomerization*. The energy of light is converted into atomic motion—a necessary part of vision. Do research on the structure of 11-*cis*-retinal and its role in vision. Construct a model to show how the *cis-trans* isomerization leads to a dramatic change in the shape of the molecule, and explain the role that this conformational change plays in vision.

Cis **and** ***trans*** **configurations differ in 3-D orientation about the double bond between the 11th and 12th carbon atoms. The** ***cis*** **configuration places both bulky groups on the same side of the double bond, leaving a large open space for the opsin molecule to bond. The** ***trans*** **configuration closes up a part of the open space and forces out the opsin molecule. Construction of a ball-and-stick model should help students visualize what happens when the double bond between C-11 and C-12 is temporarily broken, allowing 180° rotation about the resulting single bond before the double bond is reestablished. This shifting of the double bond and rotation is the** ***cis-trans*** **isomerization that occurs when the eye is exposed to light. Absorption of light energy by the** ***cis*** **form allows us to see images in the visible region.**

Name ______________________ Date __________________ Class ________________

50 ESTERS OF CARBOXYLIC ACIDS

Text Reference
Section 23.3

Time Required
40 minutes

Objectives

- Observe several different acid-catalyzed reactions of carboxylic acids with alcohols to form esters.
- Describe the odor of the ester products.

PURPOSE

To synthesize various esters from carboxylic acids and alcohols.

BACKGROUND

Did you know the aromas of bananas, strawberries, and other fruits are the result of organic chemistry? Esters account for the distinctive odors of many fruits. Many of these ester compounds have pleasant odors. You can synthesize an ester in the lab by heating a carboxylic acid in an alcohol solution containing a small amount of strong acid as a catalyst.

$$\underset{\text{carboxylic acid}}{R{-}CO_2H} + \underset{\text{alcohol}}{R'{-}OH} \overset{H^+}{\rightleftharpoons} \underset{\text{ester}}{R{-}CO_2R'} + \underset{\text{water}}{H_2O}$$

In this experiment, you will react carboxylic acids and alcohols, in the presence of a strong acid catalyst, to form esters.

Advance Preparation
Caution: Concentrated H_2SO_4 can react so vigorously with organic matter that explosions can occur. To minimize this risk, keep the quantity of 18*M* H_2SO_4 at each lab station very small. Do not dispense in dropper bottles with rubber bulbs. Caution students to read all labels carefully and never to add water to the container of 18*M* H_2SO_4.

MATERIALS (PER PAIR)

safety goggles
glass-marking pencil
5 medium test tubes
test-tube rack
10-mL graduated cylinder
dropper pipet
ring stand
ring support
2 250-mL beakers
wire gauze
gas burner
thermometer
90% methanoic acid, HCOOH [T] [F] [C]
glacial ethanoic acid, CH_3COOH [T] [F] [C]
salicylic acid, $C_6H_4OHCOOH$ [T]
methanol, CH_3OH [T] [F]
ethanol, C2H5OH [T] [F]
2-methyl-1-propanol, C_4H_9OH [T] [F]
1-pentanol, $C_5H_{11}OH$ [T] [F]
1-octanol, $C_8H_{17}OH$ [T] [F]
18*M* sulfuric acid, H_2SO_4 [T] [C]
ice
distilled water

Demonstrate the technique for wafting vapors toward the nose. Students must not attempt to taste esters!

SAFETY FIRST!

In this lab, concentrated H_2SO_4 is used to catalyze a chemical reaction. It is strongly recommended that your teacher assist during this procedure. Observe all precautions, especially the ones listed below. If you see a safety icon beside a step in the Procedure, refer to the list below for its meaning.

Caution: Wear your safety goggles. (All steps.)

Name ______________________ Date ________________ Class ________________

Some additional flavor esters are as follows:

Name: ethyl methanoate
Formula: $HCOOCH_2CH_3$
Odor/Flavor: rum

Name: ethyl butyrate
Formula: $CH_3(CH_2)_2COOCH_2CH_3$
Odor/Flavor: pineapples

Name: pentyl butyrate
Formula: $CH_3(CH_2)_2COO(CH_2)_4CH_3$
Odor/Flavor: apricots

Name: methyl butyrate
Formula: $CH_3(CH_2)_2COOCH_3$
Odor/Flavor: apples

Caution: All acids are corrosive, and several of the carboxylic acids used in this experiment are concentrated and particularly hazardous. (All steps.)

Caution: The chemicals used in this experiment are toxic. Avoid contact with these chemicals. (All steps .)

Caution: Alcohols are flammable liquids. Do not dispense these compounds near an open flame. (Step 2.)

Caution: Mix chemicals only according to directions. Never add water to 18*M* sulfuric acid. Never add 18*M* sulfuric acid to any other concentrated acid or to an alcohol.

Note: Return or dispose of all materials according to the instructions of your teacher. (Step 4.)

PROCEDURE

As you perform the experiment, record your observations in Data Table 1.

1. **CAUTION:** *The acids used in this experiment are extremely corrosive.* Label five medium test tubes with the numbers 1–5. Put the tubes in a test-tube rack. To each of the tubes, add 1 mL of a carboxylic acid and 1 mL of an alcohol, as listed in Data Table 1. In the case of the solid carboxylic acid, salicylic acid, add 1 g of acid and 1 mL of alcohol to the tube.

Step 2.
Note: It is strongly recommended that you add the drops of 18*M* H_2SO_4.

2. **CAUTION:** *Keep containers of alcohols and carboxylic acids away from flames.* Add 3–5 drops of concentrated sulfuric acid to each tube and heat the tubes in a water bath at 60°C for 10–15 minutes.
3. Turn off the burner and remove the test tubes from the hot water bath. Cool the tubes in an ice bath. Add 5 mL of distilled water to each tube. Any ester produced in the reaction will float on the water in the tube. Note the odor of the ester by wafting the fumes toward your nose with your hand. Try to relate each odor to a familiar fruit, flower, or vegetable. Record your observations in Data Table 1.

Use the following disposal method for chemical waste.

Disposal 3: All reaction solutions used in this experiment.

4. Follow your teacher's instructions for proper disposal of the materials.

Name ______________________ Date ________________ Class ________________

OBSERVATIONS

DATA TABLE 1: RESULTS AND CONCLUSIONS

Test Tube	Carboxylic Acid	Alcohol	Ester Synthesized	Odor of Ester
1	methanoic acid	2-methyl-1-propanol	isobutyl methanoate	raspberries
2	glacial ethanoic acid	ethanol	ethyl ethanoate	ripe fruit
3	glacial ethanoic acid	1-pentanol	pentyl ethanoate	bananas
4	glacial ethanoic acid	1-octanol	octyl ethanoate	oranges
5	salicylic acid	methanol	methyl salicylate	oil of wintergreen

ANALYSES AND CONCLUSIONS

1. Complete Data Table 1 by naming the esters that were synthesized in the experiment.

2. Write a general equation for the acid-catalyzed formation of an ester from an alcohol and a carboxylic acid.

$$R{-}CO_2H + R'{-}OH \overset{H^+}{\rightleftharpoons} R{-}CO_2R' + H_2O$$

3. Why was water added to the tube before you were asked to smell it? (**Hint:** What was in the water layer in the test tube?) To answer this question, discuss the relative solubility of acids, alcohols, and esters in water.

The esters are not soluble in water. The esters are also less dense than water. As a result, upon addition of water, the esters float to the surface of the test tube where they are exposed to the air. Their odor is, thus, more obvious to the investigator.

4. Why were the reactions kept free of water during heating?

The reaction for the production of an ester is reversible:

$$\text{acid} + \text{alcohol} \rightleftharpoons \text{ester} + \text{water}$$

According to Le Châtelier's principle, since water is a product of the reaction, the addition of water will force the reaction to the left. Thus, the yield of ester will decrease.

Name ______________________ Date ______________ Class ______________

5. Write equations for each of the esterfication reactions in this experiment. Use structural formulas in the equations and write the name of each compound below its structural formula.

$$HCOOH + CH_3CH(CH_3)CH_2OH \overset{H^+}{\rightleftharpoons} HC(=O)-O-CH_2CH(CH_3)CH_3 + H_2O$$

methanoic acid; 2-methyl-1-propanol (isobutyl alcohol); isobutyl formate; water

$$CH_3COOH + CH_3CH_2OH \overset{H^+}{\rightleftharpoons} CH_3C(=O)-O-CH_2CH_3 + H_2O$$

ethanoic acid; ethanol; ethyl ethanoate; water

$$CH_3COOH + CH_3CH_2CH_2CH_2CH_2OH \overset{H^+}{\rightleftharpoons} CH_3C(=O)-O-CH_2CH_2CH_2CH_2CH_3 + H_2O$$

ethanoic acid; 1-pentanol; pentyl ethanoate; water

$$CH_3COOH + CH_3(CH_2)_6CH_2OH \overset{H^+}{\rightleftharpoons} CH_3C(=O)-O-CH(CH_2)_6CH_3 + H_2O$$

ethanoic acid; 1-octanol; octyl ethanoate; water

$$C_6H_4(OH)C(=O)-OH + CH_3OH \overset{H^+}{\rightleftharpoons} C_6H_4(OH)C(=O)-OCH_3 + H_2O$$

salicylic acid; methanol; oil of wintergreen; water

6. In esterfication reactions, the products are in chemical equilibrium with the reactants. Suggest several ways of causing the equilibrium to shift in favor of the production of additional ester.

The general equation for ester formation is:

$$R-CO_2H + R' \overset{H^+}{\rightleftharpoons} R-CO_2R' + H_2O$$

One way to improve the yield of ester is to use a large excess of the alcohol. According to Le Châtelier's principle, the equilibrium will shift to use up as much of the excess alcohol as possible. One way this can happen is by adding more carboxylic acid to make more ester. Another way is to remove water, a product of the reaction. Removal of water forces more alcohol and acid to react to produce more water and more ester in order to restore the equilibrium.

Name ____________ Date ____________ Class ____________

GOING FURTHER

Develop a Hypothesis

Based on the results of this lab, predict the product formed when 5-hydroxypentanoic acid is treated with acid catalyst.

HO–$CH_2CH_2CH_2CH_2$–C(=O)–OH $\overset{H^+}{\rightleftharpoons}$ (six-membered cyclic ester, δ-valerolactone)

Propose a mechanism for this reaction. How does the acid catalyze the reaction?

The acid catalyzes an intramolecular esterification to form a cyclic ester.

Design an Experiment

Propose an experiment to test your idea(s). If resources are available and you have your teacher's permission, perform the experiment.

Name ______________ Date ______________ Class ______________

51 PREPARATION OF SOAP

Text Reference
Section 24.4

Time Required
45 minutes

Objectives
- Saponify vegetable oil to form soap.
- Observe some of the physical and chemical properties of the soap product, including pH and solubility in aqueous solutions of calcium, iron(III), and magnesium salts.
- Compare the properties of the soap product to the properties of a commercial laundry detergent and a commercial hand soap.

Advance Preparation

0.1M calcium chloride
Dissolve 1.5 g of $CaCl_2 \cdot 2H_2O$ in 90 mL of distilled water. Dilute to 100 mL.

saturated sodium chloride solution
The solubility of NaCl is approximately 360 g/L H_2O at 25°C. It is estimated that 2.5 L of solution will meet the needs of 15 lab pairs.

0.1M iron(III) chloride
Dissolve 2.7 g of $FeCl_3 \cdot 6H_2O$ in 80 mL of distilled water, and dilute to 100 mL.

0.1M magnesium chloride
Dissolve 2.0 g of $MgCl_2 \cdot 6H_2O$ in 80 mL of distilled water, and dilute to 100 mL.

50% (v/v) ethanol-water mixture
Mix 150 mL of 95% ethanol with 150 mL of distilled water.

PURPOSE

To prepare and isolate a soap by saponification of a triglyceride.

BACKGROUND

Have you ever considered that soap is one of society's major defenses against disease? The cleansing power of soap helps rinse away many disease-causing organisms, making your home and school healthier places than they otherwise would be. Soaps are alkali metal salts of carboxylic acids. They are generally produced by the reaction of metallic hydroxides with animal fats and vegetable oils. The major components of these fats and oils are triglycerides, esters of glycerol, and various fatty acids. Typically, soaps are made by hydrolyzing the ester bonds of triglycerides with solutions of sodium hydroxide. This soap-making reaction is called saponification (in Greek, *sapon* means "soap"). The products of the hydrolysis reaction are soap and glycerol.

In this experiment, you will saponify a vegetable oil and examine some properties of your product. You will compare the properties of the soap you make with the properties of a commercial detergent and a commercial hand soap.

MATERIALS (PER PAIR)

safety goggles and apron
2 250-mL beakers
2 50-mL beakers
10-mL graduated cylinder
gas burner
ring stand
ring support
wire gauze
glass stirring rod
50-mL graduated cylinder
spatula
3 medium test tubes
centigram balance
glass-marking pencil
test-tube rack
dropper pipet
3 cork stoppers
plastic wash bottle
scoopula
vegetable oil
50% (v/v) ethanol-water mixture
sodium hydroxide, NaOH [C] [T]
saturated sodium chloride solution, NaCl
paper towels
laundry detergent [I]
hand soap
wide-range indicator solution or wide-range test paper
0.1*M* calcium chloride, $CaCl_2$ [T]
0.1*M* iron(III) chloride, $FeCl_3$ [T] [I]
0.1*M* magnesium chloride, $MgCl_2$ [T]

Name ______________________ Date ______________ Class ______________

Other materials

Corn oil used for cooking works well and is inexpensive. Lard or other vegetable oils may also be used.

Most laundry detergents are sodium salts of sulfonic acids (RSO_3Na) or sulfates ($ROSO_3Na$). Sodium dodecyl sulfate ($CH_3(CH_2)_{11}OSO_3Na$) is a common detergent.

SAFETY FIRST!

In this lab, observe all precautions, especially the ones listed below. If you see a safety icon beside a step in the Procedure, refer to the list below for its meaning.

Caution: Wear your safety goggles. (All steps.)

Caution: Wear your lab apron. (All steps.)

Caution: Sodium hydroxide is corrosive and can cause severe burns. Never handle sodium hydroxide pellets with your fingers; use a small beaker and a scoopula. Solid sodium hydroxide will absorb water from the atmosphere; do not leave the container of sodium hydroxide open. (Steps 2, 3.)

Caution: Aqueous iron(III) chloride will stain clothes permanently and is irritating to the skin. Avoid contact with this material. (Step 9.)

Caution: Keep ethanol and ethanol-water mixtures away from open flames. (Step 3.)

Note: Return or dispose of all materials according to the instructions of your teacher. (Step 12.)

PROCEDURE

Part A. Preparation of Soap

1. Pour 5 mL (5.0 g) of vegetable oil into a 250-mL beaker.

2. Measure 15 mL of 50% ethanol-water mixture into a 50-mL beaker. Slowly dissolve 2.5 g of NaOH pellets in the ethanol-water mixture.

3. Add 2–3 mL of the NaOH solution to the beaker containing the oil. **CAUTION:** *Keep your face away from the beaker.* Heat the mixture over a *low flame* while stirring. Every few minutes, for about 20 minutes, add a portion of the ethanol-water mixture while continuing to stir. Heat and stir for about 10 more minutes. The oil should be dissolved and a homogeneous solution should be obtained.
4. Add 25 mL of cold water to the hot solution. Using a towel "handle," as shown in Figure 30.1, pour this solution into a 250-mL beaker containing 150 mL of saturated NaCl. Stir this mixture gently and allow it to cool for several minutes.
5. Using a spatula, skim off the top layer of soap and place it in a 50-mL beaker.

Step 2.
The solid NaOH dissolves rather slowly. The dissolution is faster if the NaOH is first dissolved in 7.5 mL of water and 7.5 mL of ethanol is added. Use this alternative procedure if time is an important factor, but caution students that significant heat is generated when the NaOH pellets are added to such a small volume of water. The addition should be done slowly and with care.

Step 3.
Caution: The reaction mixture should be watched constantly during heating.

Step 5.
Soap is fairly soluble in water, but insoluble in saturated sodium chloride solution.

Name ______________________ Date ________________ Class ________________

Step 9–11.
Typical reactions of soap and detergent with cations are as follows. The carboxylic acid salts are less soluble than the salts of the detergent acids.

$2RCO_2^-(aq) + Ca^{2+}(aq) \rightarrow (RCO_2)_2Ca(s)$

$2RCO_2^-(aq) + Mg^{2+}(aq) \rightarrow (RCO_2)_2Mg(s)$

$3RCO_2^-(aq) + Fe^{3+}(aq) \rightarrow (RCO_2)_3Fe(s)$

$2RSO_3^-(aq) + Ca^{2+}(aq) \rightarrow (RSO_3)_2Ca(aq)$

$2RSO_3^-(aq) + Mg^{2+}(aq) \rightarrow (RSO_3)_2Mg(aq)$

$3RSO_3^-(aq) + Fe^{3+}(aq) \rightarrow (RSO_3)_3Fe(aq)$

Use the following disposal methods for chemical waste.

Disposal 1: Soap in Part A.

Disposal 2: NaCl(*aq*) in Part A and the reaction solutions in Part B.

Part B. Properties of Soaps and Detergents

6. Place a pea-sized lump of your soap into a test tube. Use a scoopula to put a similar amount of laundry detergent in a second tube and a similar amount of hand soap in a third tube. Add 10 mL of water to each tube, stopper them, and shake the tubes thoroughly. In this step and throughout this experiment, use a test-tube rack as needed.

7. Estimate the pH of the solutions, using wide-range indicator solution or wide-range test paper. Record the results. Pour the contents of the test tubes down the drain. Rinse the test tubes and stoppers with water.

8. Mark three test tubes with the labels "$CaCl_2$," "$FeCl_3$," and "$MgCl_2$," respectively.

9. Prepare a detergent solution by dissolving 0.3 g of detergent in 30 mL of water. Divide this solution equally among the three test tubes. Add solutions to the test tubes as follows.

$CaCl_2$ test tube: 1.0 mL (or 20 drops) of 0.1*M* $CaCl_2$

$FeCl_3$ test tube: 1.0 mL of 0.1*M* $FeCl_3$

$MgCl_2$ test tube: 1.0 mL of 0.1*M* $MgCl_2$

Stopper each test tube and shake it to mix. Record your observations. Pour the contents of the test tubes down the drain. Rinse the test tubes and stoppers with water.

10. Repeat Step 9, but replace the detergent solution with a hand-soap solution of the same strength. Record your observations.

11. Repeat Step 9, but replace the detergent solution with a solution of your soap of the same strength. Record your observations.

12. Follow your teacher's instructions for proper disposal of the materials.

Name ____________________ Date ____________ Class ____________

OBSERVATIONS

DATA TABLE 1: PROPERTIES OF SOAPS AND DETERGENTS				
	pH of	Effect of Adding Salts		
Substance	Solution	$CaCl_2$	$FeCl_3$	$MgCl_2$
your soap	10–11	heavy white ppt.	no ppt.	light white ppt.
detergent	10–11	no ppt.	no ppt.	light ppt.
hand soap	10–11	heavy white ppt.	light ppt.	white ppt.

ANALYSES AND CONCLUSIONS

1. Write the reaction for saponification of a typical fat (or oil) with sodium hydroxide. Include structural formulas.

$$\begin{array}{l} CH_2O-\overset{\displaystyle O}{\overset{\|}{C}}(CH_2)_{14}CH_3 \\ | \\ CHO-\overset{\displaystyle O}{\overset{\|}{C}}(CH_2)_{14}CH_3 \\ | \\ CH_2O-\overset{\displaystyle O}{\overset{\|}{C}}(CH_2)_{14}CH_3 \end{array} + 3NaOH \rightarrow 3CH_3(CH_2)_{14}\overset{\displaystyle O}{\overset{\|}{C}}-O^-Na^+ + \begin{array}{l} CH_2OH \\ | \\ CHOH \\ | \\ CH_2OH \end{array}$$

2. How does the pH of the soap solution that you prepared compare with those of the solution of commercial laundry detergent and the solution of hand soap? Which of these products would have the harshest effect on the skin?

   The pH of each solution is about the same. If harshness to skin is caused by high pH, all would be equally harsh.

3. The metal ions Ca^{2+}, Fe^{3+}, and Mg^{2+} all contribute to the formation of *hard water*. What differences did you observe when the metal ions Ca^{2+}, Fe^{3+}, and Mg^{2+} were added to a soap or detergent? Do you think that a soap or detergent would make a better cleansing agent in hard water? Explain.

   The detergent does not form insoluble salts (scums) with the ions Mg^{2+} and Ca^{2+} in hard water. This is the reason that detergents are often preferred to soaps as cleansing agents in hard water.

Name ______________________ Date ________________ Class ________________

GOING FURTHER

Develop a Hypothesis

Based on the results of this lab, develop a hypothesis to explain why commercial laundry detergents do not form insoluble salts when mixed with calcium, iron, or magnesium salts.

____

____

____

____

Design an Experiment

Propose an experiment to test your hypothesis. If resources are available and you have your teacher's permission, perform the experiment. Alternatively, do research to learn more about what properties of laundry detergent enhance their solubility in hard water.

____

____

____

____

Name ______________________ Date ______________ Class ______________

52 RADIOACTIVITY AND RADIATION

Text Reference
Section 25.4

Time Required
40 minutes

Objectives
- Measure radiation, using a Geiger-Müller counter.
- Infer how distance, shielding, and time affect the degree of exposure to a radioactive source.

Advance Preparation
Alpha-, beta-, and gamma-radioactive sources may be purchased from:

The Nucleus
P.O. Box R
Oak Ridge, TN 37830

Carbon-14 emits beta radiation; cesium-137 emits beta and gamma radiation; thallium-204 emits beta and gamma radiation.

Note: It is strongly recommended that this experiment be conducted as a teacher demonstration if sealed radiation sources are used. Because a major point of the experiment is to demonstrate the inverse-square law with respect to radiation intensity, a light bulb, simple solar cell, and ammeter may be substituted for the sealed radiation sources and Geiger-Müller counter described in the text.

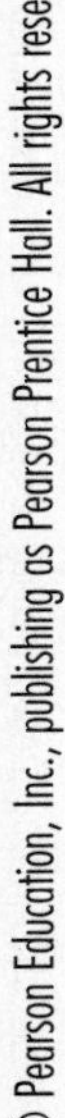

PURPOSE

To investigate the effects of distance, shielding, and time on radiation exposure.

BACKGROUND

Although radiation is generally considered dangerous to living things, radiation and radioisotopes are very important in the diagnosis and treatment of some diseases. Nevertheless, the penetrating power of some types of radiation and the ionizations they produce in the body are potentially hazardous. When radioactive elements decay, they can emit three types of radiation: alpha (α), beta (β), and gamma (γ). Radiation cannot be seen, but its presence can be detected through the ionizations produced when it interacts with matter.

How can X-ray technicians and other people who work with radioactive materials minimize their exposure to the potentially hazardous effects of radiation? In this experiment, you will investigate how to minimize your exposure to radiation from low-level radioactive sources.

MATERIALS (PER GROUP)

safety goggles
Geiger-Müller counter
forceps
meter stick
ring stand
ring support
utility clamp
radioactive sources, sealed and kept in shielded container when not in use:
- carbon-14, ^{14}C
- thallium-204, ^{204}Tl
- cesium-137, ^{137}Cs

shielding materials, 10-cm × 10-cm squares, 1 of each of the following:
- paper
- wood, 3 mm thick
- aluminum foil
- glass, picture
- lead foil
- cotton fabric
- plastic (film)

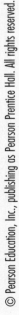

Name ______________________ Date ________________ Class ________________

Radioactive sources, no matter how "safe," must always be handled with forceps.

SAFETY FIRST!

In this lab, observe all precautions, especially the ones listed below. If you see a safety icon beside a step in the procedure, refer to the list below for its meaning.

Caution: Wear your safety goggles. (All steps.)

Caution: The amount of radiation from the sources used in this experiment presents a negligible health hazard. Nevertheless, proper handling of radioactive materials should always be practiced.

PROCEDURE

Your teacher will describe the Geiger-Müller tube and counter, and will demonstrate proper procedures for handling the sealed radioactive sources. Follow your teacher's directions! As the experiment is performed, record observations in Data Tables 1, 2, and 3.

Part A. Background Radiation

1. Remove all radioactive material from the region near the Geiger-Müller tube. Measure the detected background radiation in counts per minute and record the measurements in Data Table 1.

Part B. Effect of Distance

2. Place the Geiger-Müller tube at one end of the meter stick with a sealed source (preferably a gamma emitter) at the other end, as shown in Figure 52.1.
3. Measure the detected radiation at distances between the source and the detector of 4 cm, 2 cm, and 1 cm. Record your measurements in Data Table 1.

Step 3.
The intensity of radiation from a source decreases by the inverse-square law as you move away from the source. Mathematically, the relationship is as follows:

$$I \propto \frac{1}{d^2}$$

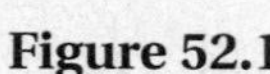

Figure 52.1

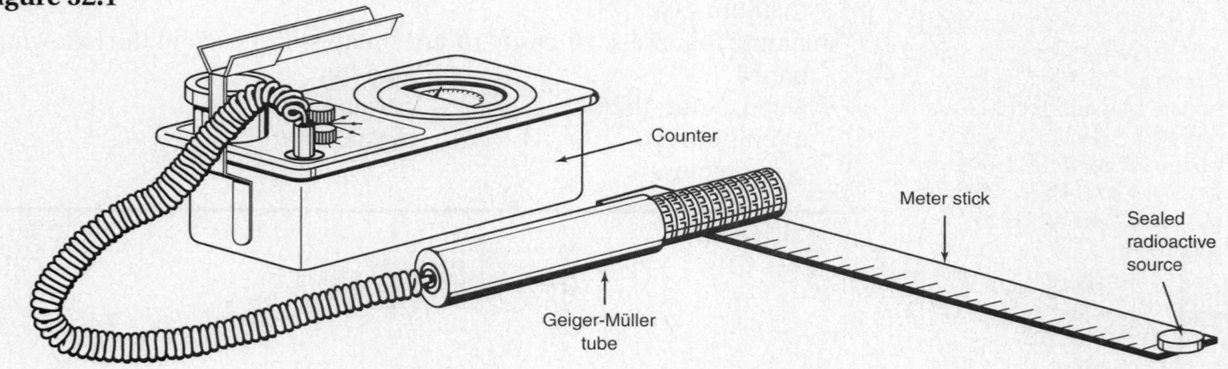

Name ______________________ Date ________________ Class ________________

Part C. Effect of Shielding

Step 5.
When testing the effect of shielding (i.e., using absorbers of different materials to reduce the amount of radiation emitted by a source), you may wish to use several layers of plastic and of paper to produce a combined thickness similar to that of the glass or wood.

4. Place a sealed source 5–10 cm below a Geiger-Müller tube, as shown in Figure 52.2. Measure the detected radiation and record your measurement in Data Table 2.
5. Place thin pieces of the various materials (paper, wood, aluminum, glass, lead, cotton fabric, and plastic) between the sealed source and the Geiger-Müller tube. Measure and record the detected radiation for each of the various materials.

Part D. Effect of Time

6. Measure and record the counts per minute from a radiation source. Calculate the total counts for 5 minutes, 30 minutes, and 60 minutes. Record your results in Data Table 3.

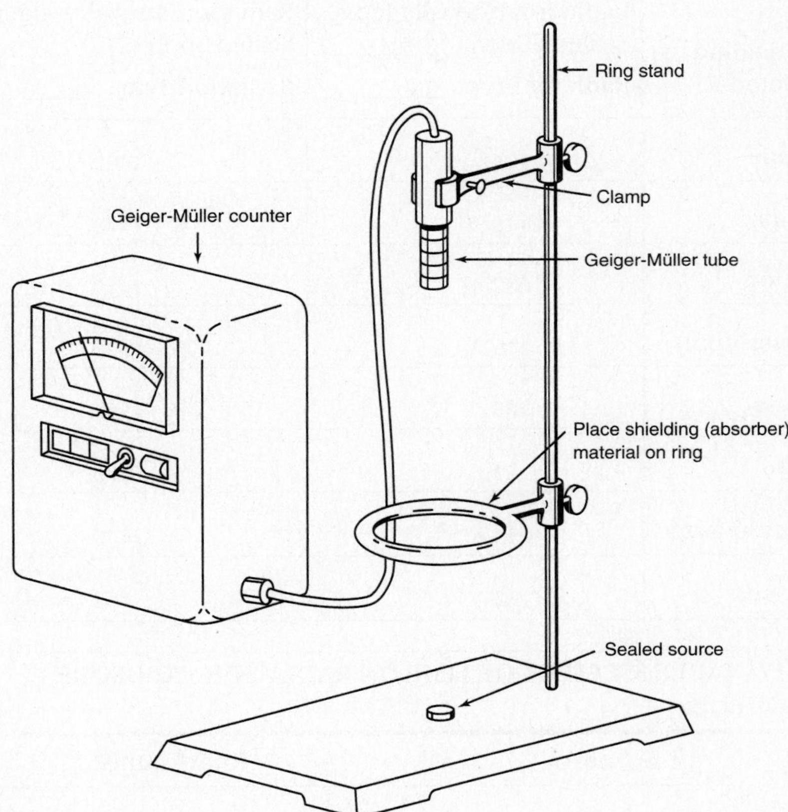

Figure 52.2

Name ________________ Date ________________ Class ________________

OBSERVATIONS

DATA TABLE 1: EFFECT OF DISTANCE ON RADIATION INTENSITY	
Distance from Source (cm)	Radiation Intensity (cpm)
4	228
2	883
1	3321
(Source: ^{204}Tl)	Background radiation: 18 cpm

DATA TABLE 2: EFFECT OF SHIELDING ON RADIATION INTENSITY		
Shielding Material	Radiation Intensity (cpm) Sealed Source ^{14}C Radiation Type β	Radiation Intensity (cpm) Sealed Source ^{137}Cs Radiation Type β, γ
none	1284	1462
paper	1140	1458
wood	862	1410
aluminum	412	1326
glass	363	1302
lead	24	1265
cotton fabric	1054	1445
plastic	1162	1452

DATA TABLE 3: EFFECT OF TIME ON RADIATION EXPOSURE (SOURCE: ^{137}Cs)	
Time (min)	Total Counts
1	1368
5	6840
30	40,800
60	81,600

Name ______________________ Date ________________ Class ________________

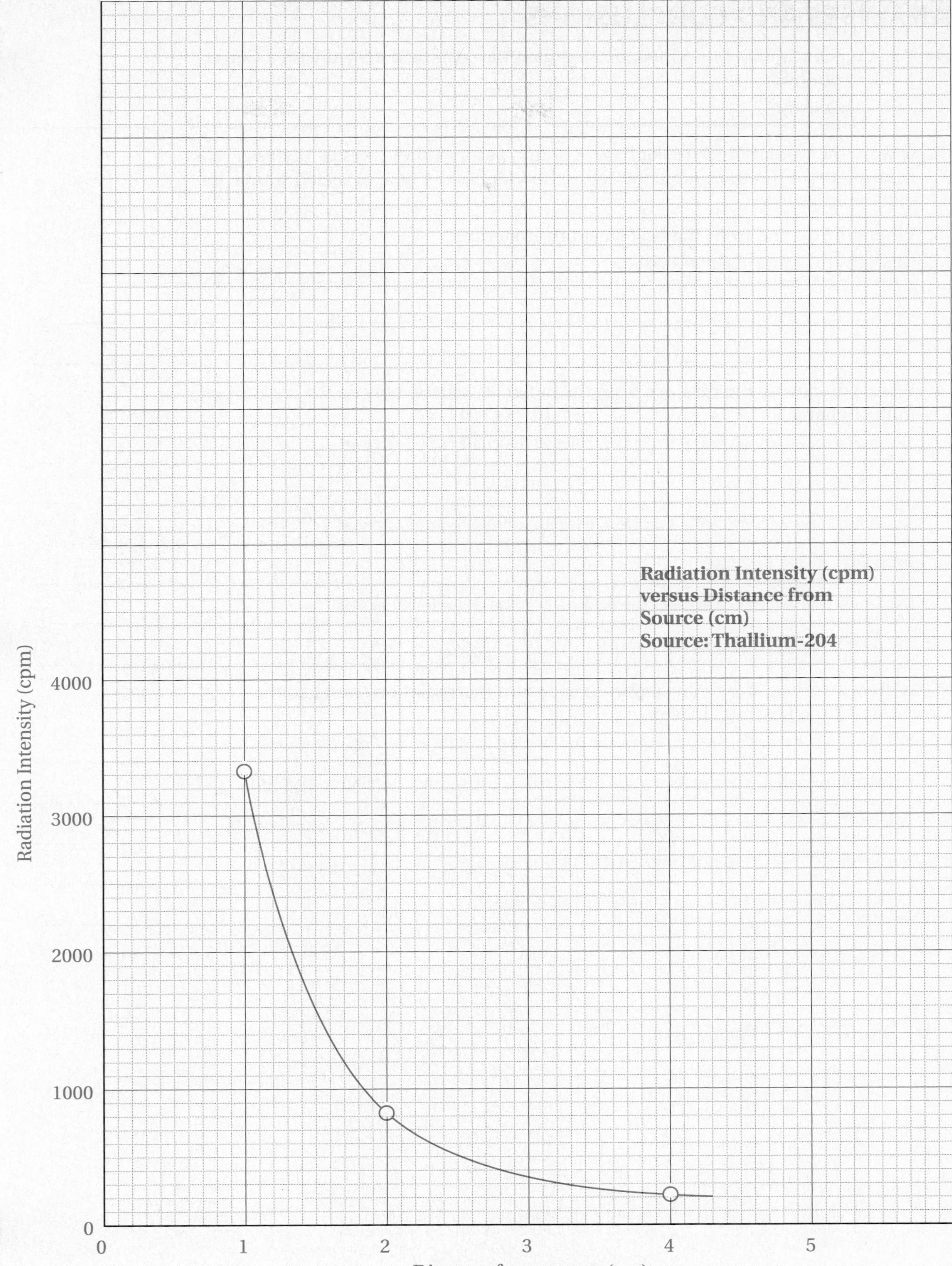

Name ______________________ Date ________________ Class ________________

ANALYSES AND CONCLUSIONS

1. What types of radiation—alpha, beta, or gamma—can be detected with a Geiger-Müller counter?

   beta and gamma

2. Graph the radiation intensity (in counts per minute) versus distance (in centimeters) from the source. Be certain to identify the type of sealed source the data represents.

3. What did you find to be the best shielding material?

   The best shielding material is lead.

4. When you double the distance from the radiation source, how do the counts per minute change?

   Doubling the distance from 1 cm to 2 cm causes the cpm to change from 3321 to 882, or 3.76:1.

   Doubling the distance from 2 cm to 4 cm causes the cpm to change from 882 to 228, or 3.87:1.

   Doubling the distance between the source and the detector tube cut the cpm by approximately one-fourth.

5. Is there an advantage in limiting your exposure to a radiation source to the shortest time possible? Explain.

   Yes. There is no safe level of exposure to ionizing radiation. Any exposure has the potential for causing harm. Because the damage caused by ionizing radiation is cumulative, the effects of radiation can be minimized by limiting your exposure to radiation sources. The data collected in Part D show that the total exposure, corresponding to total counts, increases with time.

Name ______________________ Date ________________ Class ________________

GOING FURTHER

Develop a Hypothesis

Based on the results of this lab, develop a hypothesis to explain why the radiation from the ^{14}C source could be shielded more effectively than the radiation from the ^{137}Cs source. What do your results suggest about the decay mode of each radioactive isotope?

Carbon-14 is primarily a beta emitter. Cesium-137 is primarily a gamma emitter. Gamma rays are more penetrating than beta particles and are blocked less effectively by shielding materials.

Do Research

Do research to find scientific evidence that supports or refutes your hypothesis.

____

____

____

Sample Laboratory Report

Name: Janet Blair **Class:** 2 **Date:** October 5, 2004

Experiment Number and Title: Experiment 5: Mass, Volume, and Density

Purpose: (Give a clear, concise description of exactly what the experiment was intended to demonstrate.)

The purpose of this experiment was to investigate the relationship between mass and volume for a metal and to determine if that relationship can be used as an identifying property of the metal.

Equipment/Materials: (List the equipment and materials that you actually used in the experiment.)

graduated cylinder (25-mL)
metal A
metal B
centigram balance
ruler (cm)

Methods: (Describe all laboratory techniques and types of calculations that you used in the experiment.)

Mass measurements were made by measuring clean, dry samples of metals on a centigram balance. The mass measurements were made to the nearest 0.01 g.

Volume measurements were made by the method of water displacement. A 25-mL graduated cylinder was half-filled with water and the volume recorded. The volume was read at the bottom of the meniscus. Then the metal sample was immersed in the water in the graduated cylinder. The new volume of the water and the metal sample together was read and recorded. The volume of the metal sample was determined by subtracting the initial volume of the water from the final volume. The density of each sample was calculated by dividing the mass of the sample by its volume.

Other groups in the class had different-sized samples of the same metals, A and B. Class data was pooled to obtain data points for graphing mass (the manipulated or independent variable) versus volume (the responding or dependent variable) for each metal. The slope of the line obtained for each metal is equal to mass/volume and represents the density of the metal. The slope was determined according to the formula $y = mx + b$, where x = mass value, y = the volume associated with that mass, m = slope of the line, and b = y-intercept of the line.

Procedure: (Describe the major steps of the procedure, exactly as you carried them out. Include here any qualitative observations you made during the experiment.)

We received one sample of metal A and one sample of metal B from the teacher. Metal A was shiny, smooth, and black. Metal B was dull, rough, and tan. We cleaned and dried the samples, using tap water and paper towels. Metal B was more difficult to dry than metal A. We then measured each sample on the centigram balance as described above and recorded the masses. We determined the mass of metal A first and metal B second. I did the measurements, and Paul recorded the data.

We then made the volume measurements, using the water displacement method described in the Methods section. Paul added the samples to the water, and I made the initial and final volume readings. We did this first for metal A and then for metal B. After making these measurements, we dried the samples and returned them to the teacher.

Observations: (Record here any measurements and calculations that you make during the experiment. Make sure to clearly distinguish between the two. Include units for all measurements and all calculations. Pay close attention to significant figures. If possible, present your data in the form of a table and/or graph so that patterns in the data may be more easily recognized.)

Group 1 Data and Calculations		
Quantity	Metal A	Metal B
mass	10.10 g	33.41 g
volume of water alone	12.0 mL	19.7 mL
volume of water and metal	15.8 mL	23.5 mL
volume of metal	3.8 mL (15.8 mL − 12.0 mL)	3.8 mL (23.5 mL − 19.7 mL)
density of metal	2.7 g/mL (10.10 g/3.8 mL)	88 g/mL (33.41 g/3.8 mL)

Class Data and Calculations						
Lab Group*	Metal A			Metal B		
	Mass	Volume	Density	Mass	Volume	Density
1	10.10 g	3.8 mL	2.7 g/mL	33.41 g	3.8 mL	8.8 g/mL
2	4.31 g	1.7 mL	2.6 g/mL	34.62 g	3.9 mL	8.9 g/mL
3	8.05 g	3.0 mL	2.7 g/mL	27.63 g	3.1 mL	8.9 g/mL
4	9.00 g	3.4 mL	2.6 g/mL	21.00 g	2.4 mL	8.4 g/mL
5	6.25 g	2.5 mL	2.5 g/mL	20.92 g	2.5 mL	8.4 g/mL

*1 = Janet & Paul 2 = Lin & Pat 3 = Ellen & Emilio 4 = Dave & Alice 5 = Fariq & Bill

Graph of Class Data for Metal A (Remember to plot the manipulated variable on the *x*-axis, the horizontal axis, and the responding variable on the *y*-axis, the vertical axis.)

mass (x)	volume (y)
10.10 g	3.8 mL
4.31 g	1.7 mL
8.05 g	3.0 mL
9.00 g	3.4 mL
6.25 g	2.5 mL

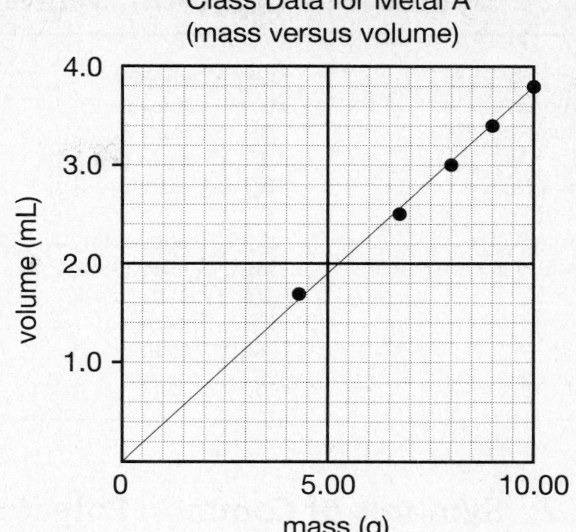

Analyses and Conclusions: (Record here the answers to all the questions in the Analyses and Conclusions section of the experiment. Also answer any additional questions that your teacher may ask.)

6. The results of this experiment indicate that the density of a specific substance is a constant. They indicate also that the densities of different substances can be quite different. For these reasons, density should be useful in the identification of substances.

(Use this model for the questions posed in the lab manual.)

Table A.1 Symbols of Common Elements

Ag	silver	Cu	copper	O	oxygen
Al	aluminum	F	fluorine	P	phosphorus
As	arsenic	Fe	iron	Pb	lead
Au	gold	H	hydrogen	Pt	platinum
Ba	barium	Hg	mercury	S	sulfur
Bi	bismuth	I	iodine	Sb	antimony
Br	bromine	K	potassium	Sn	tin
C	carbon	Mg	magnesium	Sr	strontium
Ca	calcium	Mn	manganese	Ti	titanium
Cl	chlorine	N	nitrogen	U	uranium
Co	cobalt	Na	sodium	W	tungsten
Cr	chromium	Ni	nickel	Zn	zinc

Table A.2 Symbols of Common Polyatomic Ions

$C_2H_3O_2^-$	ethanoate	$Cr_2O_7^{2-}$	dichromate	NO_3^-	nitrate
ClO^-	hypochlorite	HCO_3^-	hydrogen carbonate	NO_3^-	nitrite
ClO_2^-	chlorite	H_3O^+	hydronium	O_2^{2-}	peroxide
ClO_3^-	chlorate	HPO_4^{2-}	hydrogen phosphate	OH^-	hydroxide
ClO_4^-	perchlorate	HSO_3^-	hydrogen sulfite	PO_4^{3-}	phosphate
CN^-	cyanide	HSO_4^-	hydrogen sulfate	SiO_3^{2-}	silicate
CO_3^{2-}	carbonate	MnO_4^-	permanganate	SO_3^{2-}	sulfite
CrO_4^{2-}	chromate	NH_4^+	ammonium	SO_4^{2-}	sulfate

Table A.3 Solubilities of Compounds at 25°C and 101 kPa

	bromide	carbonate	chlorate	chloride	ethanoate	hydroxide	iodide	nitrate	oxide	perchlorate	phosphate	sulfate	sulfide
aluminium	S	—	S	S	S	I	S	S	I	S	I	S	d
ammonium	S	S	S	S	S	S	S	S	—	S	S	S	S
barium	S	I	S	S	S	S	S	S	sS	S	I	I	d
calcium	S	I	S	S	S	S	S	S	sS	S	I	sS	I
copper(II)	S	—	S	S	S	I	S	S	I	S	I	S	I
iron(II)	S	I	S	S	S	I	S	S	I	S	I	S	I
iron(III)	S	—	S	S	S	I	S	S	I	S	I	sS	d
lithium	S	sS	S	S	S	S	S	S	S	S	sS	S	S
magnesium	S	I	S	S	S	I	S	S	I	S	I	S	d
potassium	S	S	S	S	S	S	S	S	S	S	S	S	S
silver	I	I	S	I	sS	—	I	S	I	S	I	sS	I
sodium	S	S	S	S	S	S	S	S	S	S	S	S	S
strontium	S	I	S	S	S	S	S	S	S	S	I	I	I
zinc	S	I	S	S	S	I	S	S	I	S	I	S	I

Key:
S = soluble
sS = slightly soluble
I = insoluble
d = decomposes in water
— = no such compound

Table A.4 Some Properties of the Elements

Element	Symbol	Atomic Number	Atomic Mass	Melting Point (°C)	Boiling Point (°C)	Density (g/cm³) (gases at STP)	Major Oxidation States
actinium	Ac	89	(227)	1050	3200	10.07	+3
aluminium	Al	13	26.98154	660.37	2467	2.6989	+3
americium	Am	95	(243)	944	2607	13.67	+3, +4, +5, +6
antimony	Sb	51	121.75	630.74	1950	6.691	−3, +3, +5
argon	Ar	18	39.948	−189.2	−185.7	0.0017837	
arsenic	As	33	74.9216	817	613	5.73	−3, +3, +5
astatine	At	85	(210)	302	337	—	
barium	Ba	56	137.33	725	1640	3.5	+2
berkelium	Bk	97	(247)	986	—	14.78	
beryllium	Be	4	9.01218	1278	2970	1.848	+2
bismuth	Bi	83	208.9804	271.3	1560	9.747	+3, +5
bohrium	Bh	107	(264)	—	—	—	
boron	B	5	10.81	2079	3675	2.34	+3
bromine	Br	35	79.904	−7.2	58.78	3.12	−1, +1, +5
cadmium	Cd	48	112.41	320.9	765	8.65	+2
calcium	Ca	20	40.08	839	1484	1.55	+2
californium	Cf	98	(251)	900	—	14	
carbon	C	6	12.011	3550	4827	2.267	−4, +2, +4
cerium	Ce	58	140.12	799	3426	6.657	+3, +4
cesium	Cs	55	132.9054	28.40	669.3	1.873	+1
chlorine	Cl	17	35.453	−100.98	−34.6	0.003214	−1, +1, +5, +7
chromium	Cr	24	51.996	1857	2672	7.18	+2, +3, +6
cobalt	Co	27	58.9332	1495	2870	8.9	+2, +3
copper	Cu	29	63.546	1083.4	2567	8.96	+1, +2
curium	Cm	96	(247)	1340	—	13.51	+3
darmstadtium	Ds	110	(269)	—	—	—	
dubnium	Db	105	(262)	—	—	—	
dysprosium	Dy	66	162.50	1412	2562	8.550	+3
einsteinium	Es	99	(252)	—	—	—	
erbium	Er	68	167.26	159	2863	9.006	+3
europium	Eu	63	151.96	822	1597	5.243	+2, +3
fermium	Fm	100	(257)	—	—	—	
fluorine	F	9	18.998403	−219.62	−188.54	0.001696	−1
francium	Fr	87	(223)	27	667	—	+1
gadolinium	Gd	64	157.25	1313	3266	7.9004	+3
gallium	Ga	31	69.72	29.78	2204	5.904	+3
germanium	Ge	32	72.59	937.4	2830	5.323	+2, +4
gold	Au	79	196.9665	1064.43	3080	19.3	+1, +3
hafnium	Hf	72	178.49	2227	4602	13.31	+4
hassium	Hs	108	(265)	—	—	—	
helium	He	2	4.00260	−272.2	−268.934	0.001785	
holmium	Ho	67	164.9304	1474	2695	8.795	+3
hydrogen	H	1	1.00794	−259.14	−252.87	0.00008988	+1
indium	In	49	114.82	156.61	2080	7.31	+1, +3
iodine	I	53	126.9045	113.5	184.35	4.93	−1, +1, +5, +7
iridium	Ir	77	192.22	2410	4130	22.42	+3, +4
iron	Fe	26	55.847	1535	2750	7.874	+2, +3
krypton	Kr	36	83.80	−156.6	−152.30	0.003733	
lanthanum	La	57	138.9055	921	3457	6.145	+3
lawrencium	Lr	103	(262)	—	—	—	+3
lead	Pb	82	207.2	327.502	1740	11.35	+2, +4
lithium	Li	3	6.941	180.54	1342	0.534	+1
lutetium	Lu	71	174.967	1663	3395	9.840	+3
magnesium	Mg	12	24.305	648.8	1090	1.738	+2
manganese	Mn	25	54.9380	1244	1962	7.32	+2, +3, +4, +7
meitnerium	Mt	109	(268)	—	—	—	
mendelevium	Md	101	(257)	—	—	—	+2, +3
mercury	Hg	80	200.59	−38.842	356.58	13.55	+1, +2

Table A.4 Some Properties of the Elements

Element	Symbol	Atomic Number	Atomic Mass	Melting Point (°C)	Boiling Point (°C)	Density (g/cm^3) (gases at STP)	Major Oxidation States
molybdenum	Mo	42	95.94	2617	4612	10.22	+6
neodymium	Nd	60	144.24	1021	3068	6.90	+3
neon	Ne	10	20.179	−248.67	−246.048	0.0008999	
neptunium	Np	93	(237)	640	3902	20.25	+3, +4, +5, +6
nickel	Ni	28	58.69	1453	2732	8.902	+2, +3
niobium	Nb	41	92.9064	2468	4742	8.57	+3, +5
nitrogen	N	7	14.0067	−209.86	−195.8	0.0012506	−3, +3, +5
nobelium	No	102	(259)	—	—	—	+2, +3
osmium	Os	76	190.2	3045	5027	22.57	+3, +4
oxygen	O	8	15.9994	−218.4	−182.962	0.001429	−2
palladium	Pd	46	106.42	1554	2970	12.02	+2, +4
phosphorus	P	15	30.97376	44.1	280	1.82	−3, +3, +5
platinum	Pt	78	195.08	1772	3827	21.45	+2, +4
plutonium	Pu	94	(244)	641	3232	19.84	+3, +4, +5, +6
potassium	K	19	39.0982	63.25	760	0.862	+1
praseodymium	Pr	59	140.9077	931	3512	6.64	+3
promethium	Pm	61	(145)	1168	2460	7.22	+3
protactinium	Pa	91	231.0359	1560	4027	15.37	+4, +5
radium	Ra	88	(226)	700	1140	5.5	+2
radon	Rn	86	(222)	−71	−61.8	0.00973	
rhenium	Re	75	186.207	3180	5627	21.02	+4, +6, +7
rhodiuim	Rh	45	102.9055	1966	3727	12.41	+3
rubidium	Rb	37	85.4678	38.89	686	1.532	+1
ruthenium	Ru	44	101.07	2310	3900	12.41	+3
rutherfordium	Rf	104	(261)	—	—	—	
samarium	Sm	62	150.36	1077	1791	7.520	+2, +3
scandium	Sc	21	44.9559	1541	2831	2.989	+3
seaborgium	Sg	106	(263)	—	—	—	
selenium	Se	34	78.96	217	684.9	4.79	−2, +4, +6
silicon	Si	14	28.0855	1410	2355	2.33	−4, +2, +4
silver	Ag	47	107.8682	961.93	2212	10.50	+1
sodium	Na	11	22.98977	97.81	882.9	0.971	+1
strontium	Sr	38	87.62	796	1384	2.54	+2
sulfur	S	16	32.06	112.8	444.7	2.07	−2, +4, +6
tantalum	Ta	73	180.9479	2996	5425	16.654	+5
technetium	Tc	43	(98)	2172	4877	11.50	+4, +6, +7
tellurium	Te	52	127.60	449.5	989.8	6.24	−2, +4, +6
terbium	Tb	65	158.9254	1356	3123	8.229	+3
thallium	Tl	81	204.383	303.5	1457	11.85	+1, +3
thorium	Th	90	232.0381	1750	4790	11.72	+4
thulium	Tm	69	168.9342	1545	1947	9.321	+3
tin	Sn	50	118.69	231.968	2270	7.31	+2, +4
titanium	Ti	22	47.88	1660	3287	4.54	+2, +3, +4
tungsten	W	74	183.85	3410	5660	19.3	+6
ununbium	Uub	112	(277)	—	—	—	
ununquadium	Uuq	114					
unununium	Uuu	111	(272)	—	—	—	
uranium	U	92	238.0289	1132.3	3818	18.95	+3, +4, +5, +6
vanadium	V	23	50.9415	1890	3380	6.11	+2, +3, +4, +5
xenon	Xe	54	131.29	−111.9	−107.1	0.005887	
ytterbium	Yb	70	173.04	819	1194	6.965	+2, +3
yttrium	Y	39	88.9059	1522	3338	4.469	+3
zinc	Zn	30	65.38	419.58	907	7.133	+2
zirconium	Zr	40	91.22	1852	4377	6.506	+4

Periodic Table of the Elements

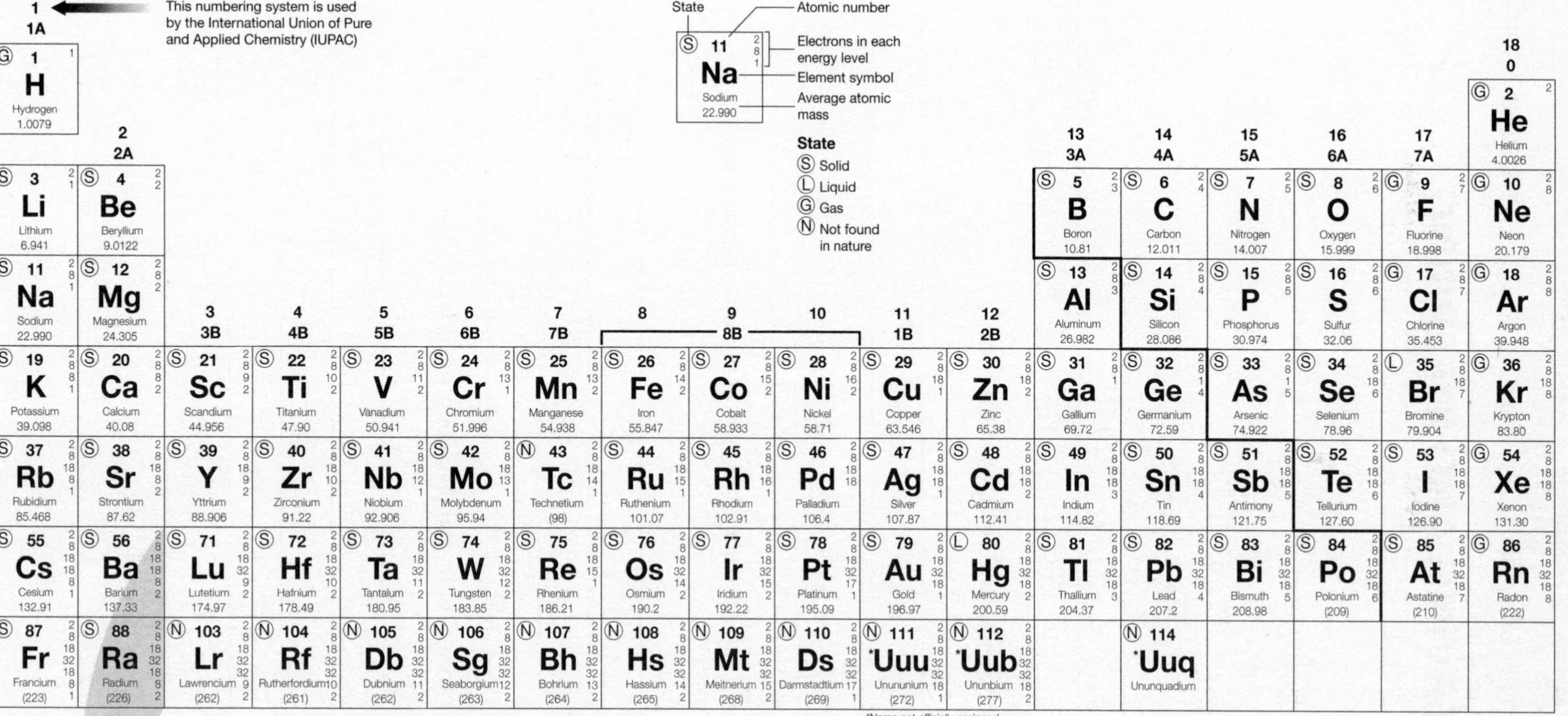

1 ← This numbering system is used by the International Union of Pure and Applied Chemistry (IUPAC)

Key: (S) 11 Na Sodium 22.990 (2-8-1) — State; Atomic number; Electrons in each energy level; Element symbol; Average atomic mass

State
(S) Solid
(L) Liquid
(G) Gas
(N) Not found in nature

1 1A	2 2A	3 3B	4 4B	5 5B	6 6B	7 7B	8 8B	9 8B	10 8B	11 1B	12 2B	13 3A	14 4A	15 5A	16 6A	17 7A	18 0
(G) 1 H Hydrogen 1.0079 (1)																	(G) 2 He Helium 4.0026 (2)
(S) 3 Li Lithium 6.941 (2-1)	(S) 4 Be Beryllium 9.0122 (2-2)											(S) 5 B Boron 10.81 (2-3)	(S) 6 C Carbon 12.011 (2-4)	(S) 7 N Nitrogen 14.007 (2-5)	(S) 8 O Oxygen 15.999 (2-6)	(G) 9 F Fluorine 18.998 (2-7)	(G) 10 Ne Neon 20.179 (2-8)
(S) 11 Na Sodium 22.990 (2-8-1)	(S) 12 Mg Magnesium 24.305 (2-8-2)											(S) 13 Al Aluminum 26.982 (2-8-3)	(S) 14 Si Silicon 28.086 (2-8-4)	(S) 15 P Phosphorus 30.974 (2-8-5)	(S) 16 S Sulfur 32.06 (2-8-6)	(G) 17 Cl Chlorine 35.453 (2-8-7)	(G) 18 Ar Argon 39.948 (2-8-8)
(S) 19 K Potassium 39.098 (2-8-8-1)	(S) 20 Ca Calcium 40.08 (2-8-8-2)	(S) 21 Sc Scandium 44.956 (2-8-9-2)	(S) 22 Ti Titanium 47.90 (2-8-10-2)	(S) 23 V Vanadium 50.941 (2-8-11-2)	(S) 24 Cr Chromium 51.996 (2-8-13-1)	(S) 25 Mn Manganese 54.938 (2-8-13-2)	(S) 26 Fe Iron 55.847 (2-8-14-2)	(S) 27 Co Cobalt 58.933 (2-8-15-2)	(S) 28 Ni Nickel 58.71 (2-8-16-2)	(S) 29 Cu Copper 63.546 (2-8-18-1)	(S) 30 Zn Zinc 65.38 (2-8-18-2)	(S) 31 Ga Gallium 69.72 (2-8-18-3)	(S) 32 Ge Germanium 72.59 (2-8-18-4)	(S) 33 As Arsenic 74.922 (2-8-18-5)	(S) 34 Se Selenium 78.96 (2-8-18-6)	(L) 35 Br Bromine 79.904 (2-8-18-7)	(G) 36 Kr Krypton 83.80 (2-8-18-8)
(S) 37 Rb Rubidium 85.468 (2-8-18-8-1)	(S) 38 Sr Strontium 87.62 (2-8-18-8-2)	(S) 39 Y Yttrium 88.906 (2-8-18-9-2)	(S) 40 Zr Zirconium 91.22 (2-8-18-10-2)	(S) 41 Nb Niobium 92.906 (2-8-18-12-1)	(S) 42 Mo Molybdenum 95.94 (2-8-18-13-1)	(N) 43 Tc Technetium (98) (2-8-18-14-1)	(S) 44 Ru Ruthenium 101.07 (2-8-18-15-1)	(S) 45 Rh Rhodium 102.91 (2-8-18-16-1)	(S) 46 Pd Palladium 106.4 (2-8-18-18)	(S) 47 Ag Silver 107.87 (2-8-18-18-1)	(S) 48 Cd Cadmium 112.41 (2-8-18-18-2)	(S) 49 In Indium 114.82 (2-8-18-18-3)	(S) 50 Sn Tin 118.69 (2-8-18-18-4)	(S) 51 Sb Antimony 121.75 (2-8-18-18-5)	(S) 52 Te Tellurium 127.60 (2-8-18-18-6)	(S) 53 I Iodine 126.90 (2-8-18-18-7)	(G) 54 Xe Xenon 131.30 (2-8-18-18-8)
(S) 55 Cs Cesium 132.91 (2-8-18-18-8-1)	(S) 56 Ba Barium 137.33 (2-8-18-18-8-2)	(S) 71 Lu Lutetium 174.97 (2-8-18-32-9-2)	(S) 72 Hf Hafnium 178.49 (2-8-18-32-10-2)	(S) 73 Ta Tantalum 180.95 (2-8-18-32-11-2)	(S) 74 W Tungsten 183.85 (2-8-18-32-12-2)	(S) 75 Re Rhenium 186.21 (2-8-18-32-13-2)	(S) 76 Os Osmium 190.2 (2-8-18-32-14-2)	(S) 77 Ir Iridium 192.22 (2-8-18-32-15-2)	(S) 78 Pt Platinum 195.09 (2-8-18-32-17-1)	(S) 79 Au Gold 196.97 (2-8-18-32-18-1)	(L) 80 Hg Mercury 200.59 (2-8-18-32-18-2)	(S) 81 Tl Thallium 204.37 (2-8-18-32-18-3)	(S) 82 Pb Lead 207.2 (2-8-18-32-18-4)	(S) 83 Bi Bismuth 208.98 (2-8-18-32-18-5)	(S) 84 Po Polonium (209) (2-8-18-32-18-6)	(S) 85 At Astatine (210) (2-8-18-32-18-7)	(G) 86 Rn Radon (222) (2-8-18-32-18-8)
(S) 87 Fr Francium (223) (2-8-18-32-18-8-1)	(S) 88 Ra Radium (226) (2-8-18-32-18-8-2)	(N) 103 Lr Lawrencium (262) (2-8-18-32-32-9-2)	(N) 104 Rf Rutherfordium (261) (2-8-18-32-32-10-2)	(N) 105 Db Dubnium (262) (2-8-18-32-32-11-2)	(N) 106 Sg Seaborgium (263) (2-8-18-32-32-12-2)	(N) 107 Bh Bohrium (264) (2-8-18-32-32-13-2)	(N) 108 Hs Hassium (265) (2-8-18-32-32-14-2)	(N) 109 Mt Meitnerium (268) (2-8-18-32-32-15-2)	(N) 110 Ds Darmstadtium (269) (2-8-18-32-32-17-1)	(N) 111 *Uuu Unununium (272) (2-8-18-32-32-18-1)	(N) 112 *Uub Ununbium (277) (2-8-18-32-32-18-2)		(N) 114 *Uuq Ununquadium				

*Name not officially assigned

Lanthanide Series

(S) 57 La Lanthanum 138.91 (2-8-18-18-9-2)	(S) 58 Ce Cerium 140.12 (2-8-18-20-8-2)	(S) 59 Pr Praseodymium 140.91 (2-8-18-21-8-2)	(S) 60 Nd Neodymium 144.24 (2-8-18-22-8-2)	(N) 61 Pm Promethium (145) (2-8-18-23-8-2)	(S) 62 Sm Samarium 150.4 (2-8-18-24-8-2)	(S) 63 Eu Europium 151.96 (2-8-18-25-8-2)	(S) 64 Gd Gadolinium 157.25 (2-8-18-25-9-2)	(S) 65 Tb Terbium 158.93 (2-8-18-27-8-2)	(S) 66 Dy Dysprosium 162.50 (2-8-18-28-8-2)	(S) 67 Ho Holmium 164.93 (2-8-18-29-8-2)	(S) 68 Er Erbium 167.26 (2-8-18-30-8-2)	(S) 69 Tm Thulium 168.93 (2-8-18-31-8-2)	(S) 70 Yb Ytterbium 173.04 (2-8-18-32-8-2)

Actinide Series

(S) 89 Ac Actinium (227) (2-8-18-32-18-9-2)	(S) 90 Th Thorium 232.04 (2-8-18-32-18-10-2)	(S) 91 Pa Protactinium 231.04 (2-8-18-32-20-9-2)	(S) 92 U Uranium 238.03 (2-8-18-32-21-9-2)	(N) 93 Np Neptunium (237) (2-8-18-32-22-9-2)	(N) 94 Pu Plutonium (244) (2-8-18-32-24-8-2)	(N) 95 Am Americium (243) (2-8-18-32-25-8-2)	(N) 96 Cm Curium (247) (2-8-18-32-25-9-2)	(N) 97 Bk Berkelium (247) (2-8-18-32-27-8-2)	(N) 98 Cf Californium (251) (2-8-18-32-28-8-2)	(N) 99 Es Einsteinium (252) (2-8-18-32-29-8-2)	(N) 100 Fm Fermium (257) (2-8-18-32-30-8-2)	(N) 101 Md Mendelevium (258) (2-8-18-32-31-8-2)	(N) 102 No Nobelium (259) (2-8-18-32-32-8-2)

Name ______________ Date ______________ Class ______________

1 OBSERVING AND INFERRING

1. Explain the steps of the scientific method.

2. What steps of the scientific method are included in Experiment 1?

3. List one flammable and two corrosive materials used in this experiment. Include the letter code in your answer.

4. What hazard is associated with handling small amounts of dry ice?

2 PHYSICAL AND CHEMICAL CHANGE

1. Give three examples of physical properties that can be easily observed or measured.

2. How is a *physical* change distinguished from a *chemical* change?

3. a. What cautions must be observed when using 6*M* HCl?

b. Why is the burning of magnesium hazardous?

4. Briefly describe how to filter a mixture.

5. What substance will you heat in a clean, dry test tube?

6. Propose a reason for why the sulfur–iron mixture must be heated in a fume hood.

Name ______________________ Date __________________ Class ________________

3 OBSERVING A CHEMICAL REACTION

1. How does an *observation* differ from an *interpretation*?

____

____

____

2. What is the difference between a *qualitative* and a *quantitative* observation?

____

____

____

____

3. What is the first thing you must do at the beginning of an experiment?

____

____

4. At the end of the experiment, how do you dispose of the solid contents of the beaker?

____

____

____

5. What two tasks are required at the end of this and all other experiments?

____

____

Name ______________________ Date ________________ Class ________________

4 MASS, VOLUME, AND DENSITY

1. a. What type of balance would you use to determine the approximate mass of a beaker?

____

b. What type of balance would you use to determine, as accurately as possible, the mass of a small piece of gold?

____

2. How could you determine the volume of a solid that has a surface too irregular to measure?

____

3. In this lab, how many different samples are used for the determination of density?

____

4. Why must a metal sample always be *dry* before its mass or volume is determined?

____

____

5. What does a graph of mass vs. volume show?

____

____

____

Name ______________________ Date ________________ Class ______________

ATOMIC STRUCTURE: RUTHERFORD'S EXPERIMENT

1. What was the major problem facing scientists working with Rutherford?

____

____

____

2. How does this experiment simulate Rutherford's work?

____

____

____

3. a. How do the entry and exit paths of the marble give clues to the shape hidden under the board?

____

____

____

b. Given the shape below and the four entry paths shown, draw probable exit paths for each marble.

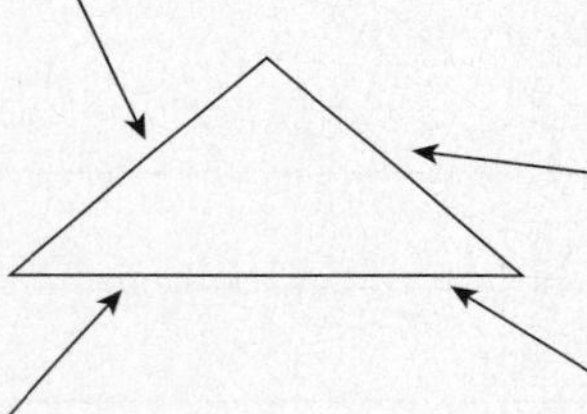

FLAME TESTS FOR METALS

1. Describe what happens to the electrons of an element when the element is heated to high temperatures.

____

____

____

2. What color of light is associated with the most energy?

____

3. Which solids must be viewed through cobalt glass when heated?

____

4. How is the loop cleaned between samples?

____

____

5. Why should you wash your hands thoroughly at the conclusion of this experiment?

____

____

7 ENERGIES OF ELECTRONS

1. What is an emission spectrum?

____

____

____

2. Explain what a spectrograph does.

____

____

____

3. How does this experiment differ from the flame tests done in Experiment 20?

____

____

____

____

4. What two health hazards are associated with concentrated HCl?

____

____

5. Why are meter sticks used in this experiment?

____

____

Name ______________________ Date ________________ Class ________________

8 INTRODUCTION TO THE SPECTROPHOTOMETER

1. List the parts of a spectrometer.

____

____

____

____

2. In general, at which wavelengths will light absorption occur?

____

____

____

____

3. Why do the cuvettes or tubes need to be clean and dry?

____

____

____

4. What health hazard is associated with chromium(III) nitrate?

____

____

____

Name ______________________ Date ________________ Class ________________

9 PERIODIC PROPERTIES

1. How are elements arranged in a periodic table?

2. What are the vertical columns in a periodic table called?

3. What determines whether two elements will have similar chemical properties?

4. What property will you measure in this experiment?

5. Briefly summarize the procedure for determining the density of an irregularly shaped solid.

Name ______________ Date ______________ Class ______________

10 CRYSTAL STRUCTURES

1. Name the three forms of packing in crystals that you will examine.

____

____

____

2. What does *coordination number* refer to?

____

____

____

3. What factor is significant in determining the coordination number of an ionic crystal?

____

____

____

Name ______________ Date ______________ Class ______________

MOLECULAR MODELS

1. Complete the following table:

Molecule	Shape
methane	
ammonia	
water	

2. Define *structural isomer.*

____

____

____

3. In the models that you will construct, how are single, double, and triple bonds represented?

____

____

____

4. What does the number of holes drilled in the wooden balls represent?

____

____

____

12 THE MASSES OF EQUAL VOLUMES OF GASES

1. When you compare the masses of two different gases, what experimental conditions must be kept constant?

____

____

____

2. How is the mass of the air in the flask determined?

____

____

____

____

3. If the flask or stopper was wet when the mass of the flask assembly was measured in Step 2, how would this affect the calculated mass of argon?

____

____

4. Define *density*.

____

____

13 EMPIRICAL FORMULA DETERMINATION

1. How does an empirical formula differ from a molecular formula?

____

____

____

____

2. Other than the reminder to wear safety goggles and dispose of materials as instructed, what are the three safety hazards in this experiment?

____

____

____

3. Why is it inadvisable to determine the mass of a hot crucible and lid?

____

____

4. State what mass is to be determined each time the balance is used.

____

____

____

5. What would happen if the crucible lid was left off during the combustion of the magnesium ribbon?

____

____

____

Name ____________________ Date ______________ Class ______________

14 TYPES OF CHEMICAL REACTIONS

1. How does a decomposition reaction differ from other types of reactions?

____

____

2. In a combustion reaction, what products form in addition to any new compound(s)?

____

____

3. Which two ions should be used in very small quantities because they are toxic and bioaccumulative, that is, build up in body tissues?

____

____

4. During which steps (give numbers) of the procedure would you expect to produce a gas?

____

5. What safety precaution applies when heating a test tube?

____

____

____

Name ______________________ Date ________________ Class ______________

15 REACTIVITY OF METALS

1. Explain why different metals show a difference in chemical reactivity.

____

____

____

2. What is the activity series of metals?

____

____

____

3. How can you determine which of two metals is more reactive?

____

____

____

____

____

4. Describe what occurs when iron is placed in a solution of copper ions.

____

____

____

5. What will happen if a strip of copper metal is placed in a solution containing iron(II) ions?

____

____

____

6. What hazards are associated with silver nitrate?

____

____

____

Name ______________________ Date ________________ Class ________________

IDENTIFICATION OF ANIONS AND CATIONS IN SOLUTION

1. How would you recognize when a precipitate has formed?

____

____

____

2. If sodium hydroxide gets in your eyes or spills on your skin, how should you treat it?

____

____

____

3. a. Give the formulas and names of the three acids used in this experiment.

____

____

____

b. Consider all the acids mentioned in your answer to question 3a. In solution, what ion do all three compounds produce?

____

c. What safety term applies to all three of the acids?

____

4. Which chemical used in this lab will stain skin and clothing?

____

5. Why is distilled water, and not tap water, used for the tests?

____

____

____

6. When you do a flame test, which ion will most likely mask the color of potassium?

____

Name ______________________ Date ________________ Class ________________

17 PRECIPITATION REACTIONS

1. Explain how ionic compounds are held together.

____

____

____

2. What compound is formed when sodium chloride is mixed with silver nitrate?

____

3. Distinguish between a *complete* ionic equation and a *net* ionic equation.

____

____

____

4. In addition to being toxic, what hazard does silver nitrate pose to skin or clothing?

____

5. Are any of the compounds in Sets 1, 2, or 3, insoluble?

____

6. Complete the following:

In a complete ionic equation, reactants are always shown as ________________,

the precipitate as ________________, and the ________________ as unchanged.

The total charge should be ________________ on both sides of the equation.

Name ______________________ Date ________________ Class ________________

18 QUALITATIVE ANALYSIS

1. Why might a single test be insufficient to identify an unknown solution?

____

____

____

____

2. Why are the spot plates or test tubes cleaned with distilled water before you test any of the solutions?

____

____

____

3. Why are the solutions and reagents not labeled in this experiment?

____

____

____

4. What is the safest approach to use when working with unknown chemicals?

____

____

____

Name ______________________ Date ________________ Class ______________

19 QUANTITATIVE ANALYSIS

1. What is the relationship between the number of moles of reactants and products, and the coefficients in a balanced equation?

2. In your own words, state the chemical reaction you will observe.

3. Identify and define the new laboratory skill learned in this experiment.

4. Identify the chemical that presents the greatest safety hazard in this experiment. What is the hazard?

Name ______________ Date ______________ Class ______________

BALANCED CHEMICAL EQUATIONS

1. Define *limiting reagent.*

____

____

____

2. Refer to the balanced equation to complete the following:

Four moles of sodium iodide will require ______________ moles of lead(II) nitrate and will produce ______________ moles of lead(II) iodide and ______________ moles of sodium nitrate.

3. Why is pipetting by mouth dangerous?

____

____

4. What is a supernatant?

____

____

5. Why is a ruler used in this experiment?

____

____

Name ______________________ Date __________________ Class __________________

 PRELAB ASSIGNMENT

21 ALLOTROPIC FORMS OF SULFUR

1. Define *allotropes.*

____

____

____

2. What factors determine which allotrope of an element will be formed?

____

____

____

3. List two allotropes of carbon.

____

4. Why must this experiment be conducted in a fume hood?

____

____

5. List three allotropes of sulfur.

____

Name ____________ Date ____________ Class ____________

CHANGES OF PHYSICAL STATE

1. a. Define *melting point.*

   b. What is the change of state called when a liquid changes to a gas or vapor?

2. a. List three physical states of matter.

   b. What two phase changes will you observe in this experiment?

3. What is the greatest safety hazard in this experiment?

4. Why must the lauric acid be stirred as it heats or cools?

Name ______________________ Date ________________ Class ______________

PRESSURE–VOLUME RELATIONSHIPS FOR GASES

1. State Boyle's law.

____

____

____

2. What disposal problem does toxic dibutyl phthalate present?

____

____

____

3. What should you do if the plunger of the syringe does not operate smoothly?

____

____

____

____

4. How will you change the volume of the experimental apparatus?

____

____

____

5. What measurement will you make to track the change in pressure?

____

____

____

Name ______________ Date ______________ Class ______________

24 TEMPERATURE–VOLUME RELATIONSHIPS FOR GASES

1. State Charles's law.

____

____

____

2. Which variable is manipulated in this experiment?

____

3. What should you do if burned by hot glass?

____

____

____

4. At what different temperatures will you be measuring the volume?

____

____

____

5. How will you measure the volume of gas in each trial?

____

____

Name ____________________ Date ____________________ Class ____________________

DIFFUSION OF GASES

1. If gas X and gas Y are at the same temperature and gas X has the larger molar mass, which gas has the greater velocity?

____

2. Define *diffusion*.

____

____

____

____

3. a. Calculate the molar mass of HCl and of NH_3.

____

____

____

b. Which of the two would travel the farthest in 3 minutes?

____

4. What safety hazard do HCl and NH_3 vapors present?

____

____

____

Name ____________ Date ____________ Class ____________

26 DISTILLATION

1. Describe the process of distillation for aqueous solutions.

2. Define *condensation*.

3. Why is $AgNO_3$ added to the distillate at the conclusion of the experiment?

4. Why are boiling chips added to the solution?

5. When will you need to use glycerin?

Name ______________________ Date __________________ Class __________________

27 THE SOLVENT PROPERTIES OF WATER

1. Explain why water is such an excellent solvent.

____

____

____

2. Explain why gasoline and oil do not dissolve in water.

____

____

____

3. What disposal problem does hexane present?

____

____

____

____

4. Which three substances used in this experiment are flammable?

____

Name ______________________ Date ________________ Class ________________

28 WATER OF HYDRATION

1. Define *hydrates*.

____

____

____

2. What is an *anhydrous salt*?

____

____

3. In the following reaction, label the hydrate and the anhydrous salt.

$$CaSO_4 + 2H_2O \rightarrow CaSO_4{\bullet}2H_2O$$

______________ ______________

4. Explain the difference between plaster of Paris and hard plaster.

____

____

____

5. Which of the hydrates used in this experiment presents a disposal problem?

____

Name ______________________ Date ________________ Class ________________

29 ELECTROLYTES AND NONELECTROLYTES

1. a. Define *electrolyte.*

____

____

b. Define *ion.*

____

2. What is an electric current?

____

____

____

3. Explain why solid ionic substances do not conduct electricity, but ionic substances in solution do conduct electricity.

____

____

____

4. What precautions must be taken to protect against electric shock when working with the conductivity apparatus?

____

____

____

____

5. What is the appropriate response if sodium hydroxide is spilled or splashes on skin?

____

____

____

Name ______________________ Date ________________ Class ________________

30 FACTORS AFFECTING SOLUTION FORMATION

1. **a.** In a solution of sodium chloride and water, identify the solute.

   b. In the same solution, what is the solvent?

2. List three factors that affects the rate at which a solute dissolves.

3. Describe the safe method of transferring boiling water from one container to another.

4. In Step 3 of the procedure, what is the purpose of shaking two of the tubes?

31 SUPERSATURATION

1. a. Define *solubility.*

____

____

   b. Define *saturated solution.*

____

____

2. Describe what occurs when a solution is supersaturated.

____

____

____

____

3. Explain the use of a seed crystal in this experiment.

____

____

____

4. How are the crystals disposed of at the end of the experiment?

____

____

____

Name ______________________ Date __________________ Class __________________

INTRODUCTION TO CHROMATOGRAPHY

1. Why is chromatography used?

____

____

____

2. What process explains the movement of the solvent up the filter paper?

____

____

3. Explain why the various compounds in the mixture separate during chromatography.

____

____

____

4. What is the R_f value?

____

____

____

5. What is the only hazard associated with food coloring?

____

____

Name ______________________ Date ________________ Class ________________

33 FREEZING POINT

1. a. What variable is manipulated in this experiment?

____

b. Why is it manipulated?

____

____

____

2. Why should the benzoic acid not be heated beyond 140°C?

____

____

____

3. What factor (other than the addition of heat) would increase the rate at which solutes dissolve in benzoic acid?

____

____

____

4. Show the conversion factor that would be used to convert from 0.0050 moles of solute to grams of solute.

____

Name ______________ Date ______________ Class ______________

THE SPECIFIC HEAT OF A METAL

1. Define *specific heat.*

____

____

____

2. List the three factors that determine the amount of heat energy involved in changing the temperature of a substance.

____

____

____

3. What happens to the heat stored in the lead shot when the shot is poured into the plastic-foam cup full of water?

____

____

4. How will you remove the test tube of lead shot from the boiling water?

____

____

5. State the three temperature measurements that you are to make.

____

____

____

____

____

Name ______________________ Date ______________________ Class ______________________

35 HEATS OF REACTION

1. Define *exothermic reaction.*

2. What three facts are needed before the amount of heat released in a chemical reaction can be calculated?

3. a. Sodium hydroxide pellets are hygroscopic. What does *hygroscopic* mean?

b. Why does this behavior present a safety hazard when you use sodium hydroxide pellets?

4. Why are both a foam cup and beaker required?

Name ______________________ Date ________________ Class ______________

FACTORS AFFECTING REACTION RATES

1. According to the collision theory, how are bonds formed or broken?

____

____

2. Define *activation energy*.

____

____

3. What variables influence reaction rates?

____

____

4. Explain how catalysts work.

____

____

5. Explain how the following conditions would affect the reaction rate:
   - **a.** Temperature is reduced.
   - **b.** Finer particles are used.
   - **c.** Reactant solutions are diluted.

____

____

____

6. In Part A, step 3, how will you know when the reaction is finished?

____

____

7. What health hazard is associated with iron(III) chloride and hydrochloric acid?

____

____

37 THE CLOCK REACTION

1. Explain why this experiment is called a clock reaction.

2. The concentrations of which two ions are varied in the experiment?

3. What method is used to analyze the data?

4. In the procedure, when do you begin timing the reaction?

5. In the procedure, when do you end timing the reaction?

Name ____________________ Date ____________________ Class ____________________

38 DISTURBING EQUILIBRIUM

1. Explain what occurs when dynamic equilibrium is reached.

2. State Le Châtelier's principle.

3. In this experiment, you will study the following reaction:

$$Fe^{3+} + SCN^{-} \rightleftharpoons FeSCN^{2+}$$

In which direction will the equilibrium shift, if any, when the following changes occur?

a. Iron(III) chloride, $FeCl_3$ is added.
b. $FeSCN^{2+}$ ions are added.
c. Potassium chloride, KCl, is added.

4. What hazards are associated with iron(III) chloride?

5. What stress is applied to the equilibrium in Part A?

Name ______________________ Date ______________ Class ______________

39 A SOLUBILITY PRODUCT CONSTANT

1. The solubility product constant of lead(II) chloride is given by the following expression:

$$K_{sp} = [Pb^{2+}]\,[Cl^{-}]^2$$

In your own words, describe what this expression means.

____

____

____

2. In the solubility product expression of lead(II) chloride given above, explain why the chloride ion concentration is squared in the calculation.

____

____

____

3. Explain the role of insoluble lead(II) chromate in this experiment.

____

____

____

____

____

4. Why is it important to wash your hands thoroughly after completing this experiment?

____

____

____

Name ______________________ Date ______________ Class ______________

ESTIMATION OF pH

1. In the Brønsted-Lowry theory, how are acids and bases defined?

____

____

____

2. What are conjugate acids and bases?

____

____

____

____

____

3. What happens when phenolphthalein is introduced into a basic solution? Explain in terms of Le Châtelier's principle.

____

____

____

____

____

4. Use Data Table 3 to answer the following questions:

a. What color is methyl red at pH = 8?
b. What color is litmus at pH = 6?
c. What color is bromthymol blue at pH = 7.5?
d. What color is phenolphthalein at pH = 5?

____

____

____

____

5. List the compounds used in this experiment that present safety hazards.

____

Name ______________________ Date ________________ Class ________________

41 REACTIONS OF ACIDS

1. In Step 3 of the procedure, how will you know which gas is evolved?

2. Write a balanced equation showing what happens when magnesium ribbon is added to 6*M* hydrochloric acid.

3. Explain why the metals should be transferred to the test tubes with a spatula or forceps, and not with your fingers.

Name ______________________ Date ________________ Class ________________

42 NEUTRALIZATION REACTIONS

1. How are Arrhenius acids and bases defined?

2. What are the products of a neutralization reaction?

3. How will you know when the sodium hydroxide has been neutralized?

4. What safety precaution must be taken when removing the evaporating dish from the beaker?

5. Describe the safety procedure to be used in the event that acid spills on the laboratory bench or on the floor.

Name ______________________ Date ________________ Class ______________

43 ACID–BASE TITRATIONS

1. In a titration, what is occurring at the exact moment of neutralization?

2. How is the number of equivalents defined?

3. Explain how the volume of a solution used in a titration is determined by using a buret.

4. Define *standard solution*.

5. What must you do in the event that the level of the solution in the buret goes below the 50-mL mark?

6. Explain why two different titrations are necessary in this experiment.

Name ______________________ Date ________________ Class ______________

SALT HYDROLYSIS

1. Define *salt hydrolysis*.

____

____

____

____

2. Under what conditions will a nonneutral salt solution result?

____

____

____

____

3. How will you determine if salt hydrolysis has occurred?

____

____

____

____

Name ______________ Date ______________ Class ______________

45 BUFFERS

1. What do buffers consist of?

2. What does a buffered solution do?

3. Describe how the carbonic acid/hydrogen carbonate buffering system in the blood works.

4. How will you determine whether or not a system tested in this experiment is an effective buffering system?

Name ______________________ Date ________________ Class ________________

OXIDATION–REDUCTION REACTIONS

1. How are *oxidation* and *reduction* defined?

____

____

____

2. When a metal reacts with an acid, what is oxidized and what is reduced in the reaction?

____

____

____

3. What characterizes a strong reducing agent?

____

____

____

4. What will you do with the metal strips when you have finished testing them?

____

____

Name ______________________ Date ________________ Class ________________

CORROSION

1. Define *corrosion.*

____

____

____

2. In the corrosion of iron, what reaction occurs at the anode and what reaction occurs at the cathode?

____

____

____

____

3. In Part B, why do you bend the nails?

____

____

4. Explain why copper and zinc are wrapped around two of the nails.

____

____

____

Name ______________________ Date ________________ Class ______________

ELECTROCHEMISTRY

1. a. Describe the process of electroplating.

____

____

____

b. Why are metals electroplated?

____

____

2. a. When a fork is silver plated, what is the anode?

____

b. What is the cathode?

____

c. What is the electrolytic solution?

____

3. Explain what occurs in this experiment at the cathode and what occurs at the anode.

____

____

____

____

4. Explain why you should never touch both terminals of the battery at the same time.

____

____

____

5. Explain why the steel wool should be held with gloves or paper.

____

____

Name ______________________ Date ________________ Class ________________

49 HYDROCARBONS: A STRUCTURAL STUDY

1. Explain why an understanding of molecular shape is important in understanding chemical behavior.

2. Distinguish between the use of the short and long sticks in the ball-and-stick models.

3. What are structural isomers?

4. Distinguish between the boat conformation and the chair conformation of cycloalkanes.

5. a. What are geometric isomers?

   b. Name the two kinds of geometric isomers.

Name ______________________ Date ________________ Class ________________

ESTERS OF CARBOXYLIC ACIDS

1. How are esters recognized?

2. How are esters synthesized?

3. In the synthesis of esters, what is used to catalyze the reaction?

4. In esterification reactions, why is water removed?

Name ______________________ Date ________________ Class ________________

51 PREPARATION OF SOAP

1. How are soaps produced?

2. What are triglycerides?

3. Describe what occurs in saponification.

4. Why is it important to remember to close the container of sodium hydroxide pellets tightly and to never touch the pellets with your fingers?

Name ______________________ Date __________________ Class ________________

RADIOACTIVITY AND RADIATION

1. What are the there types of radiation?

____

2. Give two ways that the ionizations caused by radiation can be detected.

____

____

3. Explain why a Geiger-Müller counter cannot be used to measure alpha radiation.

____

____

____

4. Give three ways that exposure to radiation can be minimized.

____

____

____

____

____

Name ______________________ Date ________________ Class ________________

SAFETY IN THE CHEMISTRY LABORATORY

A. Matching

Match each description in Column B with the correct symbol in Column A. Write the letter of the correct description in the blank provided.

Column A

_______ 1.

_______ 2.

_______ 3.

_______ 4.

_______ 5.

_______ 6.

_______ 7.

_______ 8.

Column B

a. Always wear safety goggles in the lab.

b. Avoid irritating fumes.

c. Dispose of this chemical only as directed.

d. Wear safety goggles, an apron, and gloves when working with corrosive chemicals.

e. Tie back hair and loose clothing.

f. Use sharp objects as intended.

g. Do not touch hot glassware.

h. Do not use chipped glassware.

B. True–False

Each statement is either true or false. Indicate your answer in the margin with a T for true or an F for false.

_______ **9.** If you have not handled any chemicals, you do not need to wash your hands at the conclusion of the experiment.

_______ **10.** All leftover or waste chemicals can be flushed down the drain with large amounts of water.

_______ **11.** You must wear goggles while cleaning up after an experiment.

_______ **12.** To save materials, it is a good idea to return surplus chemicals to their appropriate, labeled reagent bottles.

_______ **13.** You should always add concentrated acid slowly to a large volume of water and never the other way around. You should never add water to a concentrated acid.

_______ **14.** You may eat an apple during an experiment.

_______ **15.** When you are heating a test tube you should make sure that the mouth of the tube is pointed away from you and from others.

_______ **16.** Flammable liquids may be heated using a hot plate.

_______ **17.** If your clothing catches on fire, you should run immediately to the safety shower.

Name ______________________ Date ________________ Class ________________

C. Short Answers

In an emergency, what would you do? Write a short-answer response to each of the following hypothetical situations that might arise during a chemistry experiment. Make sure that your answer includes a description of all actions that would be reasonable to take, including first aid.

19. A small beaker of a flammable liquid near a lit burner has caught fire.

____

____

20. A small amount of a chemical labeled in the materials list with the symbol [C] has spilled on your hand.

____

____

21. A chemical has splashed into your eye.

____

____

22. You have received a small cut on your hand.

____

____

23. Your partner is heating the bottom of a test tube half-filled with liquid and the mouth of the tube is pointing at you.

____

____

24. You begin to feel faint during an experiment.

____

____

25. You think your partner has accidentally swallowed a chemical.

____

____

26. You accidentally touch a tripod that is very hot.

____

____

Name ____________________ Date ______________ Class ______________

SAFE LABORATORY TECHNIQUES

A. Multiple Choice

Write the letter of the best answer in the blank.

______ **1.** Which of the following statements is incorrect concerning the transfer of chemicals?
- **a.** You should always read the label on storage bottles.
- **b.** You should always wear goggles in the laboratory.
- **c.** You should never touch chemicals directly with your hands.
- **d.** You should always return unused chemicals to their original containers.

______ **2.** Which of the following is an appropriate technique to use when pouring liquids?
- **a.** Remove the stopper of the container and lay the stopper on a clean area of the workbench.
- **b.** Look down into the graduated cylinder to better determine when the correct volume has been reached.
- **c.** Pour the liquid slowly down a glass stirring rod into a beaker.
- **d.** Grasp the container you are pouring from by its base.

______ **3.** What equipment is essential for filtering a solid from a liquid?
- **a.** Filter paper, funnel, beaker, iron ring, and stand
- **b.** Beaker, funnel, filter paper, stirring rod, iron ring and stand
- **c.** Beaker, funnel, stirring rod, iron ring, and stand
- **d.** Filter paper, beaker, stirring rod, iron ring, and stand

______ **4.** Which of the following errors is most likely to cause you to start a filtration over again?
- **a.** Overflowing the top edge of the filter paper
- **b.** Failure to use a stirring rod
- **c.** Using too large a piece of filter paper
- **d.** Placing the tip of the funnel in the center of the beaker

______ **5.** Which of the following descriptions of gas burner flame color, air vent status, and degree of air mixing are realistic?
- **a.** Yellow flame, open air vents, good mixing of air
- **b.** Blue flame, closed air vents, poor mixing of air
- **c.** Yellow flame, closed air vents, poor mixing of air
- **d.** Blue flame, closed air vents, good mixing of air

______ **6.** When preparing to light a gas burner, which of the following should you do first?
- **a.** Determine which burner model you are working with.
- **b.** Connect the burner to the gas supply.
- **c.** Close the air vents.
- **d.** Make sure that flammable chemicals are not being used.

Name ______________________ Date ________________ Class ________________

_______ 7. Which of the following types of flame is probably the best for most laboratory work?
  a. A 2-inch-wide yellow flame
  b. A light blue, cone-shaped flame
  c. A flame with an inner yellow cone and an outer blue margin
  d. A flame with an inner blue cone and an outer margin of smoky yellow

_______ 8. Which of the following is not a correct technique for heating a liquid in a test tube while using a gas burner?
  a. Use a gentle blue flame.
  b. Heat only the bottom of the tube.
  c. Shake the tube gently.
  d. Fill the tube about one-third full.

_______ 9. A hot water or boiling water bath requires which of the following sets of equipment?
  a. Burner, wire gauze, iron ring and stand, beaker
  b. Burner, iron ring and stand, beaker
  c. Burner, tongs, beaker
  d. Burner, iron ring and stand, stirring rod, wire gauze, beaker

_______ 10. Which of the following is an appropriate procedure to follow when using a balance?
  a. Move the balance freely around the laboratory.
  b. Be especially careful when measuring an object that exceeds the balance capacity.
  c. Place solid chemicals directly on the pan.
  d. Remember to zero the balance.

_______ 11. How should the volume of a liquid in a graduated cylinder be read?
  a. At the bottom of the meniscus
  b. With your eyes focused on the top of the cylinder
  c. To the nearest 1 mL
  d. None of the above

_______ 12. Which of the following is an appropriate procedure to be used when cutting and polishing a piece of glass tubing?
  a. Make a very deep scratch in the surface of the glass, using a back-and-forth sawing motion.
  b. Place your thumbs over the scratch and snap the glass.
  c. Rotate the glass in a hot burner flame to soften the edges
  d. Apply a water or oil lubricant to make cutting easier.

_______ 13. Which of the following heating techniques produces a smooth glass bend?
  a. Heating the tubing strongly at one point
  b. Holding the tubing at a low point of the flame
  c. Bending the tubing while it is still in the flame
  d. Rotating the tubing in the flame so that the tube is heated uniformly

Name ____

SAFETY CONTRACT

I have read the pages in the *Laboratory Manual* that describe safety precautions, laboratory hazards, and safe laboratory techniques. I have asked questions about any section that is unclear.

I agree to help promote and maintain a safe laboratory environment for myself and my classmates.

I will wear safety goggles at all times during chemistry laboratory experiments and whenever my teacher thinks it is appropriate.

____
Signature

____
Date

CARE OF LABORATORY EQUIPMENT

Balances

Balances get a lot of use and abuse. Consequently, you should check the zero setting of each balance before each class period in which balances will be used. You can easily adjust this setting by turning the knob on the short end of the beam of a triple-beam balance, or by turning the small knob in the middle of a pan balance. Also, you should be sure to hang the balance pans in the correct manner, as the pans are often knocked askew. An investment in plastic balance covers makes students more aware of the fact that they should treat balances gently. Use of the covers also serves to discourage students from fiddling with balances when they are not in use.

Sometimes balances cannot be adjusted because their weight distribution has been altered by damage. This problem can be remedied in the following way. First, set the adjusting knob of the balance to its middle position. Note whether the balance is reading too heavy or too light. Then look under the pan of the balance to locate a container holding lead shot. (You can gently shake the balance to hear the shot.) Remove the screw holding the container and take it, being careful not to spill any shot. Add or remove shot. (You can add any kind of metal pellets you have.) You will have to guess about the amount to add or remove. Then replace the container, or just put it on the pan, and check the zero setting. Repeat the procedure if your guess was not correct. Do not make any other adjustments to the balance (such as trying to add weights to the short end of the arm); these changes will make the readings incorrect. Only changing the amount of shot keeps the balance readings correct because the added or removed mass is at the same distance from the fulcrum as the pan is.

Balance pans often get dirty, rusty, or bent. Have students wash the pans when they clean up at the end of a laboratory period. You can usually straighten bent pans by using two pairs of pliers. Bent pans do not affect accuracy to any large degree. Avoid the temptation to use plastic balance pans, as they often melt when students place hot beakers or crucibles on them.

Burets

Burets should be washed, with their stopcocks open, immediately after each use so that nothing is allowed to dry in the tip of the buret. Dry the burets with their tips up and their stopcocks open. Before putting a buret away, rotate its stopcock a full 360 degrees in both directions. Store the burets with their stopcocks in the open position.

If you can, store your burets in a rack with their tips up or place a small piece of rubber tubing on the tip of each dry buret before storing it. Remove the piece of tubing just prior to the actual titration. Buying burets with detachable and replaceable tips is a good idea. Attaching and removing these tips is an easy task. It is a good practice to detach and clean the tips after each use and store them separately to prevent seals from hardening.

If a buret does become clogged, try sliding a straight pin up through the tip. Use only your fingers or a pair of pliers to hold the pin; do not tap or force it, as the tip may break as a result. If this procedure fails to unclog the tip, soak it in soapy water overnight. If this approach does not work, soak the tip in concentrated acid, or an appropriate organic solvent if the clog is organic material. Note that tips that are chipped or cracked still may be usable. Throw away a buret or buret tip if it does not drip properly.

Centrifuges

A centrifuge is generally indestructible. Keep it in a permanent location away from the sites of other lab activities. The tabletop on which the centrifuge rests should be level and not slippery. If you have a “creeping” centrifuge, make sure it is leveled and try placing a rubber mat beneath it. It is not necessary to oil a centrifuge or to perform any other such routine maintenance. Also, it is not necessary to calibrate the speed of a centrifuge or to make any other adjustment. Note that every student who is allowed to use the centrifuge should be instructed to use paired tubes of equal weight to keep the centrifuge balanced.

It is recommended that you always use plastic centrifuge tubes. Glass tubes break eventually, and when they do, they leave water and chemicals in the tube holder. If any liquid does spill in a centrifuge, dry the centrifuge thoroughly.

Ceramic Ware

Ceramic ware often gets encrusted with material. Crucibles, evaporating dishes, and the like, can be cleaned in several different ways. One approach is to blast each piece in the flame of a Fischer burner until the piece becomes red hot. This is a fun task for the student to do if supervised. Another approach is to put the pieces in a self-cleaning oven that is equipped with a fan. Then, turn on the fan and set the oven to self-clean. If you have a laboratory furnace, you may use it to burn the crusts off smaller pieces. Still another approach is to soak the ceramic ware in a chromic acid–sulfuric acid solution overnight. Be certain to rinse the ceramic ware thoroughly after this acid soaking. Never allow the students to do this soaking, because it is hazardous and can result in damaged clothing or worse. Note that all these cleaning methods may cause the ceramic ware to appear dirty. But, appearances notwithstanding, the ceramic ware is perfectly usable after these cleaning procedures, as long as it is not cracked.

Electrolysis Apparatus

To care for an electrolysis apparatus, clean the electrodes in dilute acid and rinse thoroughly after each use. Also, be sure to rinse the apparatus after each use so that acids, bases, or salts do not remain in contact with, or accumulate on, the apparatus. Check the wires and their connections before each use. This apparatus requires no calibration. Note that a conductivity apparatus can be cared for in the same way as an electrolysis apparatus.

Gas Burners

Note that a burner's tubing should not be so soft that it can become kinked, and the tube should be thick enough that it is not easily cut. Clean out the gas inlet with a straight pin if the inlet hole has become clogged. Use a pair of pliers to crimp the burner air flow vents into place if the cuff or top tube has become loose.

Geiger Counter and Radioactive Materials

Check the batteries of a Geiger counter for corrosion at least every semester. Other than this inspection, the instrument requires no special care. Inform students who are using a Geiger counter that the Geiger sensory tube is relatively delicate, even though it looks quite solid. Note that you cannot calibrate a Geiger counter.

Use only radioactive materials that come sealed in plastic. An old watch with a radium dial may also be used as a radiation source, if available. All radioactive materials should be stored away from the Geiger counter. Keep all radioactive materials in one place, perhaps together with the other materials used in radioactivity experiments.

Hot Plates

Hot plates may become rusty as the result of spills. To prevent rust from forming, keep a thick sponge nearby to wipe off the top and sides of a hot plate if there is a spill. Remember that the hot plate should be unplugged before you start to clean up a spill.

Often a hot plate that fails to work has an unattached wire that can be fixed by opening up the bottom of the hot plate and reattaching the wire. Be certain to unplug the hot plate before beginning any repairs. The hot plate may also fail to work because its heating element is broken. If this is the case, do not try to fix the hot plate.

pH Meter

A pH meter should always be kept plugged in with its control knob set to "standby." Keep the pH meter in a set place in the laboratory, away from the site of any other lab activities. The meter should not be moved around.

Keep the electrode tips of the pH meter immersed in a beaker of distilled water. Keep a wash bottle of distilled water near the pH meter. Label the bottle "distilled water for the pH meter" so that it is not mistaken for a wash bottle. Change the distilled water once a week so that bacteria do not begin to grow and dust does not accumulate. At the same time, check the amount of saturated potassium chloride solution in the electrodes. Normally, you should have to add solution to the electrodes only about once a year.

Before each class involving use of the pH meter, you should calibrate the device. First set the temperature knob on the meter to the normal room temperature, if it is not there already. Then prepare three buffer solutions—one at pH 4, one at pH 7, and one at pH 10. These solutions can be obtained already prepared in plastic bottles from chemical supply houses. You can also purchase packets of solids that can be added to the distilled water to produce the buffer solutions. To calibrate the meter, do the following steps:

1. Pour 20 mL of the pH 7 buffer solution into a 150-mL beaker that has been thoroughly rinsed in distilled water. (You do not need much buffer solution because only the glass membrane at the bottom of the electrode needs to be covered.)
2. Hold the electrode above its regular beaker of distilled water and rinse the electrode thoroughly with distilled water. Never dry or wipe an electrode because its glass membrane is easily damaged by such treatment.
3. Gently lower the electrode into the beaker of buffer solution. Never allow the electrode to touch the bottom of the beaker because the glass membrane could break.
4. Turn the control knob from "standby" to "pH." Then turn the adjusting knob until the needle or display reads 7.00.
5. Repeat steps 1–4 using first the pH 4 buffer and then the pH 10 buffer. Then do a repeat check on the pH 7 solution.

It is usually hard to move the electrode holder smoothly up and down on its stand. It is a good idea to tape down, or otherwise secure, the electrode stand. This action prevents spills and makes the holder slide more easily. You can also make the holder slide more easily by greasing its pole.

If, at the beginning of a school year, you establish a pH meter station, fill the electrodes, and calibrate the meter, the meter should require only minor adjustment and maintenance for the rest of the year.

Pipets

After using a pipet, place it, tip up, in a tall plastic container that is filled with soapy water. The tips of the pipets should be under water. After enough pipets have accumulated, pour off the soapy water and rinse the pipets thoroughly. Store the pipets either vertically, with their tips up, or horizontally, with their tips elevated. You can dry and store pipets in a second tall plastic cylinder with the tips elevated. Following this procedure prevents tips from becoming clogged and makes washing pipets a relatively easy task.

Spectrophotometer

One of the most commonly used spectrophotometers, the Bausch and Lomb Spectronic 20™, has a single bulb for which you should have two spares. You can replace the bulb by removing the bulb holder located under the bottom right of the instrument. This spectrophotometer itself usually does not need any special care. However, the tube holder may become dirty or cracked. You can remove the tube holder easily from the top of the machine to clean or replace it. Although the electronics of the spectrophotometer are relatively simple, it is unlikely that you will be able to find the cause of a problem, unless it is simply a burned-out fuse, which you can replace. To calibrate the spectrophotometer, use the procedure described in the Procedure section on page 58 of the lab manual.

ANSWERS TO PRELAB ASSIGNMENTS AND SAFETY QUIZZES

Prelab 1

1. Observations are made and explanations are offered. A hypothesis is developed to explain them. Experiments are conducted to test the hypothesis, which may then need to be refined. This procedure is repeated until no further refinement of the hypothesis is needed. Well-tested explanations that are supported by many experiments can evolve into theories.
2. Observations are made and explanations are offered.
3. Flammable (F): ethanol; Corrosive (C): silver nitrate, sodium hydroxide, dry ice
4. Dry ice can cause frostbite if it comes into contact with skin.

Prelab 2

1. Odor, color, boiling point, and melting point
2. In a physical change, only the appearance or physical state of a substance is altered; in a chemical change, however, new substances with different chemical compositions are formed.
3. **a.** Hydrochloric acid is corrosive. If any spills on the body, the affected area should be immediately flushed with water for 2–3 minutes. If any gets into the eyes, flush with water for at least 15 minutes. **b.** The intense light given off may damage the eyes.
4. Fold a piece of filter paper into quarters, and form it into a cone. Place the cone in a glass funnel, moisten it with water, and place the funnel in a ring support attached to a ring stand. Pour the mixture into the funnel using a glass rod as a guide.
5. Sucrose
6. The reaction produces toxic, irritating fumes.

Prelab 3

1. An observation is a statement of fact, based on sensory data. An interpretation is a judgement about what is observed.
2. A qualitative observation does not involve measurement; it is a general description. A quantitative observation involves a measurement.
3. Put on safety goggles.
4. Follow the instructions given by the teacher (to empty the beaker into the chemical waste container).
5. 1. Wash and dry equipment. 2. Wash hands thoroughly.

Prelab 4

1. **a.** A platform balance; **b.** An analytical balance
2. By water displacement
3. Two
4. The mass of the water would introduce an error into the measurement.
5. Because density is equal to mass/volume, the slope of the line represents the density of the substance.

Prelab 5

1. Their target, the atom, was too small to be viewed directly.
2. In this game, the size and shape of an object can be indirectly determined, although the object itself cannot be seen.
3. **a.** The shape can be determined by the angle at which the marbles exit from under the board.
   b.

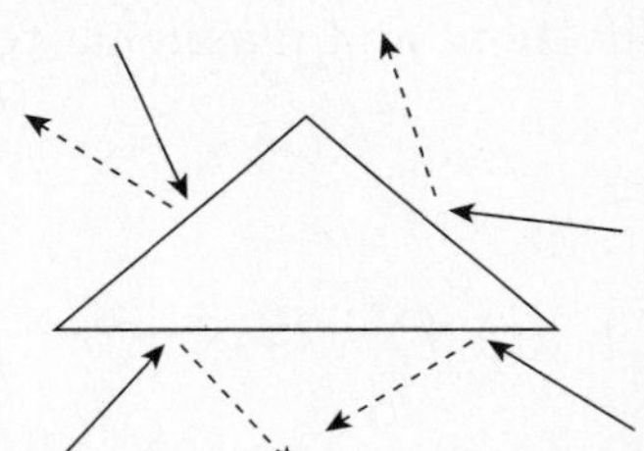

Prelab 6

1. The electrons are excited to higher energy levels. When they return to lower levels, they emit specific wavelengths of light.
2. Blue to violet light
3. Sodium nitrate ($NaNO_3$) and potassium nitrate (KNO_3)

4. The loop is cleaned by dipping it into the concentrated HCl and heating it in the hottest portion of the gas burner flame.
5. Virtually all of the solids used in this experiment are toxic.

Prelab 7

1. An emission spectrum is the pattern of lines that results when emitted light is separated into its component wavelengths.
2. A spectrograph is an instrument that causes electron excitation, separates emitted light into its component wavelengths, and records the wavelengths.
3. The color given off by the heated sodium chloride is separated into its individual wavelengths. The wavelength of the brightest line will be measured.
4. HCl is corrosive and toxic.
5. To measure the distance from the observed spectral lines to the slit and the distance from the diffraction grating to the slit.

Prelab 8

1. A spectrometer consists of a radiation source, a diffraction grating, a monochrometer, and a detector.
2. Light absorption will occur when the energy of a wavelength of light corresponds to the energy needed to excite an electron.
3. Impurities are likely to affect light transmittance, leading to erroneous results.
4. It is toxic and can irritate the skin.

Prelab 9

1. Elements are arranged in a periodic table in order of increasing atomic number.
2. Groups
3. If the two elements are in the same group in the periodic table, they will have the same number of electrons in their highest occupied energy level.
4. Density
5. Determine its mass. Record the volume of water in a graduated cylinder before and after the solid has been added. The difference in these two measurements is the volume of the solid. Divide the mass by the volume.

Prelab 10

1. Hexagonal closest packing, face-centered cubic packing, and body-centered cubic packing
2. The number of nearest neighbors of a particle
3. The relative size of the anions and cations that make up the crystal

Prelab 11

1.

Molecule	Shape
methane	tetrahedral
ammonia	trigonal pyramidal
water	bent

2. Structural isomers have identical molecular formulas but different structural formulas.
3. Single bonds are represented by short wooden sticks. Double and triple bonds are represented by springs.
4. The number of holes represents the maximum number of bonds that an atom can have.

Prelab 12

1. Their volume, temperature, and pressure must be the same.
2. Find the density of the air. Then use the value for volume, found in Step 7, to calculate the mass of the air according to the following equation:
$$\text{mass} = \text{density} \times \text{volume}$$
3. The added water would increase the calculated mass of argon.
4. Density is equal to the ratio of mass to volume.
$$\text{density} = \frac{\text{mass}}{\text{volume}}$$

Prelab 13

1. An empirical formula gives the simplest whole-number ratio of the different atoms in a compound. A molecular formula indicates the exact number of atoms in a single molecule of the compound.

2. 1. Burns from the hot crucible; 2. Eye damage from the intense light given off by the burning magnesium; 3. Inhalation of magnesium oxide smoke
3. Inaccurate mass reading and damage to the balance may result.
4. 1. Crucible and lid 2. Crucible, lid, and magnesium ribbon 3. Crucible, lid, and magnesium oxide
5. Some magnesium oxide would be lost, and there would be greater danger of inhalation of the smoke produced.

Prelab 14

1. In a decomposition reaction, there is always a single reactant.
2. Heat and light are given off.
3. Lead and copper ions
4. Steps 3, 4, 5, and 6
5. Be careful to point the mouth of the tube away from yourself and others. Never heat the bottom of the tube.

Prelab 15

1. The differences in chemical reactivity depend on the ease with which metals give up electrons.
2. In the activity series, metals are listed in the order of ease of loss of electrons.
3. Place a piece of a pure metal A in a solution containing the ions of metal B. If metal A is more reactive than metal B, electrons will be transferred from metal A to the ions of metal B.
4. Because iron is above copper in the activity series, iron corrodes and particles of copper metal are deposited on the iron.
5. Because copper is below iron in the activity series, no reaction will occur.
6. Silver nitrate will stain skin and clothing. It can also cause chemical burns and is toxic. Skin contact should be avoided.

Prelab 16

1. The solution will have the appearance of cloudy water or thick paint. The precipitate will slowly settle out of the solution.
2. Flush the affected area with running water continuously for 10–15 minutes.
3. **a.** HCl, hydrochloric acid; HNO_3, nitric acid; H_2SO_4, sulfuric acid; **b.** H^+ ion; **c.** Corrosive
4. Silver nitrate
5. Tap water contains dissolved minerals that could affect the outcome of the tests.
6. Sodium ion

Prelab 17

1. They are held together by electrostatic attractions between the positive and negative ions.
2. Silver chloride
3. A complete ionic equation includes the spectator ions; a net ionic equation does not.
4. Silver nitrate can stain skin or clothing.
5. No
6. In a complete ionic equation, reactants are always shown as __ions__, the precipitate as __a solid__, and the __spectator ions__ as unchanged. The total charge should be __zero__ on both sides of the equation.

Prelab 18

1. Different ions can have similar reactions to a single reagent.
2. Tap water contains ions that could interfere with the test results.
3. They are not labeled to enable the development of a systematic strategy to identify the unknown.
4. Assume that each chemical is toxic and corrosive unless you are told otherwise by your teacher.

Prelab 19

1. The coefficients represent the number of moles of each reactant and product.
2. Iron metal will react with a solution of copper(II) chloride to produce copper metal and iron(II) chloride.
3. Decanting: Pouring a solution into a waste container, leaving the solid reaction product in the original beaker
4. Hydrochloric acid; which is corrosive.

Prelab 20

1. The limiting reagent is the reactant that is the first to be completely consumed. It determines the number of moles of product produced.

2. Four moles of sodium iodide will require two moles of lead(II) nitrate and will produce two moles of lead(II) iodide and four moles of sodium nitrate.
3. Toxic or corrosive chemicals could be ingested.
4. The liquid above a settled precipitate
5. The ruler is used to measure the height of the precipitate formed.

Prelab 21

1. Allotropes are different structural forms of the same element in the same physical state.
2. Environmental conditions such as pressure and temperature
3. Diamond and graphite
4. Sulfur fumes should not be inhaled.
5. Orthorhombic, monoclinic, and plastic

Prelab 22

1. **a.** The melting point is the temperature at which a substance changes from a solid to a liquid. **b.** Vaporization
2. **a.** Solid, liquid, and gas; **b.** Solid to liquid, and liquid to solid phase changes will be observed.
3. Burns from hot water or heated glass
4. The temperature reading would be inaccurate if the material near the bulb of the thermometer was not representative of the total sample.

Prelab 23

1. At constant temperature, the volume of a fixed amount of gas is inversely proportional to its pressure.
2. It should not be poured down the drain.
3. Apply a thin film of silicone grease.
4. Depress the syringe plunger to the desired mark and hold it there.
5. The height of the column of DBP will be related to the pressure.

Prelab 24

1. At constant pressure, the volume of a sample of gas is directly proportional to its temperature in kelvins.
2. Temperature
3. Hold the burned area under cold running water until the burning sensation stops. Notify your teacher immediately.
4. At about 10°C (ice water), at room temperature, and at 20°C intervals until 100°C is reached.
5. The volume of gas is represented by the numerical value for the height of the air column.

Prelab 25

1. Gas Y
2. Diffusion is the tendency of particles to move from an area of higher concentration to an area of lower concentration until a uniform concentration of particles is reached.
3. **a.**

H: 1.0 g/mol	N: 14 g/mol
Cl: 35.5 g/mol	H_3: 3.0 g/mol
HCl: 36.5 g/mol	NH_3: 17 g/mol

   b. NH_3
4. Both are significant respiratory irritants. The vapors should not be inhaled.

Prelab 26

1. The aqueous solution is boiled, causing the water to vaporize. Dissolved non-volatile solid materials are left behind.
2. During condensation, vapor cools to a liquid.
3. It is added to test for the presence of chloride ions.
4. To prevent the "bumping" that occurs when bubbles of vapor rise rapidly to the surface
5. To lubricate the thermometer and the sidearm of the distillation flask when inserting them into the one-holed stopper

Prelab 27

1. The polarity of the water, along with its ability to form hydrogen bonds, makes it an excellent solvent.
2. Gasoline and oil are nonpolar molecules.
3. Students may infer that hexane and TTE are water pollutants because they are not flushed down the drain with the other substances.
4. Hexane, kerosene, and ethanol

Prelab 28

1. Hydrates are ionic solids that contain water as an integral part of their crystal structure.
2. The material that remains after water of hydration has been removed

3. $CaSO_4 + 2H_2O \rightarrow CaSO_4{\bullet}2H_2O$
   anhydrous salt   hydrate
4. They differ in the degree of hydration of calcium sulfate.
5. Copper(II) sulfate pentahydrate

Prelab 29

1. **a.** Electrolytes are substances that dissolve in water to produce solutions that conduct electricity. **b.** An ion is a charged atom, or a group of atoms with a charge.
2. An electric current is the movement of charged particles.
3. The ions in the solid are not free to move; those in solution are.
4. The plug should be removed from the outlet and the switch turned off before the equipment is handled. The operator should not stand in water or touch any metal objects while operating the conductivity apparatus.
5. Wash thoroughly with lots of water until the skin no longer feels soapy. Notify the teacher immediately.

Prelab 30

1. **a.** Sodium chloride is the solute. **b.** Water is the solvent.
2. Temperature, particle size, and degree of mixing
3. Use a rolled paper towel handle as shown in Figure 30.1. Pinch the towel close to the beaker and pour.
4. To determine the effect of agitation on the rate of dissolving

Prelab 31

1. **a.** Solubility is the maximum amount of a solute that will dissolve in a given amount of solvent at specified conditions. **b.** A saturated solution contains the maximum amount of solute that can dissolve in the solution at a particular temperature.
2. Under certain conditions, a solution may contain more solute than is normal for the specified temperature.
3. The addition of a single crystal to a supersaturated solution often causes the excess solute to crystallize.
4. They should be washed into the sink and flushed down the drain.

Prelab 32

1. Chromatography is a method for separating the substances in a mixture.
2. Students may infer that the solvent is drawn up the paper by attractive forces.
3. Differences in solubility and absorption affect the rate at which the compounds travel.
4. The R_f value is the distance that a substance moves relative to the solvent.
5. It may stain hands and clothing.

Prelab 33

1. **a.** The concentration of the solute; **b.** To determine the effect of solute concentration on the freezing point of the solution
2. It may begin to emit toxic fumes.
3. The use of fine particles of solute rather than coarse particles
4. $0.0050 \text{ moles solute} \times \frac{\text{molar mass}}{1 \text{ mole}} = \text{grams solute}$

Prelab 34

1. The specific heat of a substance is the amount of heat required to raise the temperature of 1 g of the substance by 1°C.
2. 1. The specific heat of the substance; 2. The mass of the sample; 3. The magnitude of the temperature change
3. Heat is transferred to the water.
4. Using the utility clamp as a holder
5. After heating the shot for 10 minutes, (1) record the water temperature in the foam cup, and (2) in the boiling bath. After pouring the shot into the water, watch the thermometer, and (3) record the maximum temperature reached.

Prelab 35

1. In an exothermic reaction, energy is released in the form of heat.
2. 1. The specific heat of the reaction mixture; 2. The temperature change; 3. The mass of the reaction mixture
3. **a.** Hygroscopic pellets readily absorb moisture from the air. **b.** If the NaOH pellets absorb enough water, the clear caustic solution can be mistaken for water.
4. The foam cup acts as an insulator to minimize the loss of heat. The beaker provides support and catches any leaks from the foam cup.

Prelab 36

1. Bonds are formed or broken when molecules collide with sufficient energy to break old bonds or form new ones.
2. Activation energy is the minimum energy that colliding molecules must have for reaction to occur.
3. Temperature, concentration of reactants, particle size, and catalysts
4. They provide a path of lower activation energy for reactions.
5. **a.** The reaction rate decreases. **b.** The reaction rate increases. **c.** The reaction rate decreases.
6. It is over when the bubbling stops or when no zinc remains.
7. Both compounds are irritants. Skin contact should be avoided.

Prelab 37

1. The appearance of a blue color signals that the reaction is complete. The rate of reaction can be determined from the color signal.
2. I^- and $S_2O_8^{2-}$
3. The data is plotted in a graph.
4. You should begin timing the reaction as soon as solutions A and C are poured into the beaker.
5. You should stop timing when the blue color appears.

Prelab 38

1. When dynamic equilibrium is reached, there is no further change in the concentration of reactants or products. The rate of the forward reaction equals the rate of the reverse reaction.
2. Le Châtelier's principle states that if a stress is placed on a system that is at equilibrium, the system will shift in the direction that relieves the stress.
3. **a.** Toward products; **b.** Toward reactants; **c.** No change
4. Iron(III) chloride is an irritant.
5. Change in temperature

Prelab 39

1. For any system containing solid $PbCl_2$ in equilibrium with its ions, the product of the lead ion concentration multiplied by the chloride ion concentration squared will be a constant.
2. The balanced equation indicates that two moles of chloride ions are produced from one mole of lead(II) chloride.
3. The Pb^{2+} ions are precipitated as lead(II) chromate. From the amount of lead(II) chromate obtained, the concentration of Pb^{2+} ions in the saturated solution can be determined. This, in turn, enables calculation of the concentration of Cl^- ions.
4. Compounds of lead and chromate salts are toxic.

Prelab 40

1. An acid is a hydrogen ion donor. A base is a hydrogen ion acceptor.
2. Each acid has a corresponding base, called a conjugate base, that is formed when the acid loses a hydrogen ion. Each base has a corresponding acid, called a conjugate acid, that is formed when the base accepts a hydrogen ion.
3. Phenolphthalein will turn pink in a basic solution. The base accepts hydrogen ions from the phenolphthalein, shifting its equilibrium toward the pink form.
4. **a.** Yellow **b.** Red **c.** Blue **d.** Colorless
5. Hydrochloric acid, sodium hydroxide, and ammonia

Prelab 41

1. A burning splint placed at the mouth of the test tube will produce the sound of a pop when hydrogen gas is present; it will be extinguished when carbon dioxide is present.
2. $Mg(s) + 2HCl(l) \rightarrow MgCl_2(aq) + H_2(g)$
3. Your fingers may transfer oils, dirt, or other substances that might affect the reaction.

Prelab 42

1. An Arrhenius acid is a substance that produces hydrogen ions in aqueous solution. An Arrhenius base produces hydroxide ions in aqueous solution.
2. A salt and water are produced in a neutralization reaction.
3. The phenolphthalein will lose its color when the sodium hydroxide has been neutralized.
4. Use tongs to remove the evaporating dish.
5. Neutralize the spill with solid sodium hydrogen carbonate until bubbles of gas no longer appear. Then wipe the area with a sponge or paper towels.

Prelab 43

1. At neutralization, the number of equivalents of acid is equal to the number of equivalents of base.
2. The number of equivalents of a solution equals the volume of the solution multiplied by the normality of the solution.
3. The volume is determined by subtracting the initial volume reading of the buret from the final volume reading.
4. A standard solution is a solution whose concentration is known to a high degree of accuracy.
5. You must discard the sample and start again.
6. The first titration is done to standardize the sodium hydroxide solution. The standardized sodium hydroxide solution is then used to titrate vinegar.

Prelab 44

1. In salt hydrolysis, one of the ions produced in a salt solution reacts with water to produce hydronium ions or hydroxide ions.
2. A nonneutral salt solution will form when a strong acid is mixed with a weak base, or a weak acid is mixed with a strong base.
3. The pH of various salt solutions will be measured. Any nonneutral pH reading implies that salt hydrolysis has occurred.

Prelab 45

1. Buffers are solutions of a weak acid and its salt, or of a weak base and its salt.
2. Buffered solutions maintain a relatively constant pH when limited amounts of acid or base are added to them.
3. This buffering system helps to maintain the blood at a pH between 7.35 and 7.45. It buffers against a build-up of either hydrogen ions or hydroxide ions in the blood.
4. The system is an effective buffering system if it resists changes of pH as small quantities of acid or base are added.

Prelab 46

1. Oxidation involves a loss of electrons. Reduction involves a gain of electrons.
2. H^+ ions from the acid are reduced. The metal loses electrons and is oxidized.
3. A strong reducing agent is easily oxidized; it readily donates electrons to other substances.
4. Return the metal strips for reuse.

Prelab 47

1. Corrosion is an oxidation–reduction reaction in which metals are converted to their oxides or other compounds.
2. At the anode, iron is oxidized to iron(II) ions, Fe^{2+}. At the cathode, hydroxide ions, OH^-, are produced by the reduction of oxygen gas.
3. The nails are bent to determine if the application of a structural stress will influence the corrosion process.
4. To determine if iron can be protected from corrosion by the presence of other metals

Prelab 48

1. **a.** During electroplating, a layer of one metal is deposited on another. **b.** To protect their surface from corrosion, or for decoration
2. **a.** Silver **b.** The fork **c.** Silver nitrate
3. At the cathode, the fork becomes silver-plated as a result of the reduction of Ag^+ ions. At the anode, the silver ions are replenished by oxidation of silver atoms.
4. Doing so would complete an electric circuit; electricity would pass through your body.
5. To avoid getting steel slivers in your hands

Prelab 49

1. The physical and chemical properties of molecules are determined, to a large extent, by their three-dimensional shapes.
2. Short sticks are used to represent bonds with hydrogen. Long sticks are used to represent all other single covalent bonds.
3. Molecules that have the same molecular formula, but different structural formulas
4. In the boat conformation, two of the carbons are directly across the ring from each other and above the plane of the other carbons. In the chair conformation, one of the carbons is above the plane of the other carbons, and one of the carbons is below.
5. **a.** Atoms are arranged in the same order but with different positions of substituted atoms around a double bond. **b.** *cis-* and *trans-*

Prelab 50

1. Many esters have pleasant odors. Esters account for the distinctive odors of fruit, such as bananas, pineapples, and oranges.
2. By reacting a carboxylic acid with alcohol
3. A strong acid
4. In esterification reactions, the products are in equilibrium with the reactants. The reaction seldom goes to completion unless the water produced is removed, driving the reaction in the direction of the products.

Prelab 51

1. Soaps are produced by the reaction of metallic hydroxides with animal fats or vegetable oils.
2. Triglycerides are esters of the trihydroxyl alcohol called glycerol and various long-chain fatty acids.
3. A triglyceride (tristearin) is reacted with sodium hydroxide to break the ester's bonds. The products of this reaction are soap (sodium stearate) and glycerol.
4. Solid sodium hydroxide is hygroscopic. An open container will allow moisture to enter, creating a corrosive sodium hydroxide solution.

Prelab 52

1. alpha (α), beta (β), and gamma (γ)
2. 1. The darkening of a film badge detector 2. With a Geiger-Müller counter
3. Because of their large size and charge, alpha particles cannot penetrate the window of a Geiger-Müller counter.
4. 1. Keep a maximum distance from the radiation source. 2. Place shielding between you and the source. 3. Spend the minimum amount of time in the vicinity of the source.

Answers - Safety Quiz 1

1. e 2. f 3. a 4. b
5. g 6. h 7. c 8. d
9. F 10. F 11. T 12. F
13. T 14. F 15. T 16. T
17. F

19. Turn off the burner. Move away any other combustible materials. Smother the fire with a watch glass or damp cloth. Notify the teacher immediately.
20. Wash the hand with large amounts of cool running water for several minutes.
21. Call for help while removing contact lenses, if wearing them. Go to the nearest eyewash station and flood the eye with continuously running water for at least 20 minutes. Report all details of the accident to the teacher.
22. Allow the cut to bleed freely under running water. Notify the teacher. Bandage the wound, if necessary.
23. Ask your partner to point the tube away from you and others. Explain that the tube should be heated evenly, not just at the bottom, to avoid cracking the tube.
24. Notify the teacher. Walk outside into the fresh air. Position your head so that it is lower than your heart.
25. Notify the teacher immediately. Note the name of the swallowed substance.
26. Place the burned hand or fingers under cold running water until the feeling of pain is reduced. Notify the teacher.

Answers - Safety Quiz 2

1. d 2. c 3. b 4. a
5. c 6. d 7. b 8. b
9. a 10. d 11. a 12. c
13. d